Data Analytics: Principles, Tools, and Practices

A Complete Guide for Advanced Data Analytics Using the Latest Trends, Tools, and Technologies

Dr. Gaurav Aroraa
Chitra Lele
Dr. Munish Jindal

www.bpbonline.com

FIRST EDITION 2022

ISBN: 978-93-88511-95-7

Distributors:

BPB PUBLICATIONS
20, Ansari Road, Darya Ganj
New Delhi-110002
Ph: 23254990/23254991

DECCAN AGENCIES
4-3-329, Bank Street,
Hyderabad-500195
Ph: 24756967/24756400

MICRO MEDIA
Shop No. 5, Mahendra Chambers,
150 DN Rd. Next to Capital Cinema,
V.T. (C.S.T.) Station, MUMBAI-400 001
Ph: 22078296/22078297

BPB BOOK CENTRE
376 Old Lajpat Rai Market,
Delhi-110006
Ph: 23861747

Published by Manish Jain for BPB Publications, 20 Ansari Road, Darya Ganj, New Delhi-110002 and Printed by him at Repro India Ltd, Mumbai

www.bpbonline.com

Dedicated to

Col. Manoj Rana – a man of principles
who always inspires me to put more efforts in life, and show more courage, love and support.

--- Gaurav Aroraa

My Parents: Asha Lele and G. G. Lele
"Through thick and thin you are always by my side
You both are the essence of my life and spirit —
My true pride."

---Chitra Lele

Ms. Nirmal Jindal - My Mother who made me to reach beyond the stars and who taught me that not even sky's the limit. Whatever I am today, whenever I am today, it's the result of all her relentless efforts, the lifelong learnings she taught me, the discipline she inculcated in me. Life doesn't come with a manual, it comes with mother. I attribute excellence in my life to the moral and intellectual education I received from her.

---- Munish Jindal

About the Authors

Gaurav Aroraa is a Technology enthusiast, with Doctorate in Computer Science. Gaurav is a Microsoft MVP award recipient. He is a lifetime member of the Computer Society of India (CSI), an advisory member and senior mentor at IndiaMentor, certified as a Scrum trainer and coach, ITIL-F certified, and PRINCE-F and PRINCE-P certified. Gaurav is an open-source developer and a contributor to the Microsoft TechNet community. He has authored books across-the-technologies, including Microservices by Examples Using .NET Core (BPB).

Chitra Lele is a young software engineer, software solution architect, record-setting author, poet, mentor, award-winning technology professional, and research scholar. She is a merit-holder and holds degrees in software engineering and computer management. She runs her own software startup firm, Chitra Lele & Associates, which designs software solutions based on Ethically-Aligned Design principles. She is also the founder of 'Chitra Cares', a social transformation initiative dedicated towards community building projects. Through her software projects, peace campaigns, academic books and social transformation initiatives, Chitra strives to contribute to the greater good of the world.

Dr. Munish Jindal is the CEO of HoverRobotix & the Founding President of MENTORx. Honored with the highest civilian honor "Karmaveer Chakra" by United Nations iCongo, he is the Noble Asian. MBA and CPA from Australia, he is PhD. from USA. Dr. Munish Jindal is Serial Entrepreneur, Robostronaut, International Business Consultant, Philanthropist, Fashion Icon, Brand Ambassador, Intellectual Speaker, Corporate Trainer, Mentor, Startup Evangelist & Angel Investor. He is the one who launched the concept of Hoverboards, Autobots & Mobility Robots in India and he envisioned to "Educate, Empower, Elevate" globally. He has been conferred with 500+ awards. He has established multiple Centre of Excellence, Incubators, Accelerators, EDCs. He is a seasoned professional with experience of almost two decades, providing sustainable living with a futuristic technological vision.

About the Reviewer

Rohit Gupta has six years of experience in Data Science and Engineering. Previously he had worked with companies like Jio, Citi in building Big Data processing systems and Analytics applications. Currently, he is working in the Data Team of Paytm as Sr Software Engineer. Rohit holds B.Tech from Delhi College of Engineering.

Foreword

When thinking to write software for huge data, engineers naturally gravitate towards solutions that avoid any glitches and provide a complete insight/ analysis. We are naturally Big Data - a large volume of structured and unstructured data - often without thinking about it! Developers naturally compartmentalize functionality, create reusable methods, and make helpful classes. These are useful, general, reusable solutions to problems you'll see every day.

Gaurav, Chitra, and Munish have assembled the best and most common topics and presented them in the form of examples. The explanation of Charts using Excel-sheet is commendable. You'll start with basic, learn the theory, recognize the various technologies and then use these to analyze your data.

This book is built with basic blocks and can be a ready reckoner for any software engineer. You'll learn and understand them theoretically to implement various topics.

These techniques have been written in such a way that covers today's industry needs. This book is theory-heavy so it will be very helpful for students who are seeking their career in Database Engineering or appearing for any Software Engineering exam.

I hope you appreciate this book as much as I did. And I hope you enjoy working on data analytics.

Enjoy!

Dr. Vishal Jain

Associate Professor,

School of Engineering and Technology,

Sharda University, Greater Noida

Acknowledgments

There are people I want to thank for the continued and ongoing support they have given me during this project. First and foremost, I would like to thank my wife and daughter, Shuby, and Aarchi for putting up with me while I was spending many weekends and evenings on writing—I could have never reached to the conclusion of this book without their support.

Secondly, I would thankfully say - this book wouldn't have happened if I hadn't had the support from the author team; the key co-authors Chitra and Munish. This is the result of their dedication and hard-work that today, we're going to complete this book.

Thirdly, my thanks to few faces behind the scene who helped me directly, indirectly to make the good contents of the book. I am thankful to Ms. Payal, Dr. Vishal Jain, and Ms. Baishakhi Banerjee for their support and valuable feedback.

Finally, I would like to thank Anugraha, Surbhi, Priyanka, Sonali, and editorial team at BPB Publications for giving me this opportunity to write for them.

--- Gaurav Aroraa

I use this opportunity to express my heartfelt thanks to all those who supported me in one way or the other during the completion of this book project.

Special thanks to my exceptional Publishers, the BPB Publications team, for the valuable support provided throughout the entire process. The ceaseless cooperation by the team is greatly acknowledged.

A million thanks to my co-authors: Gaurav Aroraa Sir and Munish Jindal Sir. Their expertise and knowledge are admirable. I thoroughly enjoyed working with them on this collaborative book initiative.

What I have learned over the years comes as a result of being a daughter of wonderful parents, Asha Lele and G. G. Lele. They have been the motivation that has helped me to maintain laser-sharp focus on my goals. Thanks to them for their superb support and endless encouragement.

I offer my deep gratitude to the divine essence within me for bestowing on me the strength to follow my heart.

I owe my sincere gratitude to my company colleagues and my higher studies batch-mates who gave me the time and space to complete this book. Their ceaseless cooperation in adjusting to my software project work schedule, higher studies timetable and book writing schedule helped me to maintain balance between all these aspects.

Very special thanks must go to you all, my readers, for investing your time in reading this book.

Last but not least, I beg forgiveness of all those who have been with me over the course of my journey and whose names I have failed to mention. Your support and encouragement is deeply appreciated..

--- Chitra Lele

In the prologue, which focused on the habit of showing gratitude, I recognized and acknowledge you, the reader. If you didn't read my books, I wouldn't write them. So once again, thank you! There are plenty of people who helped bring this book to fruition, and I am grateful to all of them. Once this book started to go from a concept in my head to a manuscript, there were many people involved who deserve to be acknowledged and thanked.

First, I would like to thank my co-author Gaurav Aroraa. I have turned down every other tech geek, who asked me to co-write a book with them, but I took on this book because I believed Gaurav Aroraa would do something no one else would do and he actually did. This book is deep and so real in a way that every few other books are. I am glad Chitra Lele is part of this book with us. I am proud of my co-authors and proud to have worked with them.

I would like to thank my family for always being around and for those late-night coffee cuppas helping me remain dedicated towards writing this book. I would like to thank my younger brother Gaurav Jindal for co-creating, innovating futuristic technologies at the robotics lab of HoverRobotix, which helped me big time to gain momentum towards this book.

I shall remain grateful to my co-founder at MENTORx Dr. Nancy Juneja for always being there as the pillar of strength.

The unsung hero Ms. Payal Garg, whose ideas and suggestions helped me get this manuscript that made me say. "Yes, it's finally a book!" I am thankful to Ms. Payal Garg who helped me with scripting and writing the book.

I pay the heartfelt gratitude to Dr. Sangeeta Ahuja, Ms. Namrita Sharma, Ms. Rishita Garg, and Ms. Shweta Vakil for being the source of enlightenment.

Finally, I have to thank Anugraha, Surbhi, Priyanka, and the editorial team at BPB Publications, which helps people write and publish their books. Without them, this doesn't happen.

--- Munish Jindal

Preface

A database is a well-ordered collection of data, generally stored and retrieved electronically from a computer system. The database management system (DBMS) is a process which interacts with end users, applications to capture and analyse the data.

An entity–relationship model (ER model) describes interconnected things of interest in a specific domain of knowledge. A basic ER model is composed of entity types (which classify the things of interest) and specifies relationships that can exist between instances of those entity types. ER model is an abstract data model that defines a data or information structure which can be implemented in a database.

Data warehouse is a repository of historical and real-time data. This system is used to support the decision-making process and helps to understand the historical trends of the business by analyzing the past data.

The importance of data visualization is growing at a rapid rate in this era where the use of data is vital in different fields. Data visualization techniques allow people to use their perception to better understand the deeper dynamics of data.

Advanced data visualization software offers new ways to view data, through visuals such as bubble charts, word clouds and geospatial heat maps. Used correctly, visualization technology can deliver business insights to users faster than they can get it with traditional BI tools, and visualizing data can also simplify the process of analyzing big data sets. Once data processing is completed, it demands rich visuals to reflect those trends and hence advanced data visualization performs a vital role here. However advanced visualization tools are somehow complex to deploy and use, requiring support from outside consultants or the services of internal data scientists.

The explosion of social media and the computerization of every aspect of social and economic activity resulted in the creation of large volumes of mostly unstructured data: web logs, videos, speech recordings, photographs, e-mails, tweets, etc. In parallel development, computers keep getting ever more powerful and storage ever cheaper. Today, we have the ability to reliably and cheaply store huge volumes of data, efficiently analyze them, and extract business and socially relevant information.

The key objective of this book is to familiarize the readers, business professionals, students with the most important information technologies used in manipulating, storing and analyzing big data. Big Data, is not just about storing and extracting data, but much more than that. Big Data, itself comprises of so many technologies that it is difficult to recall which one to start learning with. Some of the technologies big data consists of are Hadoop, MapReduce, Apache, Pig, Hive, Flume, Sqoop, Zookeeper, Oozie, Spark, Cassandra, Mongo DB.

Chapter 1: To make optimized use of data and to convert it into actionable business intelligence and insights, we need to store and arrange data in an organized manner. However, business intelligence and insights that lead to operational excellence is only achievable if the necessary components are in place. The two key components are a database (DB) and a database management system (DBMS). Chapter 1 discusses these two components and their dynamics.

Chapter 2: Online Transaction Processing and its characteristics, merits and demerits, Data Warehouse and its characteristics, main components and approaches for constructing the same, Dimensional Modeling and its various components like Facts, Dimensions and Attributes used in DW Design, and also topics like types of schemas, and ETL and other tool sets available in market are dealt with in this chapter.

Chapter 3: Chapter 3 discusses Business Intelligence and its deeper dynamics in terms of characteristics, data quality and its best practices, structured versus unstructured data, data lake, and modern business intelligence systems

Chapter 4: Data visualization, its aims, types, history, importance and much more is discussed in this chapter. Apart from this, visualization dashboards and introduction to different reporting tools is also dealt with.

Chapter 5: This chapter focuses on advanced visualization, types of advanced data visualization charts, data visualization trends, data visualization tools like Tableau, Power BI, QlikView, etc., and data visualization best practices.

Chapter 6: The explosion of social media and the computerization of every aspect of social and economic activity resulted in creation of large volumes of mostly unstructured data: web logs, videos, speech recordings, photographs, e-mails, Tweets, and similar. In a parallel development, computers keep getting ever more powerful and storage ever cheaper. Today, we have the ability to reliably and cheaply store huge volumes of data, efficiently analyze them, and extract business and socially relevant information. The key objective of this course is to familiarize the students with most important information technologies used in manipulating, storing, and analyzing big data. Big Data, is not just about, storing and extracting data, but much more than that. Big Data, itself comprises of so many technologies that it is difficult to recall which one to start learning with. Some of the technologies big data consists of is Hadoop, MapReduce, Apache, Pig, Hive, Flume, Sqoop, Zookeeper, Oozie, Spark, Cassandra, Mongo DB

Chapter 7: NoSQL is an approach to database design that can used for a wide variety of data models, including key-value, document, columnar and graph formats. NoSQL, which stands for "not only SQL," is an alternative to traditional relational databases in which data is placed in tables and data schema is carefully designed before the database is built. NoSQL databases are especially useful for working with large sets of distributed data.

Map reduce is a programming technique for processing and generating big data sets with a parallel, distributed algorithm on a cluster. It consists of an algorithm using two functions, Map and Reduce. The Map function is applied on the input data and produces a list of intermediate pairs. The Reduce function is applied to all intermediate pairs with the same key. It typically performs merging operation and produces zero or more output pairs. Finally, the output pairs are sorted by their key value. In the simplest form of MapReduce programs, the programmer provides just the Map function.

Chapter 8. Big Data has been playing a very important role of big game changer for almost all the industries over the last few years. The primary goal of Big Data applications is to help companies make more informative business decisions by analyzing large volumes of data. It could include web server logs, Internet click stream data, social media content and activity reports, text from customer emails, mobile phone call details and machine data captured by multiple sensors.

Organizations from different domains are investing in Big Data applications, for examining large data sets to uncover all hidden patterns, unknown correlations, market trends, customer preferences and other useful business information.

Chapter 9: Machine Learning is the science of getting computers to learn/train and act like humans do, and improve their learning over time in autonomous fashion, by feeding them data as an input and information in the form of observations and real-world interactions. The basic premise of machine learning is to build algorithms that can receive input data and use statistical analysis to predict an output while updating outputs as new data becomes available.

Chapter 10: AI and machine learning (ML) - which include technologies such as deep learning, neural networks, and natural-language processing - can also encompass more advanced systems which understand, learn, predict, adapt, and potentially operate autonomously.

Chapter 11: The beauty of applications that employ machine learning is that it seems to be extremely simple on the surface, hiding away much complexity from users.

Code Bundle and Coloured Images

Please follow the link to download the
Code Bundle and the *Coloured Images* of the book:

https://rebrand.ly/147eac

The code bundle for the book is also hosted on GitHub at **https://github.com/bpbpublications/Data-Analytics-Principles-Tools-and-Practices**. In case there's an update to the code, it will be updated on the existing GitHub repository.

We have code bundles from our rich catalogue of books and videos available at **https://github.com/bpbpublications**. Check them out!

Errata

We take immense pride in our work at BPB Publications and follow best practices to ensure the accuracy of our content to provide with an indulging reading experience to our subscribers. Our readers are our mirrors, and we use their inputs to reflect and improve upon human errors, if any, that may have occurred during the publishing processes involved. To let us maintain the quality and help us reach out to any readers who might be having difficulties due to any unforeseen errors, please write to us at :

errata@bpbonline.com

Your support, suggestions and feedbacks are highly appreciated by the BPB Publications' Family.

Piracy

If you come across any illegal copies of our works in any form on the internet, we would be grateful if you would provide us with the location address or website name. Please contact us at **business@bpbonline.com** with a link to the material.

If you are interested in becoming an author

If there is a topic that you have expertise in, and you are interested in either writing or contributing to a book, please visit **www.bpbonline.com**. We have worked with thousands of developers and tech professionals, just like you, to help them share their insights with the global tech community. You can make a general application, apply for a specific hot topic that we are recruiting an author for, or submit your own idea.

Reviews

Please leave a review. Once you have read and used this book, why not leave a review on the site that you purchased it from? Potential readers can then see and use your unbiased opinion to make purchase decisions. We at BPB can understand what you think about our products, and our authors can see your feedback on their book. Thank you!

For more information about BPB, please visit **www.bpbonline.com**.

Table of Contents

CHAPTER 1
Database Management System

In today's technology-driven world, especially in corporate settings, data is the biggest player. It is defined as the *"new oil or new currency"*. Data can refer to facts related to any object that is storable, manageable and accessible through some form of the organized electronic system. Examples of such data objects can be students, employees, orders, and so on.

To optimize the use of data and convert it into actionable business intelligence and insights, we need to store and arrange data in an organized manner. However, business intelligence and insights that lead to operational excellence are only achievable if the necessary components are in place. The two key components are a **database** (**DB**) and a **database management system** (**DBMS**). DB and DBMS facilitate easy maintenance of a huge amount of data. Collectively, these two components, along with the data, form the lifeline of businesses.

Database and database management systems are about building a digital backbone for businesses. After all, what use is a great repository of data and information if no one is able to access it; this is where database and database management systems come into play.

Structure

This chapter will highlight the following topics:

- Database management system
  - Database and database management system
  - History of DBMS
    - Characteristics of DBMS
    - DB three-tier architecture
  - Keys
  - Entity-relationship model
  - Functional dependencies
  - Normalization
  - Database objects
  - Stored procedures and triggers
  - SQL and PL/SQL
  - Basic SQL query structure
  - Joins
  - Query optimization

Objectives

After studying this chapter, you will be able to.

- Understand the concepts of database, database management system, history of DBMS, characteristics of DBMS, and DB three-tier architecture.
- Discuss keys, entity-relationship model, functional dependencies, and normalization.
- Understand deeper dynamics like stored procedures and triggers, SQL and PL/SQL, basic SQL query structure, join, and query optimization.

Database and database management system

Without any doubt, these days, most organizations have become data-driven. This is where the need for a database emerges. A database (also known as DB) is an electronic data structure that stores an organized collection of data. It is used by organizations as an effective way of storing, managing, and retrieving information.

Databases in current times are managed through a database management system. The word *"data"* in database is derived from the Latin word *"datum"* and this means *"a piece of information"*.

A **database management system** (also known as **DBMS**) is a group of software programs designed to define, store, manage, and retrieve data from a database. A database is a logical collection of inter-related information, which is stored in the form of records. The main aim of a DBMS is to centralize and store information into and retrieve information from a database in an organized and efficient manner. Essentially speaking, a DBMS is a set of programs used to access the data in the database.

Examples of popular DBMSs are Sybase, Oracle, Microsoft SQL server, and so on. DBMS organizes, stores, and manages data in such a way that the **data manipulation language (DML)** operations of addition, updation, and deletion can be performed in an efficient and effective manner. A DML is usually a sublanguage of the parent language such as SQL, and it is used for inserting, modifying, and deleting data in a database.

Database and database management system form the backbone of all major business processes and applications today. Business growth and operational efficiency depend on the various robust DBMS implemented today. For organizations and companies to survive and thrive in the competitive landscape, they need to have an effective DBMS in place so as to collect, manage, analyze, and derive timely business insights for creating the edge. In other words, DB and DBMS provide a centralized repository for data and provide a mechanism for a highly efficient method for handling multiple types of data.

Relational databases (RDBMS) are more widely known and used than their NoSQL peers. NoSQL stands for *"not only structured query languages"* or *"non-SQL"* or *"non-relational"* database that provides a mechanism for storage and retrieval of data that is modeled in a way that is different from the relational databases. The main features of modern database systems are: apart from the feature of having a data manipulation language and a data definition language; most modern systems have at least one way of interfacing or communicating with other systems. The type of storage and the purpose are some of the main criteria for classifying the various databases into cloud-based, container, software in silicon, and so on.

A database management system is made up of software, data, hardware, users, and procedures. Each component plays an important role in the database management system environment. Software is the primary component, and it consists of a set of programs that manages the database, and it also acts as an interface between the users and the database. Data in terms of user/operational data and metadata (data about data; description of the structure of the database) is stored, accessed, managed, and processed by the DBMS. Hardware is a collection of storage devices, computers, hard disks, and so on, and these act as a bridge between the computer system and the real world. Users of different types are categorized on the basis of their access level and what operations they can perform: the main types are end-users, database administrators, and application programmers/developers (refer to *figure 1.1*). Procedures guide how to use the database management system, design the database, install the database management system, generate reports based on the data in the database, create backup copies of the database, and so on.

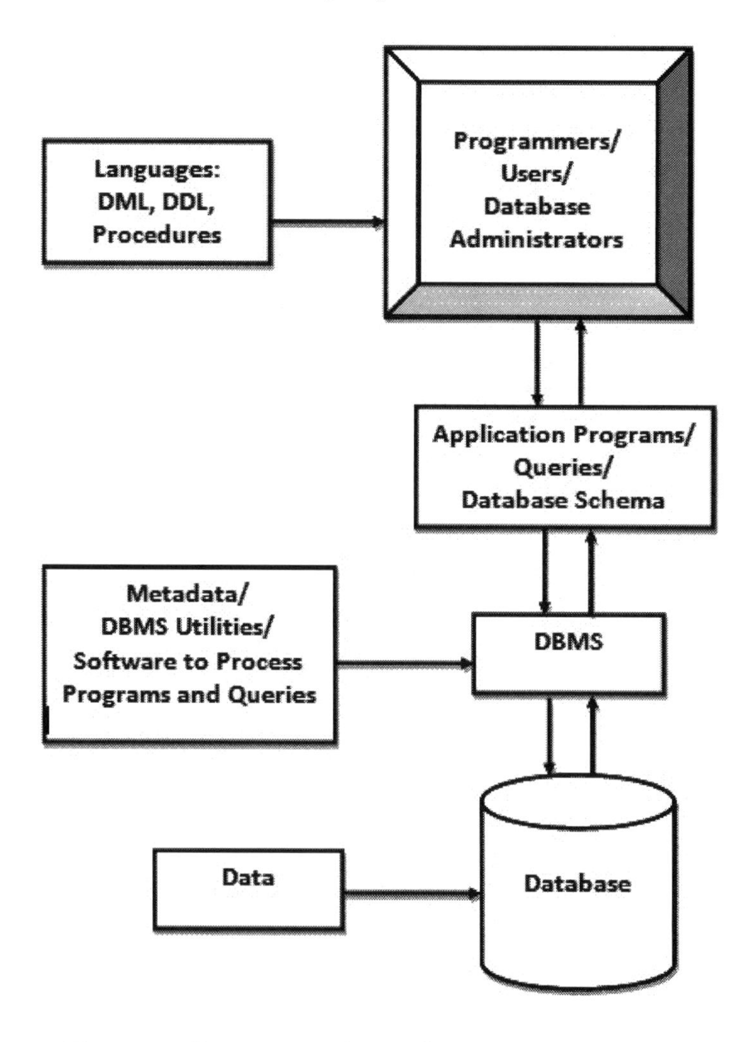

Figure 1.1: *Components of a Database Management System*

Database and database management system and their respective components form the backbone of most businesses today. They help organizations to become strategic users of the vast amount of data stored in their setups.

History of DBMS

In the initial period of database systems, they were built on top of a file system. But such systems had a large set of drawbacks like duplication of data leading to redundancy, inconsistency in data leading to integrity problems, difficulty in accessing data leading to writing more and more programs, and so on.

Electronic or computerized database systems entered the digital landscape in the 1960s. There were two main data models that came into the picture from late 1960s: a hierarchical model called IMS and a network model called **conference on data systems languages** (**CODASYL**). Intensive research was done during the 1960s. As a result of which North American Aviation, now known as Rockwell International, developed software called **generalized update access method** (**GUAM**). Later on, IBM joined hands with North American Aviation to further develop GUAM into **information management system** (**IMS**).

Information management system is a hierarchical system, and in this kind of system, data is arranged in binary tree format. It was written for NASA's space program, Apollo. This software was based on the concept that smaller components come together as a part of larger components and so on until the final product is assembled. Here, the data is organized into a tree-like structure with the records representing the nodes and fields representing the branches of the tree. It represents data using parent/child relationships: each parent can have many children, but each child has only one parent; a hierarchical model cannot represent many-to-many relationships. In this model, files are related in a parent–child manner. Although this model overcame all the cons of the file-based system by giving advantages like less redundant data, data-program independence, better security, and efficient searching, it also had some disadvantages of its own: complex implementation, lack of portability standards, programming became complex as the programmers needed to know the physical access paths to access the data items.

Example of a hierarchical model: The great grandparents are the root/base of the whole model. Parents can have many children, and this indicates one to many relationships. The great grandparents record is termed as the root of the tree. The grandparents and children are the dependents or children of the root. A root may have any number of dependents. Each of these dependents may have any number of lower-level dependents, and this nesting can go on.

Conference on data systems languages is a network model in which data is organized into records of different types, and records are organized into sets of different types. It became the basis and the framework for new commercial database systems, such as the **integrated database management system** (**IDMS**) from *Cullinane Corporation*. This type of system had many disadvantages. *Charles W. Bachman*, an American computer scientist, and industrial researcher designed the **integrated database system** (**IDS**), the first-ever network DBMS, to overcome the disadvantages of the hierarchical DBMS. In the network model, there is a three-schema approach—structure or organization of the database, data management language, and a sub-schema, which refers to the views of the database per user. Both database systems of IMS and CODASYL are described as the forerunners of the DBMS revolution.

In 1970s, *Edgar F. Codd*, an English computer scientist (also known as the "*Father of Database Management Systems*"), who while working at IBM, invented the relational model for database management—this type of system laid the roadmap for dealing with big data and database setups. Along with the E. F. Codd rules explained in the paper titled "*A Relational Model of Data for Large Shared Data Banks*", *E. F. Codd* also proposed replacing the then systems with tables and rows. This concept, later on, came to be known as relational DBMS. *Eugene Wong* and *Michael Stonebraker* from UC Berkeley performed further research on relational database systems, and their project was named **interactive graphics and retrieval system** (**INGRES**); and they were able to successfully show that a relational model is practical and efficient. INGRES used a query language known as QUEL that, in turn, made IBM develop SQL, which was more advanced.

In year 1976, *Peter Chen*, a Taiwanese American computer scientist, defined and explained the dynamics of the entity-relationship model in his paper "*The Entity-Relationship Model: Toward a Unified View of Data*". The ER model is based on the concept that the real world consists of entities and relationships. In 1980s, more and more relational databases were developed and implemented.

In mid-1980s, **object-oriented database management system** (**OODBMS**) came into the picture; it was incorporated in relational DBMS. Some popular names are Versant, Object, Design, and so on. The need for this new model arose to handle complex objects and structures like those used in CASE, CAD, and so on. To accomplish the complex tasks, the database had to be able to deal with aspects like classes and objects; hence, the object-oriented DBMS (OODBMS) came into play. OODBMS represents and model data in the form of objects and classes. In the decade of 1990s, object-oriented model in relational database lead to development of new areas like **online analytical processing** (**OLAP**), data warehousing, and so on.

In year 1995, Internet-based DBMS were introduced and NoSQL became popular with such systems as it provided faster processing of unstructured data. In the year 1997, the XML database design was introduced. An XML database is a database that stores data in XML format. It is usually associated with document-oriented databases (refer to *Figure 1.2*).

Modern day DBMS are flexible, scalable, dynamic, versatile, and secure systems that are capable of handling extremely large amounts of data.

Some of the popular current relational databases include DB2, Oracle, and so on. Platforms like *Caspio, Quickbase, TeamDesk,* and so on, are some of the popular online database building platforms that help users to build custom applications in an easy manner through the point and click interface.

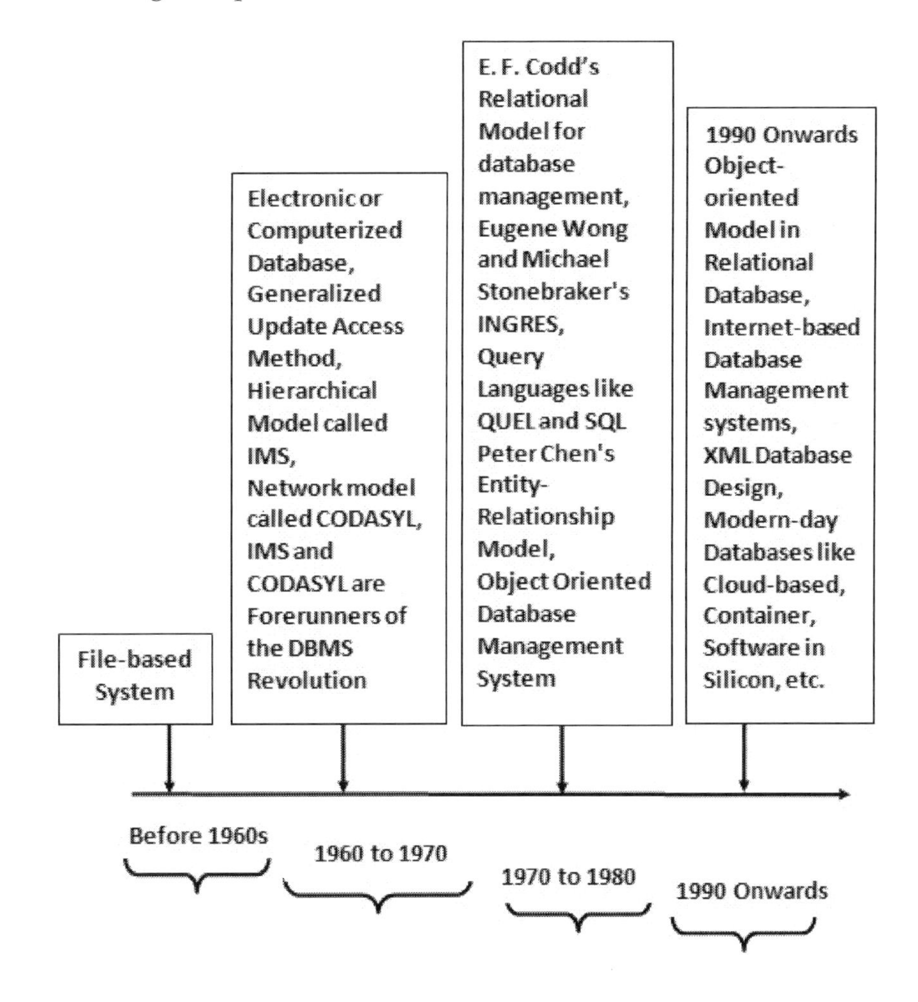

Figure 1.2: *History of DBMS*

We end by discussing the history of modern day DBMS. The main features of modern database systems are apart from the main feature of having a data manipulation language and data definition language, most modern systems have at least one way of interfacing or communicating with other systems. The type of storage and the purpose are the criteria for classifying the various databases in terms of modern-day DBMS like cloud-based, container, software in silicon, and so on.

Characteristics of DBMS

The various characteristics of DBMS help organizations and businesses to become strategic users of the vast amount of data that they possess.

- **Isolation**: DBMS is completely independent of the data it stores. DBMS is said to be an active entity, whereas data is considered passive; hence, there should be a clear differentiation between them. There is also insulation or separation between the data and the programs accessing this data.
- **Multiple views**: DBMS offers multiple views for different users based on their specific requirements. For example, the finance department will have a different view of the database than the people working in the production department. It is an abstract view of the data as DBMS hides all the underlying details.

  A *view* is a subset of the data stored in a database; it is different for each user/group of users depending on their requirements. DBMS provides multiple views of data through various tools like reports. The stored data should be made available for access by different users simultaneously through different views. It provides a multi-user, concurrent access environment and allows users to access and manipulate data in parallel. Multiple users should be able to access and manipulate the same database without affecting the other users.
- **Major elements**: There are five major elements/components of DBMS: software, hardware, procedures, data, and users (which we have already discussed).
- **Data integrity**: It is a critical characteristic and fundamental tenet of data security. DBMS ensures the accuracy, quality, consistency, and reliability of the data in the database. It maintains three types of integrity: domain, referential, and entity. If an integrity violation is detected, DBMS takes appropriate actions like reporting the violation, rejecting the violation, and many more, and if needed, it can also return the database to a consistent state.

- **ACID**: A true DBMS must adhere to the ACID properties of accuracy, consistency, isolation, and durability. DBMS must ensure that the real purpose of data should not be compromised while performing transactions like insertion, deletion, and modification. For example,, if an employee's name is updated, then it should make sure that there is no duplicate data and no mismatch of employee data anywhere in the whole employee database system.

  A transaction represents a logical unit of a program made up of related operations. A transaction must maintain atomicity, consistency, isolation, and durability as these properties are a must to ensure data completeness, accuracy, and integrity. Atomicity indicates that a transaction must be treated as an atomic unit—either all of its operations are executed or none. Consistency means that if the database was in a consistent state before the execution of a transaction, it must remain in a consistent state even after the execution of the transaction is over. Isolation implies that a transaction that is in progress and not yet committed must remain isolated from any other transaction. Durability means once a transaction is completed successfully, the changes it has made should be permanent even if there is a system failure.
- **Data persistence**: All the data is maintained as long as it is not deleted or removed explicitly.
- **Reduces redundancy**: As DBMS follows the normalization rules, it helps to minimize redundancy.
- **Security and rights**: DBMS will have a proper rights and permissions policy in place. Some users will be allowed to see the whole database and some will have only partial rights. It has a system of access controls, permissions, and privileges to create, maintain, and control various types of user accounts. For example, an instructor who teaches a particular subject will have access to view and update the marks of her/his subject. She/he will not have access to other subjects. But the HOD will have full access to all the subjects.
- **Various utilities**: A backup utility that takes regular backups/copies of the database to tackle crashes, a recovery utility to perform recovery of the DB from the history and using backup procedures, a data loading utility that facilitates easy loading of data from an external source and format without any additional programming, and many more.

Because of these characteristics of DBMS, the data in the database is therefore stored, structured, and integrated into the database in a meaningful way. And this makes it easier to retrieve, manipulate, and delete data.

DB three-tier architecture

The database architecture deals with and focuses on designing, developing, implementing, and maintaining software programs that store and organize data.

Figure 1.3 is a pictorial depiction of the types of DBMS architecture.

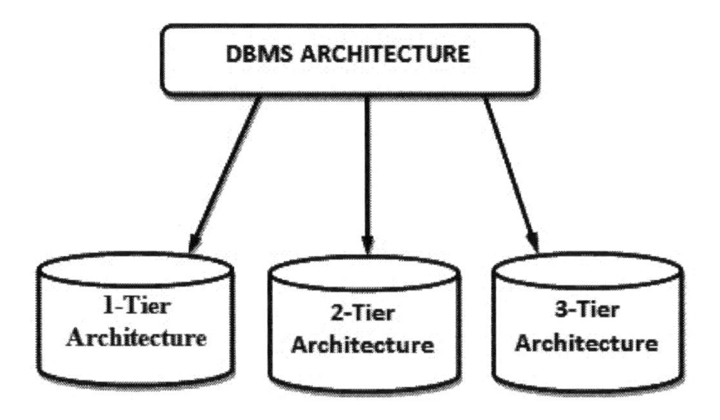

Figure 1.3: *Types of DBMS Architecture*

A. **The 1-tier architecture is the simplest form of DB architecture where the client, server, and database all reside on the same machine. Any request made by the client does not require a network connection to perform any action on the database. But such architecture is rarely used in the production environment.**

B. **In 2-tier** architecture, there is an application layer between the user and the DBMS, and its main responsibility is to communicate the user's request to the database management system and then transmit the response from the DBMS to the user. There is direct communication between the client and server. The DB is on the server machine, and the DBMS application is on the client machine, and these two are connected through a network.

C. **The 3-tier architecture (refer** *to figure 1.4***)** is the most widely used architecture to design a DBMS.

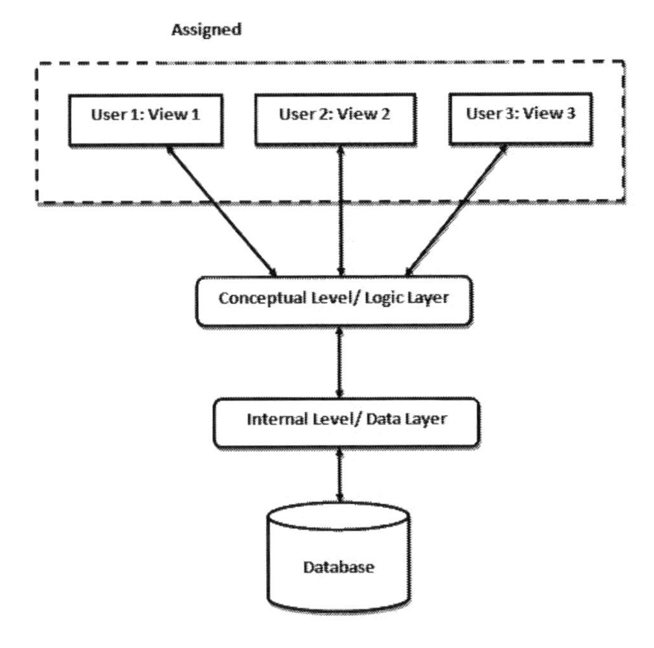

Figure 1.4: *3-Tier Architecture*

The 3-tier architecture has three inter-related but independent levels/modules/layers: external level/view level, conceptual level, and physical level. At the physical level, the information about the location of database objects in the data store is maintained. It is most commonly used for web applications. Various users of DBMS are unaware of the locations of these objects. At the external level or presentation layer, there is the **graphical user interface** (**GUI**) part of the system or application; and for the design purpose, where data is either presented to or input is received from the user. At the conceptual/logic level or business layer, all the logic for insertion, retrieval, calculation, and so on are present, and this layer act as the interface/link between the presentation layer and data layer. At the conceptual level, the design of the database in the form of a schema of data, constraints, relationships, and so on are defined. At the physical level or data layer, the actual database comes into the picture. This level is not only responsible for how the data is stored but also for allocating space to this data.

Keys

A key is an attribute (a field or combination of fields; unique identifier for data) in a table that uniquely identifies each record or a row (tuple) of data in the table. Its main purpose is that of arranging, identifying, and sorting rows. It also uniquely identifies a row in a table by a combination of one or more columns in that table based on a certain requirement or condition. A key is required to establish or identify a relation between tables. It helps to bring about the integrity of data by eliminating duplicate data. It does not allow columns to have null or duplicate values. According to *E. F. Codd's* third rule: "*Every single data element (value) is guaranteed to be accessible logically with a combination of table-name, primary-key (row value), and attribute-name (column value).*" In most relational databases, there are two main keys present: primary and foreign. A primary key enforces entity integrity, and a foreign key maintains referential integrity.

Figure 1.5 is a pictorial depiction of the types of keys.

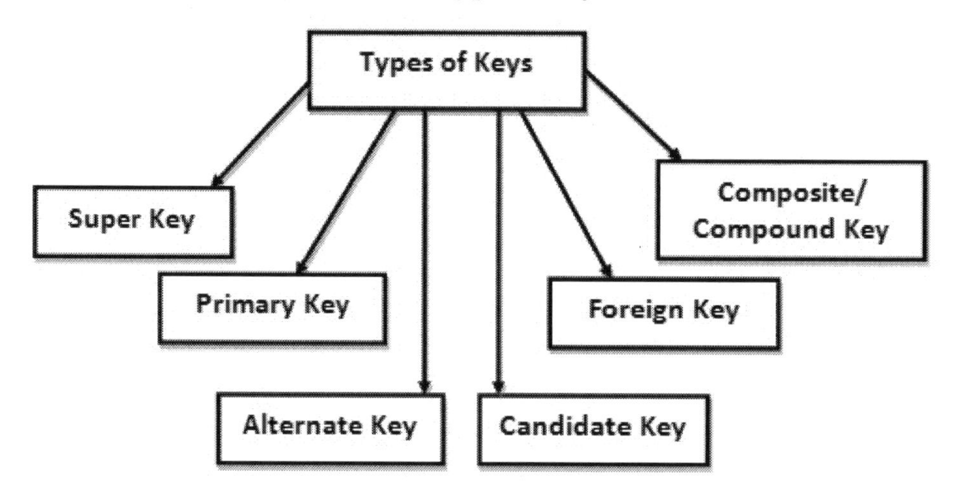

Figure 1.5: *Types of Keys*

There are several types of keys:

A. **Super**: It is a group of single or multiple keys whose values can help to uniquely identify rows in a table. A super key may have additional attributes that are not needed for unique identification.

   For example, the customer master details table is used to store customer details; it will contain columns such as **`Customer_ID Customer_Name`**, **`Customer_SSN`**, **`Customer_Birthdate`**, **`Customer_Address`**. In this case, a certain set of columns can be considered unique to each customer. Examples of super keys in this example could be ID + Name + SSN or Name + SSN + Birthdate or even just ID (which is a candidate key), but to have an absolute uniqueness, a composite key of ID + SSN can be used.

   Often, people tend to get confused between a super key and a candidate key. A candidate key is selected from a set of super keys. While doing so, it is important to ensure that a candidate key should not have any redundant attribute. Hence, a candidate key is also called a **minimal super key**.

B. **Primary**: It is used to uniquely identify a record in a table. It has to have a unique value; it cannot be duplicated. This key is a set of one or more fields. The value in a primary key column can never be modified or updated if any foreign key refers to that primary key. The primary key field cannot be null. For example, in the table Employees, the `Employee_Id` is the primary key as it is unique for each employee. In another example, the Citizens table, there could be multiple primary keys like `Citizen_ID`, `Citizen_PassportNo`, or `Citizen_SSN`; in this case, selection of the primary key is based on requirements. A primary key with two or more attributes is referred to as a composite key.

C. **Alternate**: All the keys that are not primary keys are called **alternate keys**. It is a candidate key that is currently not the primary key, and it is also called the **secondary key**.

D. **Candidate**: A super key with no redundant attribute is known as a **candidate key**. The minimal set of an attribute that can uniquely identify a row is known as a candidate key. The candidate key is as strong as the primary key. A table can have multiple candidate keys, but each table can have only one primary key. Among the set of candidates, one candidate key is chosen as the primary key. When a key is composed of more than one column, it is known as a composite key.

   For example, in the Employees table, `Employee_Id` is best suited as the primary key, whereas the remaining attributes like `Employee_SSN`, `Employee_PassportNo`, and so on are considered as candidate keys.

E. **Foreign**: A column that links with another table. It acts as a cross-reference between two tables; it typically links to the primary key of another table.

F. **Composite/compound**: is a combination of more than one attribute (and each attribute is a simple key) that can be used to uniquely identify each row. A composite key may be a candidate or primary key.

ER model

ER model stands for the **entity-relationship** model. It is a high-level data model that describes the logical structure and conceptual design of a database using a diagram known as ER diagram: **entity-relationship diagram**. This diagram is widely used in database design, and its main aim is to define the data entities/elements and relationships between them.

Entity-relationship model is the blueprint or graphical representation of a database that can be later on be implemented as a database. Each entity has a set of properties, and properties can have values. For example, a particular student studying in a particular school is an entity. If "*Asha*" is a student at Daffodils School, she will have attributes (properties) like name, age, birthdate, and so on. In most cases, a single attribute will have one value. But it is also possible for attributes to have multiple values. For example, Asha's age has a single value, but her phone number could have multiple values. An entity has a set of properties, and these properties can have values. ER model is a powerful way of communicating a common way of viewing data and hence avoiding confusion.

There are five main types of attributes: First, the simple attribute is an atomic value, which cannot be divided further. For example, an employee's phone number is an atomic value of 8 digits, and it cannot be broken down further. Second, the derived attribute does not exist in the physical database, but its value is derived from other attributes present in the database; it is calculated based on other attributes. For example, age can be derived from the attribute of a birthdate. Third, a composite attribute consists of more than one simple attribute. For example, an employee's complete name has **`First_Name`** and **`Last_Name`**. Fourth, a single-value attribute contains a single value, for example, **`Employee_SSN`**. Last, a multi-value attribute may contain more than one value; for example, a person can have more than one **`Email_Address`**.

Entities have relationships with each other. Let us consider an example: assume that each student is given an ID card. Hence Asha has an ID card. Asha's ID card is also an entity. Asha is using this ID card, and Asha uses the same ID card. There is a mutual relationship between Asha and her ID card. A set of relationships of a similar type is called a relationship set. Just like an entity, a relationship too can have attributes, which are referred to as descriptive attributes. The degree of a relationship is defined by the number of entities that participate in it. There are four main types: unary = degree 1 (one entity is involved in the relationship), binary = degree 2 (two entities are involved in the relationship), ternary = degree 3 (three entities are involved in the relationship), and N-ary ('*n*' number of entities is involved in the relationship).

Enhanced entity-relationship (EER) model is an expanded, specialized, high-level data model which provides extensions to the original **entity-relationship (ER)** model. EER models provide precise, detailed designs that cater to complex databases.

Entity-relationship model consists of many specialized symbols that have a unique meaning. The main components of the ER model are as follows:

1. **Entity**: An entity can be any person, object, or place. In the ER diagram, an entity can be depicted as a rectangle (refer to *figure 1.6*). For example, in a

company, the various entities could be employees, products, departments, and others.

Figure 1.6: *Entity Rectangle Symbol*

An entity that depends on another entity is called a **weak entity** as it does not contain any key attribute of its own, whereas an entity that has a primary key (refer to *figure 1.7*) is called a **strong entity**.

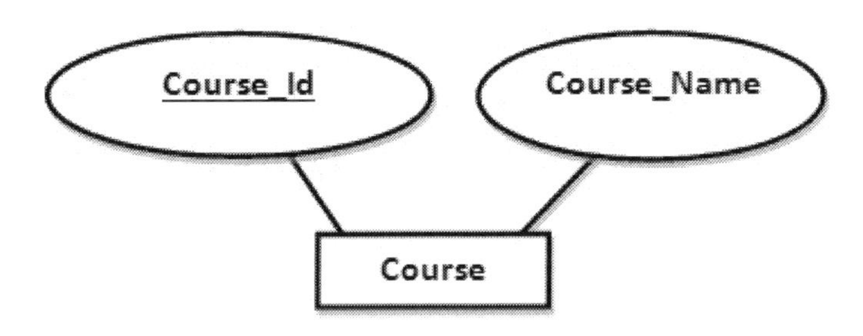

Figure 1.7: *Primary Key*

A weak entity is always dependent on strong/owner entities as they have sufficient attributes to form a primary key. The primary key of a strong entity set is represented by underlining it. The weak entity is represented by a double rectangle (refer to *figure 1.8*).

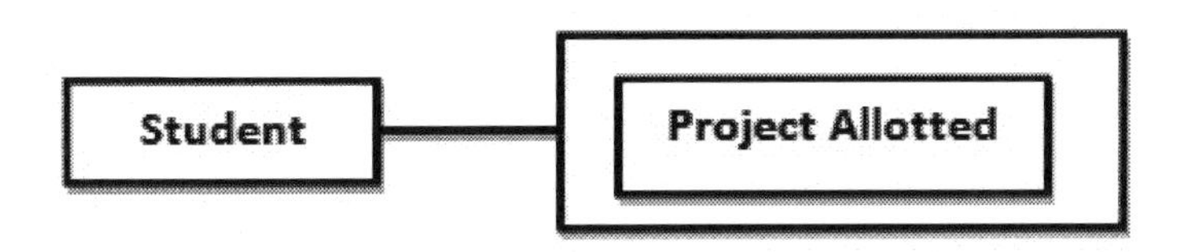

Figure 1.8: *Weak Entity*

A member of a strong entity set is called a **dominant entity,** and a member of a weak entity set is called a **subordinate entity**. The relationship between a weak entity and a strong entity is denoted with a double diamond.

2. **Attribute**: It is shown as ellipses. An attribute (ellipses) represents one that is directly connected to its entity (rectangle) (refer to *figure 1.9*).

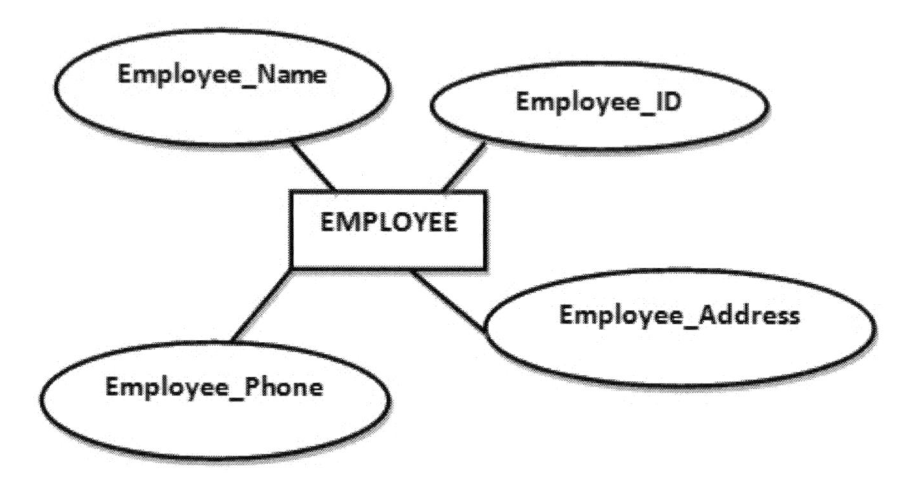

Figure 1.9: Attribute Ellipses Symbol

In the case of a composite attribute (refer to *figure 1.10*), they are depicted in a tree-like structure, i.e., a composite attribute is represented by an ellipsis that is connected with another parent ellipse.

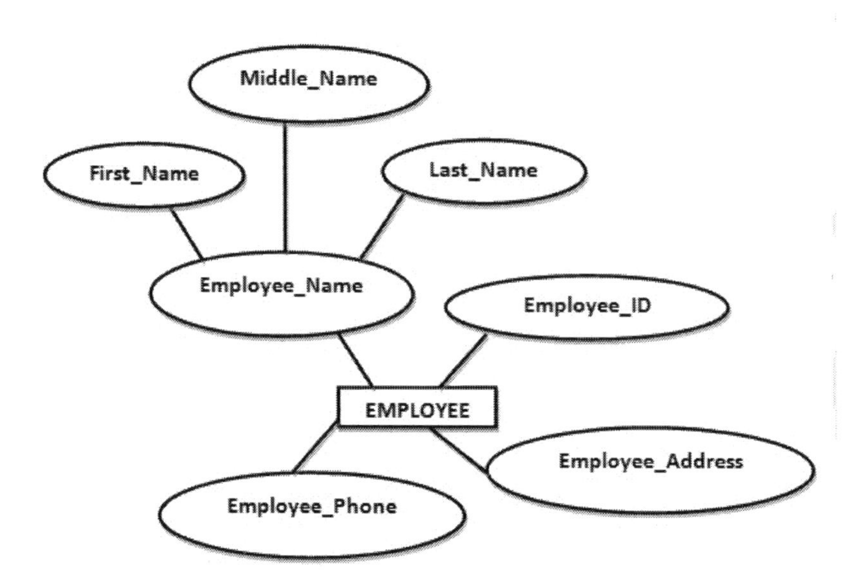

Figure 1.10: Composite Attribute

A multivalued attribute (refer to *figure 1.11*) is shown as a double ellipsis. For example, an employee can have more than one phone number.

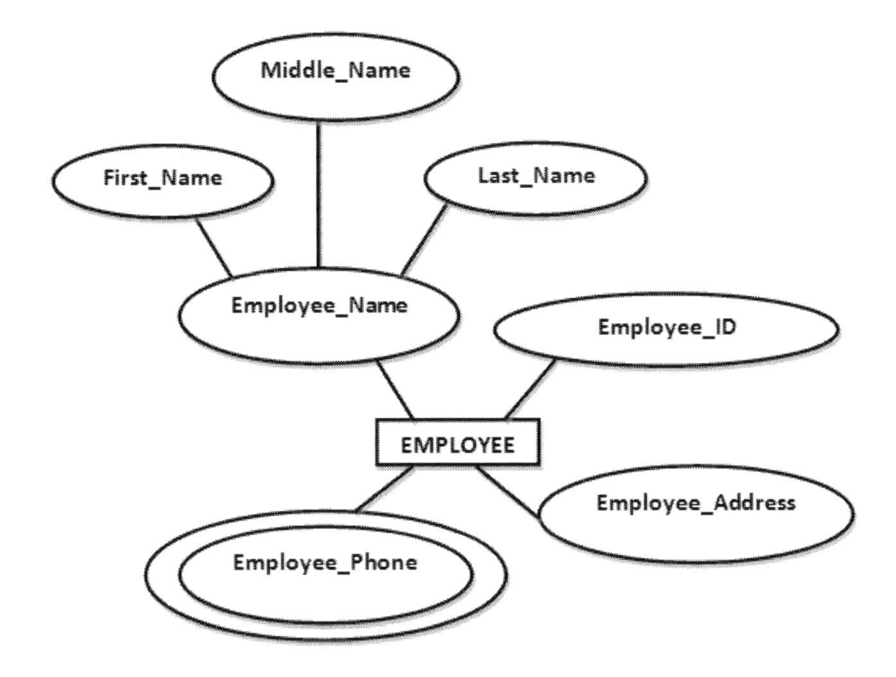

Figure 1.11: *Multivalued Attribute*

An attribute that can be derived from another attribute is known as a **derived attribute**. It is depicted by a dashed ellipse (refer to *figure 1.12*). For example, an employee's age and can be derived from another attribute like the date of birth.

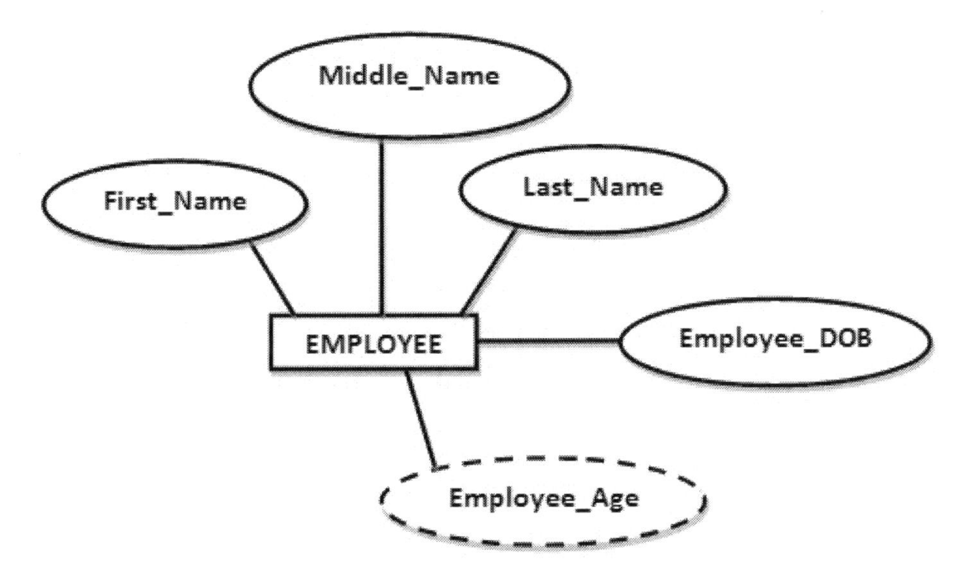

Figure 1.12: *Derived Attribute*

3. **Cardinality**: It denotes the relationship between two tables; it is about the maximum number of entities of one entity set that are linked with the maximum number of entities of the other entity set. There are four main types of cardinality ratios.

   One-to-one: when only one instance of an entity is related with the relationship (refer to *figure 1.13*), and it is marked as "1:1"; for example, a person can have only one passport, and a passport can be assigned to only one person (one row in table A relates to one row in table B).

Figure 1.13: One-to-One Cardinality

   One-to-many: Here a single instance of an entity is associated with more than one instance of another entity (refer to *figure 1.14*), and it is marked as "1:M", for example, a single customer might place an order for multiple products (one row in table A maps to many rows in table B).

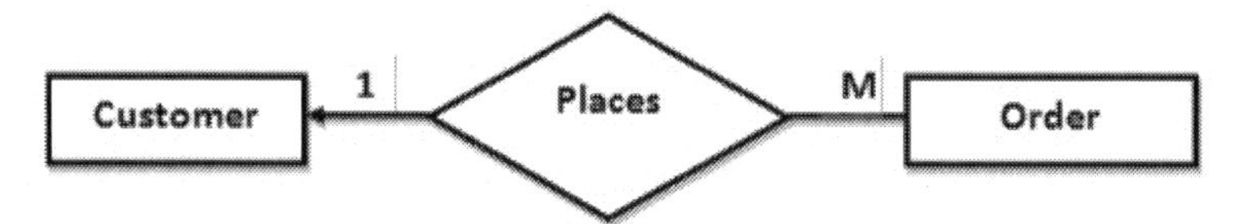

Figure 1.14: One-to-Many Cardinality

   Many-to-one: When more than one entity from entity set A can be linked with at most one entity of entity set B (refer to *figure 1.15*), and it is marked as "M:1", for example, an employee can work in at most one department, and a department can have several employees in it (many rows in table A relate to one row in table B).

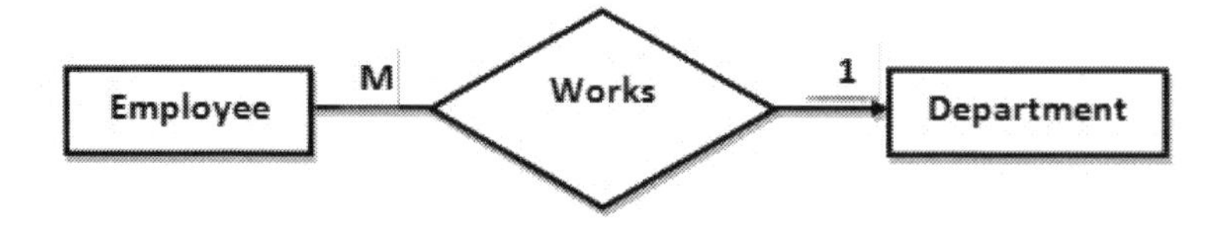

Figure 1.15: Many-to-One Cardinality

   Many-to-many: When one entity from A can be associated with more than one entity from B and vice-versa (refer to *figure 1.16*), and it is marked as

"M:N" doctors have many patients, and a patient can have several doctors (many rows in table A relate to many rows in table B).

Figure 1.16: *Many-to-Many Cardinality*

Functional dependencies

A **functional dependency** (**FD**) refers to a relationship that exists between two attributes, wherein it determines the relation of one attribute to another. It is a relationship between the primary key and other non-key attributes within a table. It is a critical part of relational database design and helps in the process of normalization and prevents data redundancy. For example, in the Employees table, there are attributes: **Employee_Id**, **Employee_Name**, and **Employee_Age**. Here **Employee_Id** attribute uniquely identifies the **Employee_Name** attribute of this table because if we know the employee id, we can easily identify the employee name associated with it. This refers to a functional dependency and can be written as follows:

- **Employee_Id** -> **Employee_Name**
- Or in words, we can say **Employee_Name** is functionally dependent on **Employee_Id**

  A -> B where A is the left side is known as a determinant, and the right side is called as a **dependent**; B is functionally dependent on A. For example, we have a student table with attributes: **Student_Id**, **Student_Name**, **Student_Address,** and many more. Here the attribute of **Student_Id** can uniquely identify the attribute of **Student_Name** in the student table because once we know the **Student_Id**, we can identify that particular student name associated with it. Functional dependency can be written as follows:

- **Student_Id** -> **Student_Name**
- We know that **Student_Id** is unique for each student. So **Student_Id** -> **Student_Name**,
  Student_RollNo -> **Student_Address** and **Student_Birthdate** all will be true.

  There are three main types of functional dependencies: transitive, trivial, and multivalued.

Transitive dependency: It is an indirect dependency, and it occurs when an indirect relationship results in a functional dependency. It normally follows this pattern

- A→B and B→C.
- Therefore A→C.
- The rule is that A is a transitive dependency of C (A→C) if A is functionally dependent on B (A→B), and B is functionally dependent on C (B→C) but not on A.

Anomalies in regards to insertion, modification, and deletion can occur due to transitive dependency. To achieve the normalization standard of **third normal form** (3NF), all transitive dependencies need to be eliminated so as to be able to maintain data integrity and minimize data duplication.

Trivial functional dependency: if a functional dependency: A → B holds, where B is a subset of A, then it is called a trivial functional dependency. Non-trivial: if a functional dependency A → B holds where B is not a subset of A, then it is called non-trivial functional dependency.

Multivalued functional dependency: when two attributes in a table are independent of each other, but both depend on a third attribute. A multivalued dependency is shown as follows:

Student_Name	Student_Discipline	Student_ Hobbies
Kaya	Science	Badminton
Asha	Science	Swimming
Asha	Science	Traveling
Citra	Arts	Singing
Citra	Arts	Kayaking

***Table 1.1:** Multivalued Functional Dependency*

In *table 1.1*, we can see students Asha and Citra have an interest in more than one hobby. This is a multivalued dependency because the discipline of a student is independent of hobbies, but it is dependent on the student. Hence the multivalued dependency is shown as follows: **`Student_Name->->Student_Discipline`** and **`Student_Name->->Student_Hobbies`**. But such multivalued dependencies violate the normalization rules, so in order to correct such violations, we need to split the preceding table into two tables to dissolve or break these multivalued dependencies.

Normalization

Normalization is a database schema design technique that aims to reduce redundancy, data dependency, and anomalies by systematically organizing tables and their data. The process is about decomposing large tables into smaller, manageable tables and associating them with relationships. The main aim of normalization is to organize data in such a manner that it meets two main requirements: there is no data redundancy, and data dependencies are logical.

Normalization can be carried out by following a set of rules called " **forms**". *E. F. Codd*, along with *R. F. Boyce*, proposed the theory of normalization with the introduction of the first normal form, second normal form, and third normal form. This theory is called the **Boyce–Codd normal form**.

- **First normal form (1NF):** Here, each column is unique. A table in this form cannot contain sub-columns; for example, if you are listing several cities, you cannot list them in one column and separate them with a semicolon. For a table to be in the first normal form, it should comply with the following four rules:

  a. It should only have single-valued columns; it means they should not contain multiple values.

  b. Values stored in a column should be of the same domain.

  c. All the columns should have unique names.

  d. The order in which data is stored does not matter.

  For example, the following table of student contact details is not in the 1NF as the column `Student_ContactNumber` has multiple values for student, Asha, and as per the rules of this form, each column should hold atomic values.

Student_Id	Student_Name	Student_ContactNumber
S1	Asha	8453495349 9043433434
S2	Kaya	4753475734
S3	Richard	8453488348

Table 1.2: *Before First Normal Form*

After normalization, *table 1.2* will appear as follows (refer to *table 1.3*):

Student_Id	Student_Name	Student_ContactNumber
S1	Asha	8453495349
S1	Asha	9043433434
S2	Kaya	4753475734
S3	Richard	8453488348

Table 1.3: *First Normal Form*

- **Second normal form (2NF):** for a table to be in the **second normal form (2NF)**, it should follow these norms:
  a. It has to be in the 1NF.
  b. It should not have any partial dependency. All non-key attributes are fully functional dependent on the primary key.

  For example, the following table of a customer order is in the 1NF as all attributes have atomic values, but it is not in 2NF as there are still partial dependencies. In this example, the combined key of **`Customer_Id`** and **`Order_Id`** form the primary key. **`Customer_Name`** is dependent on **`Customer_Id`,** and there is no real link between a customer's name and what she/he have ordered. The order details and order date are dependent on the **`Order_Id`**, but they are not dependent on the **`Customer_Id`**.

Customer_Id	Customer_ Name	Order_Id	Order_ Details	Order_Date
C1	Jake Nest	O89	2 Bundles of Paper	19/10/2019
C2	Asha Gill	O90	5 Punch Machines	20/10/2019
C3	Hema Natu	091	12 Spring Files	22/10/2019

Table 1.4: *Before Second Normal Form*

To make *table 1.4* compliant with 2NF, it needs to be split into three tables as follows (refer to *table 1.5*): customer details, order details, and third table to keep track of all the orders for a customer.

Customer_Id	Customer_Name
C1	Jake Nest
C2	Asha Gill
C3	Hema Natu

(a)

Order_Id	Order_Details
O89	2 Bundles of Paper
O90	5 Punch Machines
091	12 Spring Files

(b)

Customer_Id	Order_Id	Order_Date
C1	O89	19/01/2021
C2	O90	20/01/2021
C3	091	22/01/2021

(c)

Table 1.5: *The Second Normal Form: (a) Customer details, (b) Order details, (c) Tracking order*

- **Third normal form (3NF):** a table is said to be in the third normal form when it meets the following criteria:
  a. It is in the 2NF and 1NF.
  b. It should not have transitive functional dependency: transitive functional dependency of non-prime attribute on any super key should be eliminated. An attribute that is not part of any candidate key is known as a non-prime attribute.

  In the following tables, **super keys are `Student_Id`**, **`Student_Id`** + **`Student_Name`**, **`Student_Id`** + **`Student_Name`** + **`Student_Pincode`**, and so on, and **candidate key is `Student_Id`**. **Non-prime attributes**: all attributes except **`Student_Id`** are non-prime as they are not part of any candidate keys. Here, **`Student_State`**, **`Student_City`**, and **`Student_District`** are dependent on **`Student_Pincode`**, and **`Student_Pincode`** is dependent on **`Student_Id`**, and that makes non-prime attributes of **`Student_State`**, **`Student_City`**, and **`Student_District`** transitively dependent on the super key of **`Student_Id`**. This dependency violates the rule of 3NF.

Student_ Id	Student_ Name	Student_ Pincode	Student_ State	Student_City	Student_ District
S1	Asha	6453495	MH	Mumbai	Dadar
S2	Kaya	8753475	GJ	Ahmadabad	Anandnagar
S3	Richard	9453348	PB	Amritsar	Atam Nagar

Table 1.6: *Before Third Normal Form*

To make *table 1.6* 3NF compliant, we need to split it into tables to remove the transitive dependency (refer to *table 1.7*).

Student_Id	Student_Name	Student_Pincode
S1	Asha	6453495
S2	Kaya	8753475
S3	Richard	9453348

(a)

Student_Pincode	Student_State	Student_City	Student_District
6453495	MH	Mumbai	Dadar
8753475	GJ	Ahmadabad	Anandnagar
9453348	PB	Amritsar	Atam Nagar

(b)

Table 1.7: *The Third Normal Form with tables (a) and (b)*

- **Boyce and Codd normal form (BCNF)**: It is an advanced form of 3NF, and it is also termed 3.5NF. A table is said to be in the BCNF form if it complies with the following rules: it is in 3NF, and for every functional dependency, $X \rightarrow Y$, X should be the super key of the table.

Student_Id	Subject	Teacher
S1	Economics	Rose Ray
S1	Computers	Megan Chase
S2	Math	Jillian Bolt
S3	English	Heather Grace
S4	English	Neil Rhodes

Table 1.8: *Before Boyce and Codd Normal Form*

In *table 1.8,* we can notice that one student can enroll in multiple subjects. For example, a student with **`Student_Id`** S1 has opted for two subjects of economics and computers, and for each subject, a teacher is assigned to the student. And there can be multiple teachers teaching one subject, like in the case of English. **`Student_Id`** and subject form the primary key. There is one dependency, teacher → subject, and while a subject is a prime attribute, the teacher is a non-prime attribute, and this is not allowed by BCNF.

To make *table 1.8* BCNF compliant, we need to split it into two tables: one which contains **`Student_Id`** and **`Teacher_Id,`** and the other one contains **`Teacher_Id`**, **`Teacher,`** and **`Subject`** are as follows (refer to *table 1.9)*:

Student_Id	Teacher_Id
S1	T1
S1	T2
S2	T3
S3	T4
S4	T5

(a)

Teacher_Id	Teacher	Subject
T1	Rose Ray	Economics
T2	Megan Chase	Computers
T3	Jillian Bolt	Maths
T4	Heather Grace	English
T5	Neil Rhodes	English

(b)

Table 1.9: *Boyce and Codd Normal Form: (a) Student_Id and (b) Teacher_Id*

- **Fourth normal form (4NF):** A table is said to be in the fourth normal form when it complies with the following rules:
  a. It is in the Boyce–Codd normal form.
  b. No multivalued dependency should be present.

Subject	Student_Name	TextBook_Name
Economics	Rose Ray	Comprehensive Economics Essentials
Economics	Rose Ray	The A to Z of Economics

Economics	Jillian Bolt	Macroeconomics
English	Heather Grace	English Grammar
English	Heather Grace	English Leads to Global Growth

Table 1.10: *Before Fourth Normal Form*

In *table 1.10*, **Subject-->-->Student_Name** and **Subject-->--> TextBook_Name** are multivalued dependencies. To eliminate these dependences, this table is decomposed into two tables as follows (refer to *table 1.11*):

Subject	**Student_Name**
Economics	Rose Ray
Economics	Jillian Bolt
English	Heather Grace

(a)

Subject	**TextBook_Name**
Economics	Comprehensive economics essentials
Economics	The A to Z of economics
Economics	Macroeconomics
English	English grammar
English	English leads to global growth

(b)

Table 1.11: *Fourth Normal Form with tables (a) and (b)*

DB objects

The database itself is a huge data object that holds all other data objects. A database object in a relational database is a data structure used to either store or reference data. DB objects are the backbone of a database. Apart from the most common and primary object, table, there are several other typical DB objects like stored procedure, index, view, schema, synonym, and sequence. These objects can be created by explicitly executing statements or through a graphical user interface. Keywords like **CREATE** or **ALTER** are **DDL** statements used to deal with these objects.

- **Table**: It is where you keep all the records, and they are made up of columns and rows. It contains information about one subject or entity like an employee, student, and so on.

- **Stored procedure**: It is SQL code / subroutine (set of SQL statements) assigned a particular name that can be compiled and saved in a DB so that it can be accessed and shared by a number of programs time and again.
- **Index**: It contains a set of pointers that are logically ordered by the values of one or more keys. The pointers can refer to rows in a table, data in an XML storage object, and so on.
- **View**: It is a virtual or logical table and it is based on a table or another view. A view is an effective and efficient way of showing data as it contains no data of its own, but it is like a window through which data from tables can be seen or changed. It requires no storage as it acts as a virtual table.
- **Schema**: It is the organization or structure of the DB; it represents the logical view of the database.
- **Synonym**: It is an alternative name for the base object like a table, sequence, procedure, view, and so on, and it is generally used for security purposes. It provides a layer of abstraction that helps in protecting a client application from changes made to the name or location of the base object.
- **Sequence**: It lets users to generate unique integer values. The initial value specifies the starting value for the sequence, the increment value is the value by which the sequence will be incremented, and the maximum value specifies the upper limit up to which a sequence will increment itself.

Stored procedures and triggers

A stored procedure is SQL code/subroutine (set of SQL statements) assigned a particular name that can be compiled and saved in a DB so that it can be accessed and shared by a number of programs time and again. Most database servers like Oracle, SQL Server, and so on provide stored procedure support. When a stored procedure is called for the first time, the SQL server creates an execution plan and stores it in the plan cache, and in subsequent executions, the server executes the procedure based on this plan, and hence the execution is fast and optimized. It provides data integrity as the compilation step is required once only when the stored procedure is created, and this also leads to maintainability. As they are stored and cached on the server, this results in optimization.

The following is the general syntax for a stored procedure:

```
CREATE [OR REPLACE] PROCEDURE proc_name [list of parameters]
IS
   Declaration section
```

```
BEGIN
   Execution section
EXCEPTION
  Exception section
END;
```

IS keyword marks the starting point of the stored procedure's body. The code between **IS** and **BEGIN** forms the Declaration section. The syntax within the brackets [ ] indicates they are optional. Using **CREATE OR REPLACE** together, the procedure is created if no other procedure with the same name exists or the existing procedure is replaced with the current code.

A trigger is a special type of stored procedure that is executed when specific actions occur. A trigger can be invoked in response to system events like a startup, shutdown, and so on, and it can also be invoked in response to user events like logon, logoff, and so on. DDL triggers run in response to a variety of **data definition language (DDL)** events like create, drop, and so on. DML triggers run when a user tries to modify data through a DML event. A trigger is similar to a stored procedure but differs in the way it is invoked. A trigger is generally used for auditing purposes, enforcing referential integrity, preventing unauthorized transactions, implementing security authorization, and so on. A trigger is made up of three main components: event, condition, and action. And the event is the occurrence of some event that will cause the execution of the trigger. A condition is an optional component, and if the condition is specified, then it will check the rules to determine whether the trigger should be executed. An action is a set of statements that will be executed on the execution of the trigger.

Table 1.12 clearly helps us to understand the differences between a stored procedure and a trigger.

Stored procedure	Trigger
Executed when it is explicitly invoked	Executed automatically before or after an event occurs
We can call a stored procedure from the front end	This is not possible with a trigger
Execute or Exec statement to execute stored procedure directly by a user	Cannot be called directly by the user
We can schedule a job to execute stored procedure at a predefined time	This is not possible with a trigger

A stored procedure can be called inside a trigger	A trigger cannot be called inside a procedure
It may return a value on execution.	Never returns a value on execution
Can pass parameters to a procedure	This is not the case with a trigger

Table 1.12: *Stored Procedure Versus Trigger*

The following is the general syntax for a trigger:

```
create trigger [trigger_name]
[before | after]  (specifies when the trigger will be executed)
{insert | update | delete} (DML Operation)
on [table_name] (table name associated with the trigger)
[for each row] (the trigger will be executed for each row being affected)
[trigger_body] (the code here is executed when the trigger is fired)
```

SQL and PL/SQL

SQL stands for **structured query language,** and it is the standard language used to access, query, and manipulate a database. SQL is used to add, modify and delete the data in the database. In other words, SQL is a non-procedural, structured query language used for data manipulation. SQL statements start with keywords like **SELECT**, **INSERT**, **UPDATE**, **DELETE**, **DROP**, **ALTER**, and so on, and all the statements end with a semicolon. A simple example of a SQL query is as follows:

```
SELECT * FROM Students;
```

or

```
SELECT Customer_Name, Customer_City FROM Customers;
```

PL/SQL is a combination of procedural features of programming and SQL. It is a block-structured, procedural language, and it defines how things need to be carried out. It stands for procedural language extension to SQL as it combines the power of SQL with procedural statements. It was developed by the Oracle Corporation to enhance the capabilities of SQL. With PL/SQL, the users generally interact with an application that uses SQL to access a relational database on the back-end. PL/SQL is a procedural language to design applications. It is used to format, build and display web pages, user screens, and so on. The basic structure of PL/SQL code is as follows:

```
DECLARE
    declaration statements;
```

```
BEGIN
    executable statements;

EXCEPTIONS
    exception handling statements;
END;
```

It is in the **DECLARE** block, constants, variables, and so on, can be declared which store data temporarily. This part of the code is optional. In the Execution section, the program logic is written between the **BEGIN** and **END** keywords. This is a compulsory section. In the Exception section, statements that are executed when a run-time error occurs are written. This part of the code is optional.

An example of PL/SQL program:

```
BEGIN
dbms_output.put_line ('Hello World');
END;
```

Structured query language is declarative as it defines what needs to be done rather than how things need to be done, whereas PL/SQL is a block-structured, procedural language, and it defines how the things need to be done.

Table 1.13 clearly helps us to understand the differences SQL and PL/SQL.

SQL	PL/SQL
It is executed as a single query	It is executed as a block
As it executes one statement at a time, it is slower	As it executes a block of code, it is faster
It cannot contain PL/SQL code in it	As it is an extension of SQL, it can contain SQL code in it
It is a declarative and data-oriented language used to deal with sets of data	It is a procedural language used to create database-centric applications
SQL can be embedded in a PL/SQL statement or program	Vice versa is not possible
One can write queries and commands with the help of DDL and DML statements	One can write blocks of code that can contain variables, procedures, and so on

Table 1.13: *SQL Versus PL/SQL*

Basic SQL query structure

The basic SQL query structure contains three clauses of **`select`**, **`from,`** and **`where`**. These clauses help to filter and analyze data quickly. The select clause is the starting point/declarative statement of SQL queries. It specifies the columns from which data values are to be retrieved. The from clause specifies the table/s to retrieve data from or any other database objects, and it is the first clause that the database system looks at when it parses the SQL statement. The where clause defines the comparison predicate and returns only those results that fulfill the condition of the comparison predicate; it acts as a filter.

Data definition language (**DDL**) consists of keywords and commands that are used to define the database schema. **`CREATE`**, **`ALTER`**, and **`RENAME`** are the main examples. **Data query language** (**DQL**) is used to perform queries on data; the **`SELECT`** clause is the main one. DML consists of keywords and commands that are used to insert, delete and modify data. **`INSERT`**, **`DELETE`** and **`UPDATE`** are the main examples.

Some examples are as follows:

```
SELECT First_Name
FROM  Students
WHERE First_Name = 'Asha';

CREATE TABLE Students (
         Student_Id Int,
         First_Name varchar (30) Not Null,
         Last_Name varchar (30) Not Null,

         .....
         columnN datatype,

         PRIMARY KEY( Student_Id)
         );

DELETE FROM Students
WHERE Age >= 10;
```

Table 1.14 gives us an overview of SQL clauses and functions and what is the exact function they perform.

SQL clauses and functions	Function performed
`SELECT`	Extracts data from one or more columns
`FROM`	Identifies the tables/views that are being queried
`WHERE`	Retrieves rows that meet specified criteria
`UPDATE`	Updates data in a database
`DELETE`	Deletes data from a database
`CREATE`	Creates a new table, database, or any other database object (view, index)
`RENAME`	Renames a table
`INSERT`	Inserts a new row in a table
`ALTER`	Modifies columns in a table
`ORDER BY`	Sorts data in ascending or descending order
`COUNT`	Returns the number of rows
`MIN`	Returns the smallest value
`MAX`	Returns the largest value
`SUM`	Returns the sum value
`ROUND`	Rounds a number to a specified number of decimal places
`COUNT`	Returns the number of records returned by a select query
`SYSDATETIME`	Returns the date and time of the server
`CURRENT_TIMESTAMP`	Returns the current date and time
`CHAR`	Converts an ASCII value to a character
`ASCII`	Returns the ASCII value of a character
`CONCAT`	Joins two or more strings into one string
`LOWER`	Converts a string to lowercase
`UPPER`	Converts a string to uppercase

Table 1.14: *SQL Clauses and Functions*

Joins

A join is used to fetch data from two or more tables based on a common field between them. It is used for combining columns from two or more tables by using values common to both tables.

There are four basic types of joins: inner, right, left, and full. Let us understand these joins with the help of Venn diagrams, which depict all possible logical relations between data sets. The circles in the Venn diagram represent the tables, and where they overlap, they indicate the rows satisfying the join condition.

1. **Inner join**: It returns rows that have matching values in both tables; in other words, the only records that need to be returned on output are those referenced in both tables. It returns records that have matching values in both tables. The **`INNER JOIN`** keyword selects all rows from both the tables as long as the condition satisfies. It is usually used to perform lookup operations, for example, to get the student's name from the student id.

   The general syntax for inner join is as follows:

   ```
   SELECT column_name(s)
   FROM table1
   INNER JOIN table2
   ON table1.column_name = table2.column_name;
   ```

   For example, let us consider the following two tables of **`Customers`** and **`Orders`** (refer to *table 1.15*):

C_Id	Customer_Name	Customer_Address
C1	Ron Stint	Mumbai
C2	Asha Rhimes	Bangalore
C3	Citra Lele	Delhi

Order_Id	Customer_Id	Order_Amount
11	C3	5000
12	C3	2000
13	C2	1000

Table 1.15: *Base Tables Customers and Orders for Joins*

Let us join these two tables using the INNER JOIN as follows:

```
SELECT  C_Id, Customer_Name, Order_Amount

FROM Customers

INNER JOIN Orders
```

```
ON Customers.C_Id = Orders.Customer_Id;
```

This join would return the following result (refer to *table 1.16)*:

C_Id	Customer_Name	Order_Amount
C3	Citra Lele	5000
C3	Citra Lele	2000
C2	Asha Rhimes	1000

Table 1.16: *Inner Join Results*

As shown in the following figure:

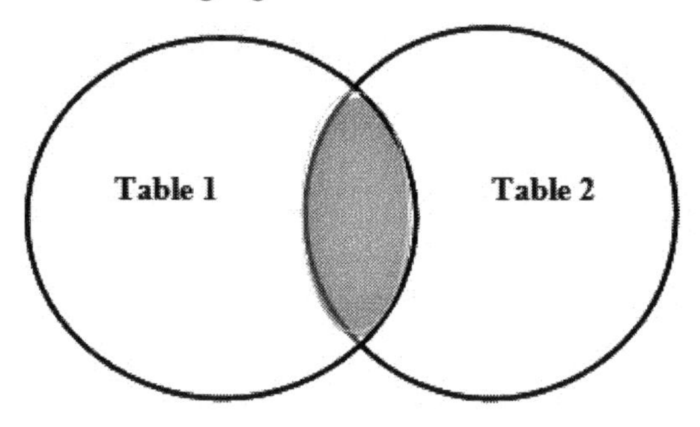

Figure 1.17: *Inner Join*

2. **Right (outer) join**: Returns all records from the right table and the matched records from the left table. The rows for which there is no matching row on the left side, the result-set will return null. If the **`ON`** clause matches 0 records in the left table, the join will still return a row in the result, but with NULL in each column from the left table.

   The general syntax for right join as follows:

   ```
   SELECT column_name(s)
   FROM table1
   RIGHT JOIN table2
   ON table1.column_name = table2.column_name;
   ```

   For example, let us consider the earlier two tables of **`Customers`** and **`Orders`** and let us join these two tables using the **`RIGHT JOIN`** as follows:

   ```
   SELECT  C_Id, Customer_Name, Order_Amount
   FROM Customers
   RIGHT JOIN Orders
   ON Customers.C_Id = Orders.Customer_Id;
   ```

   This join would return the following result (refer to *table 1.17)*:

C_Id	Customer_Name	Order_Amount
C3	Citra Lele	5000
C3	Citra Lele	2000
C2	Asha Rhimes	1000

Table 1.17: *Right Join Results*

As shown in *figure 1.18*:

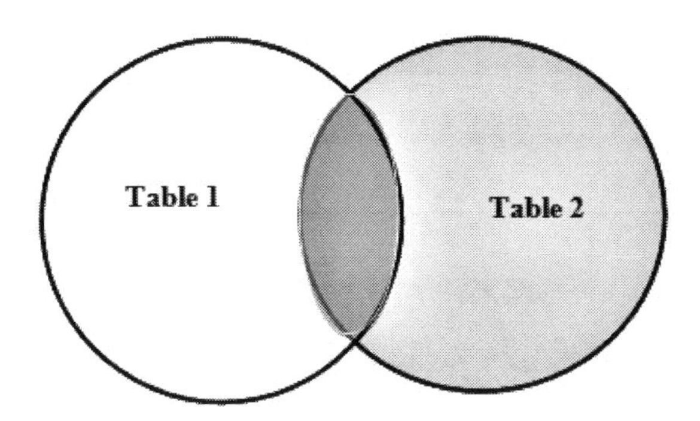

Figure 1.18: *Right Join*

3. **Left (outer) join**: This join returns all the rows of the table on the left side of the join along with matching rows of the table on the right side of the join. The rows for which there is no matching row on the right side, the result-set will return null. If the **ON** clause matches 0 records in the right table, the join will still return a row in the result, but with NULL in each column from the right table.

   The general syntax for left join as follows:

```
SELECT column_name(s)
FROM table1
LEFT JOIN table2
ON table1.column_name = table2.column_name;
```

   For example, let us consider the earlier two tables of **Customers** and **Orders** and let us join these two tables using the **LEFT JOIN** as follows:

```
SELECT  C_Id, Customer_Name, Order_Amount
FROM Customers
LEFT JOIN Orders
ON Customers.C_Id = Orders.Customer_Id;
```

   This join would return the following result (refer to *table 1.18*):

C_Id	Customer_Name	Order_Amount
C1	NULL	NULL
C3	Citra Lele	5000
C3	Citra Lele	2000
C2	Asha Rhimes	1000

***Table 1.18:** Left Join Results*

As shown in *figure 1.19*:

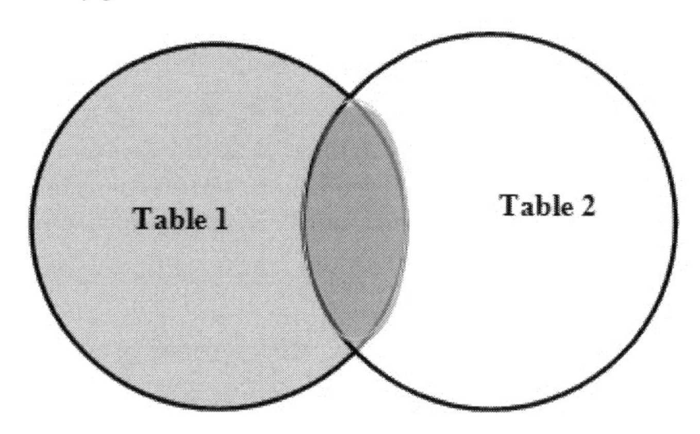

***Figure 1.19:** Left Join*

4. **Full join**: Returns all rows from an inner join; when no match is found, return nulls for that table. It combines the functions of left and right joins (refer to *figure 1.20*).

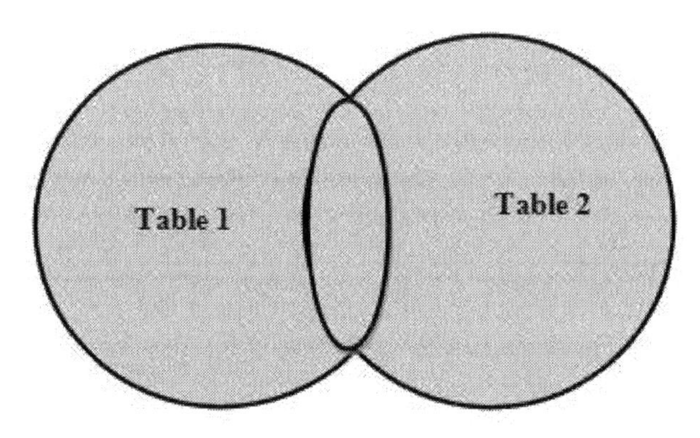

***Figure 1.20:** Full Join*

The general syntax for full join is as follows:

```
SELECT column_name(s)
FROM table1
FULL OUTER JOIN table2
ON table1.column_name = table2.column_name
WHERE condition;
```

Query optimization

A query is a request for information from a database. A query plan is a well-defined set of steps used to access data in a DBMS. A query optimizer is required to minimize issues of table locking, data corruption, slow server performance, and so on. DBMS usually have in-built tools for query optimization; for example, the SQL server profiler is a tool that is bundled with an MS SQL server.

A query optimizer is a DB component that is responsible for generating the most optimal execution plan for a query/statement by considering all the possible query plans, and this is also called query tuning based on the requirement. It typically works in the background and chooses the query plan/strategy with the least expected cost. A query optimizer generates one or more query plans for each query, and it selects the most efficient query plan to run a particular query. The query plan provides a graphical representation of how the query optimizer chooses to execute a particular query. It estimates the cost of each plan based on statistics in the data dictionary.

A query is passed to the query optimizer where optimization occurs and provides faster query processing. The main aim of an optimizer is to consume less memory, put less stress on the system, achieve less cost per query, and improve the system performance. Continuous benchmarking and profiling are a must to minimize the system bottlenecks.

An optimizer performs three main steps: parsing, binding, and optimization. Parsing is about checking query syntax in terms of the rules of the language used. In case of such errors, the optimizer will continue throwing up messages until all errors have been resolved. Binding checks whether objects are both valid and referenced correctly. The result of this step is a query tree that is made up of a basic list of the processes needed to execute the query. This contains basic instructions but does not include detailed specifics like which joins, indexes, and so on to use. Optimization works like the game of chess. It has to consider millions of combinations of possible moves, eliminate hampering moves or wrong choices, and finish the process with the best possible move/way/plan.

The process of query optimization facilitates the system to process more queries in the same amount of time as each request takes less time than un-optimized queries.

Some common tips for optimizing the queries are as follows:

1. The query executes faster if one uses the actual columns names in the **SELECT** clause instead of "*". Only retrieve the data that you need. In other words, avoid using unnecessary columns in the **SELECT** statement.

   ```
   SELECT Student_Id, Student_Name FROM Student_Details;
   ```

   Instead of:

   ```
   SELECT * FROM Student_Details;
   ```

2. Use the **WHERE** clause carefully; for example, it is better to write the query as follows:

   ```
   SELECT Student_id, Student_Name FROM Student_Details WHERE Student_
   Age > 10;
   ```

   Instead of

   ```
   SELECT Student_id, Student_Name FROM Student_Details WHERE Student_
   Age!= 5;
   ```

3. Use wildcards at the end of a phrase. If wildcards are used at the beginning, it results in the widest search/full scan possible by the database, and hence it is inefficient. Avoid using wildcard "%" at the beginning of a predicate.
4. Create joins with **INNER JOIN** rather than **WHERE**: using **WHERE** creates a Cartesian join, and this can create a problem in the case of large databases.
5. Operators like **UNION** and **DISTINCT** need to be used sparingly as they result in sorting and sorting large amounts of data slows down the execution.
6. Always better to prefix object names with the owner or schema name. The server will not search for the object outside of its owner or schema if the owner or schema name is provided.
7. Use stored procedures for frequently used data and also for tackling complex queries.
8. Use inner join instead of outer join wherever possible. The outer join should be used sparingly as it slows down the execution.

Apart from the preceding general rules, the following are some query optimization strategies too for performing optimization:

1. **Index**: It is the first strategy one should adopt to speed up a query. An index is a copy of information from a table that speeds up the retrieval data. The lack of indexes or poorly designed indexes impacts the system performance

in a negative manner. Indexes are presorted, and because of this factor, the search can be performed faster because everything is already presorted. Moreover, as an index is smaller than the table, it allows the database server to search and scan the index rather than the whole table.

2. **Vertical partition**: This strategy decreases the amount of data a SQL query needs to process; here, there is a partitioning of the table by columns.
3. **Server parameters**: Tuning of server parameters so that it can fully take advantage of the hardware resources can significantly speed up query performance.

Conclusion

In this chapter, we covered several important topics related to the database management system in terms of definition, characteristics, three-tier architecture, keys, ER model, functional dependencies, normalization, DB objects, stored procedures and triggers, SQL and PL/SQL, basic SQL query structure, joins, and query optimization.

The knowledge of these topics will help the readers to become well-versed with DBMS and its dynamics.

In the next chapter, we will discuss the basic dynamics of data warehousing and business intelligence.

Questions

1. What are the various types of relationships in a database?
2. What is the main aim of ACID properties?
3. What is the purpose of ER Model?
4. Why is the use of DBMS recommended?
5. What is the purpose of SQL?
6. What are the different types/forms of normalization?
7. What are integrity rules?
8. What is a foreign key?
9. What is the difference between DDL and DML?

CHAPTER 2
Online Transaction Processing and Data Warehouse

For a long time, **Business Intelligence** (**BI**) and **Data Warehouse** (**DW** or **DWH**) were considered to be synonymous, but in current times, their dimensions have changed considerably. They both are critical for the smooth functioning of business entities, especially medium and large-sized organizations. Today, data from various sources need to be collected and processed concurrently, and instant results need to be produced and analyzed to carry out critical customer-centric processes and operations. Data warehousing is the process of constructing and using a data warehouse by collecting different data from different sources. It usually holds historical, concise data derived from transaction data; for example, in an organization, there will be data related to operational applications and data related to data warehouse subjects; hence, there could be an operational application related to "*customer billing*" and the data warehouse related to it can hold data related to a particular subject—in this case, "*customer*".

Structure

In this chapter, we will discuss the following topics:

- Online transaction processing and data warehouse
  - Online transaction processing

- OLTP systems characteristics
- OLTP merits and demerits
- Need of data warehouse
    - Characteristics of data warehouse
    - Main components of data warehouse

Approaches for constructing a data warehouse

- Dimensional modeling used in DW design
    - Facts, dimensions, and attributes
- Types of schemas
- ETL and other toolsets available in market

Objectives

After studying this unit, you will be able to.

- Understand the concepts of online transaction processing and its characteristics, merits, and demerits, and also delve into the data warehouse and its characteristics, main components, and approaches for constructing the same.
- Discuss dimensional modeling and its various components such as facts, dimensions, and attributes used in DW design.
- Furthermore, understand topics such as types of schemas, and ETL, and other toolsets available in the market.

Introduction

Business intelligence framework deals with the collection of data, data integration, data storage, data analysis, data distribution, and reaction/decision-based on insights. This framework is responsible for linking all the elements of a business to help businesses to use data in an intelligent and insightful manner. This framework also helps to implement BI strategies in an effective and efficient manner. Data warehousing is an architectural construct that supports the BI framework and facilitates data and information processing by providing a solid platform of integrated, historical data from which businesses can do analysis. BI and DW are all about applying intelligence to data (*figure 2.1*).

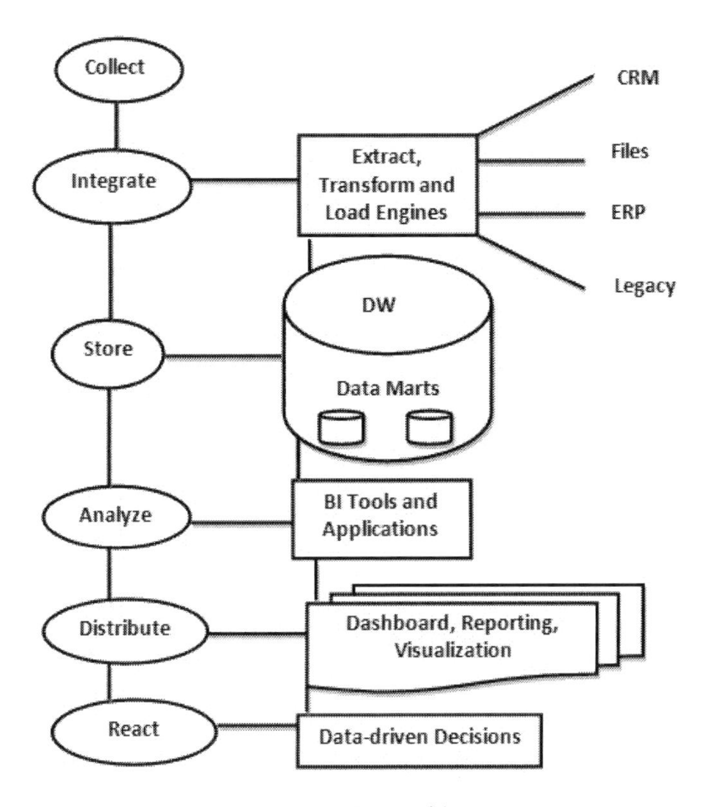

Figure 2.1: *BI-DW Architecture*

For strategic business purposes such as business insights and business intelligence, secure, cost-effective, and scalable BI and DW solutions are needed. For example, the finance department of an organization is one of the most important operations, and BI and DW tools and solutions can be used to perform what-if scenarios, predictive analysis and deal with complex tasks such as budgeting, reporting, and so on, in an efficient manner and with greater accuracy.

Online transaction processing

Online transaction processing (**OLTP**) records transactions in real-time and caters to the real-time operational needs of organizations, whereas DW acts as a storehouse of current and historical data. OLTP is a system that facilitates high transaction-oriented applications, typically for data entry and retrieval transaction processing. The transaction is not only in the context of computer or database transactions but also is defined in terms of business. Many everyday applications involve OLTP like online shopping, order entry, ticket reservation, inventory control, online banking, and so on. OLTP facilitates users to analyze database information from multiple database systems at one time. It is characterized by a large volume of data. For large and complex systems, OLTP is often integrated into web services and service-oriented architecture, and even OLTP brokering programs might be used to distribute the load of transaction processing among multiple computers. In large applications, efficient OLTP may depend on sophisticated transaction management software to facilitate the processing of large numbers of concurrent updates to the database.

Online transaction processing acts as a single source and platform for all types of business analytical needs such as analysis, planning, forecasting, and so on. OLTP applications cater to transactions that involve small amounts of data and cater to a large number of users. As OLTP systems need to be available all the time and need to maintain data integrity, they need to be ACID properties compliant. OLTP systems must typically facilitate the real-time processing of SQL transactions to support time-critical applications. A data warehouse is typically used for online transaction processing, and its main aim is to maximize the transaction processing capacity.

OLTP system characteristics

Now we will discuss OLTP characteristics as follows:

- The two main characteristics of OLTP are atomicity and concurrency. Atomicity guarantees that if one step is incomplete or fails during the transaction, the entire transaction will not be continued. According to the tenets of atomicity, each transaction must succeed or fail as a complete unit, and it cannot remain in an intermediate state. Concurrency prevents multiple users from altering the same data at the same time (one user cannot change a piece of data before another user has finished working with it). Other characteristics include frequent queries and updates, many users being involved, and there is indexed access to data.
- OLTP transactions deal with a single record or a small set of records. And all the transactions related to the record/s are handled in real-time, and processing involves more simple joins than complex ones. And the results are then stored separately from the data sources and can be presented in a variety of formats like graphs, charts, and so on. And the response time of OLTP transactions is quick.
- It has the ability to cater to a large base of users and their requests. And due to its concurrency characteristic, it is able to deal with multiple users who are trying to access the same data at the same time.

OLTP merits and demerits

The benefits of OLTP are as follows:

- Simplifies things for organizations and business entities.
- Reduces paperwork and paper trails.
- Gives more accurate forecasts for various aspects of business such as expenses, revenues, and so on.
- Provides quick response time; it is capable of handling large user volumes and data and performing complex calculations.
- Broadens the customer base by simplifying and speeding up individual processes.

The downside includes the following:

1. More susceptible to cyber attackers, intruders, and so on, as they hold private, sensitive customer information, and again for implementing computer security systems, heavy investment is needed.
2. Costly design and maintenance are involved as extra software packages are needed to maintain concurrency.
3. There could be considerable loss due to downtime caused by hardware failure, network outage, and so on.

Table 2.1 clearly helps us to understand the differences between OLTP and DW.

OLTP	DW
Data is dynamic; it is volatile.	Data is usually static; it is non-volatile.
It is transaction-driven and application-oriented.	It is analysis-driven and subject-oriented.
It has normalized data.	It has denormalized data.
It deals with transaction processing.	It deals with query processing.
It supports thousands of concurrent users.	It supports a few concurrent users.
The main purpose is that of running the business.	The main purpose is that of analyzing the business.
It has high-level transaction throughput.	It has medium to low-level transaction throughput.
It is optimized for a common set of transactions. It usually involves adding or retrieving a single row at a time per table.	It is optimized for bulk loads. It usually involves large, complex, unpredictable queries that access many rows per table.

Table 2.1: *Differences between OLTP and DW*

Need of data warehouse

Business intelligence is an umbrella term that refers to a suite of software programs, tools, and methods that facilitate the process of studying and analyzing data and deriving accurate, granular, and actionable insights to help businesses make effective and better-informed decisions. It uses various tools and methods for tactical and strategic decision-making. It converts raw data into business intelligence and insights. **Customer relationship management** (**CRM**), **decision support system** (**DSS**), **management information system** (**MIS**), and so on are some of the common BI systems.

A data warehouse is a database that collects data and information from different sources. It is subject-oriented and stores large amounts of data. It also stores a series of snapshots for an organization's operational data generated over a period of time. The DW represents the flow of data through time. Data is periodically uploaded then time-dependent data is recomputed.

Spotlight
BI systems are based on data warehouse systems; a data warehouse is the core of a BI system because that is where all the data is stored. A DW is a consolidation of data from a variety of sources that is designed to support strategic and tactical decision-making, and this is where business intelligence and its tools come into the picture. BI and DW are about blending tools, technologies, and systems in such a way that they aid the strategic uses of data.

Business intelligence and data warehouse solutions and tools help to improve the availability of data and information. They significantly simplify the data analytics architecture. They also provide data security and business continuity. These tools and solutions impact the business bottom-line positively.

Data in a data warehouse is derived from various sources, and it can be unstructured, structured, or semi-structured. By cleaning, processing, and merging data from various sources, a data warehouse and BI tools can provide organizations with a holistic view of all their data. This also facilitates the process of data mining. Data mining is the process of discovering patterns in large data sets to identify patterns and predict future trends. The data or knowledge extracted by data mining can be used for many purposes, such as risk management, market analysis, market profiling, customer retention, summary reports on various dimensions, and so on.

There are three main types of data warehouses. A data mart is usually designed to cater to the needs of a specific department or functional unit, and it is a subset of a

DW. The operational data store contains the latest snapshot of operational data, and it is widely used in routine activities. It acts as an interim area for a data warehouse. Enterprise data warehouse is a centralized, strategic repository that consolidates data from multiple sources and provides analytical information about the core operations of an enterprise.

Characteristics of DW

Some characteristics of DW are as follows:

- A DW is non-volatile in nature, which means the previous data is not overwritten or erased when new data is added to it. Therefore, historical data will never undergo any change.
- As a DW provides information specific to a particular subject and helps organizations to make decisions related to particular subjects such as customers, products, and so on, and not around an organization's operations, it is subject-oriented in nature.
- In a DW, data from several disparate sources are integrated, and the DW provides a unified view of this integrated data. For example, sources A and B may have different ways of identifying a customer, but in a DW, there will be only a single way of identifying a customer.
- Data in a DW is related to a particular time period. This time-variant characteristic is related to historical data. Unlike transaction-based systems where real-time data is the main focus, in DW, it is all about historical data; for example, the focal point can be 3–6 months of historical data.

Main components of data warehouse

There are several logical and physical components. Apart from the logical components such as raw or source data coming from various sources, schemas, tables, reports, data visualization, data sets, and so on, and physical components such as the data warehouse itself, platforms, and so on, the following are the main components of a DW.

- **Database**: It is the foundation or core component of DW architecture.
- **Metadata**: It is data about data, and it describes the DW and its objects. It is used for building, maintaining, managing, implementing, and using the DW. It is managed with the help of accompanying software.

  There are three main categories: operational, business, and technical. Operational metadata holds information in terms of the currency of data and data lineage. Currency of data refers to the data being active, archived, or purged. The lineage of data is about the history of data migrated, and the transformation applied to it. It also holds business information, algorithms for granularity, summarization, aggregation, and so on, rules related to data refresh, data purge, data transformation, and so on. Business metadata contains a business definition, data ownership information, and changing policies. Technical metadata contains primary and foreign key attributes, tables and columns, database system names, data types, and so on.

Metadata is a shorthand depiction of data that leads us to detailed data. It is a directory that helps us to locate objects in a DW. It is often used to describe rules, aggregations, transformations, and so on.

- **Load manager**: It is the front-end component, and it performs all the operations associated with the extraction and loading processes of data. It is responsible for transforming and preparing the data before it enters the DW; it performs transformations into a structure similar to one in the DW.

  The higher the degree of overlap between the data sources, the larger the load manager will be.

- **Warehouse manager**: It performs operations associated with the management of the data in the DW. It deals with operations like analysis of data to ensure consistency, creation of indexes and views, generation of denormalization and aggregations, transformation and merging of source data and archiving and backing up data. It consists of C programs, shell scripts, third-party software programs, and so on.

  It is also responsible for creating partition views, indexes, and business views. It updates the existing aggregations and creates new ones as well. It keeps track of the data to perform referential integrity checks. It also performs backup operations on the data in the DW.

- **Query manager**: It is the back-end component, and it performs all the operations related to the management of user queries. By directing the queries to appropriate tables, the query manager speeds up the query request and response process. It is responsible for scheduling the execution of the queries, and it also presents the data to the users in an understandable format.

- **End-user access tools**: There are various areas related to the DW where such tools can be utilized. They are used for data reporting and querying, data mining, online analytical processing, executive information systems, and so on. Data dippers are basic tools that facilitate the generation of standard reports. Reporting tools provide reports in various formats. OLAP tools facilitate the generation of complex charts and graphs and provide complex online analysis against live data.

Figure 2.2 is the pictorial depiction of all the main components of a data warehouse.

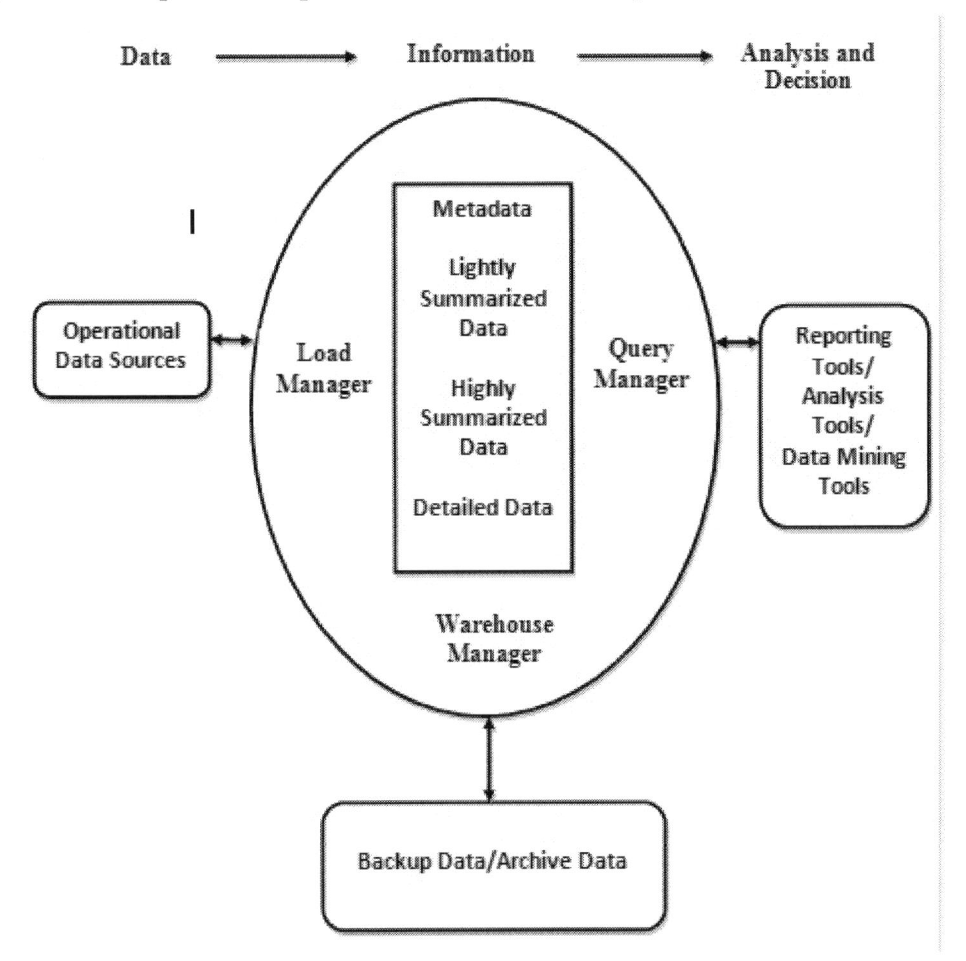

Figure 2.2: *Main Components of Data Warehouse*

Approaches for constructing a data warehouse

There are three major ways/approaches of constructing a DW: bottom-up, top-down, and hybrid.

- **Bottom-up**: In the bottom-up design approach (depicted in *figure 2.3)*, all the data marts are created first to facilitate analysis and reporting capability; DW is created from a series of incremental data marts. Data marts are directly loaded with the data from the source systems. These data marts are then integrated to build a complete larger DW. The integration of data marts is implemented using *Ralph Kimball's* (is the one who introduced the data warehouse/business intelligence industry to the world of dimensional modeling) data warehousing architecture, also known as bus architecture. The different data marts are connected via a dimensional bus system. In this type of architecture, a dimension is shared between facts in two or more data marts. These dimensions are called **conformed dimensions**. These conformed dimensions are integrated from data marts, and then the complete DW is built. *Kimball* defines DW as *"a copy of transaction data specifically structured for query and analysis."*

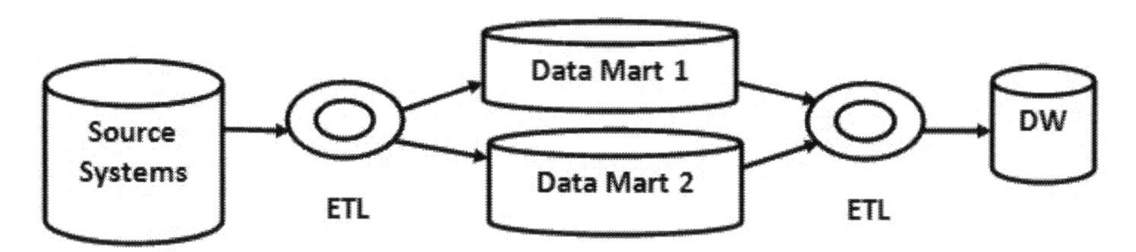

Figure 2.3: *Bottom-Up Approach*

The benefits are high flexibility, quick delivery, and user-friendliness as it contains consistent data marts and is based on the individual business departments' information needs. The integration of new data can be easily done, and it is easier to expand the DW as it provides a light infrastructure. The link between all data marts makes queries through all data possible. As the data marts are created first, reports can be generated quickly. The disadvantages are redundant data is present, and it is subject to several revisions; and hence, the process of maintenance becomes difficult. It needs to integrate incremental data marts, which is time-consuming, and it also needs the coordination of multiple teams.

- **Top-down**: In the top-down approach (depicted in *figure 2.4*), the data warehouse is built first. Data is extracted from the various sources, and then it is loaded and validated in the staging area, and after its accuracy is confirmed, it is used to populate the data warehouse. The data marts are then created from the data warehouse. It uses a normalized enterprise data model. "*Atomic*" data, which is data at the lowest level of detail, are stored in the data warehouse. Thereafter, dimensional data marts containing data needed for specific departments are created from the data warehouse. This approach is based on *Bill Inmon's* (recognized by many as the father of the data warehouse) design approach.

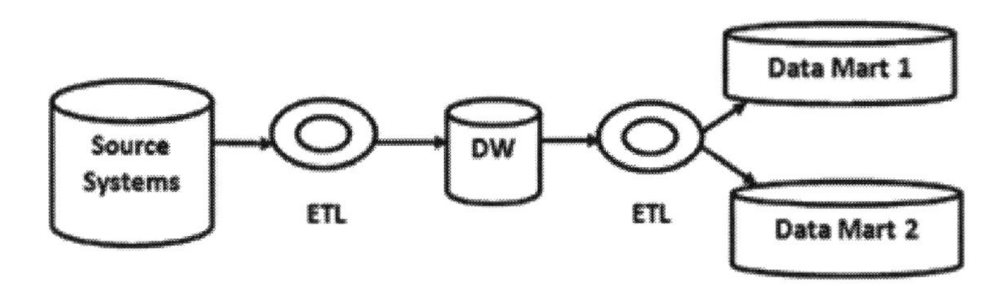

Figure 2.4: *Top-down Approach*

The advantages are facilitated easy creation of new data marts from the DW and allows easy maintenance. It gives consistent dimensional views of data across data marts since all the data marts are created from the data warehouse. It provides integrated, flexible architecture and a single point of control. The downside includes: the implementation cost and risk are high, and this approach is not so flexible to the changing needs of various departments during the implementation process. It needs longer start-up time, and too much time can be spent in analyzing and figuring out problems.

- **Hybrid**: In the hybrid approach, Kimball-style dimensional data warehouse and Inmon-style normalized relational database are combined. It attempts to blend the best of both bottom-up and top-down design approaches. It tries to blend the speed of the bottom-up approach with the aspect of integration in the top-down approach. It is in 3NF to eliminate data redundancy. It provides an environment that combines physical integration with virtual integration techniques. Examples include *Apache Hadoop*, *IBM Information Server*, and so on. The benefits include: improved query performance, lower cost of storage, supports more data sources, and need less maintenance. The disadvantages are as it relies heavily on ETL tools, it is not always guaranteed that all tools will comply with the architecture. Moreover, backfilling a DW can be quite a daunting task.

Dimensional modeling used in DW design

Dimensional modeling was developed by *Ralph Kimball* (one of the original architects of data warehousing), and it is a set of concepts and techniques used in data warehouse design, and it is used for decision support and business analysis. It is different from ER modeling; ER Modeling is a structural diagram/a graphical representation that depicts the attributes of entities and the relationships among them. Dimensional modeling is the underlying data model used by many of the OLAP systems. It does not necessarily involve a relational database.

Different types of modeling techniques have a different purposes; for example, entity-relationship model is used to eliminate data redundancy and quickly perform the operations of insert, update and delete, whereas dimensional modeling deals with denormalized structures that are designed and optimized for performing the operation of select (that is a retrieval of data). The base of the dimensional model is built from fact tables and dimension tables.

The benefits of dimensional modeling are as follows:

- Allows the data warehouse to be flexible enough to change and be easily extensible as it allows new requirements to be incorporated.
- Provides a better understanding of business processes in the form of facts and dimensions.
- Facilitates faster retrieval of data, especially for ad-hoc queries, as it is optimized due to its denormalized schema.

It is best suited for the snowflake schema and star schema. It involves the following stages:

- The first step is that of identifying the business objectives and processes that need to be modeled. Their identification depends on the quality of data available and the data analysis needs of the business in question.
- The second step is that of identifying granularity, and granularity is the lowest level of information stored in the table. It is important to define this level of detail as the business problem, and its solution is described in terms of grain. A grain describes exactly what a record in a fact table represents (the level of detail). For example, if a table contains sales data for every day, then it should be daily granularity. The fact tables should be consistent with the pre-defined granularity.
- The third step is that of identifying dimensions and their attributes. Dimensions are things or objects, or nouns that categorize and describe data warehouse facts and measures so as to derive answers for a business problem or question. A data warehouse stores descriptive attributes in the form of columns in dimension tables.
- The fourth step is that of identifying the fact. A fact table contains all the measurable data like numeral values (cost per unit, price, and more).
- The fifth step is that of building the schema, which is a database structure and is used to implement the dimensional model.

Figure 2.5 depicts the various steps involved in data warehouse design.

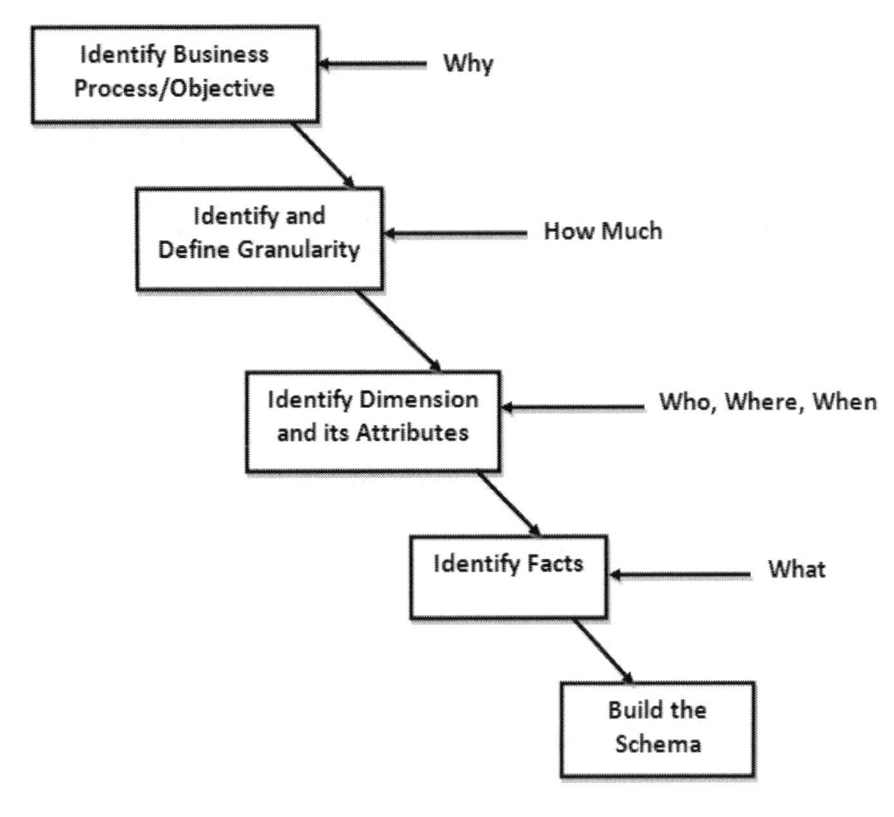

Figure 2.5: *Dimensional Modeling*

Facts, dimensions, and attributes

The following are important components or constructs of dimensional modeling:

- **Facts**: They are business metrics or measurements, either factual data or quantitative, derived from the business processes. Facts point to the key-value at the lowest level of each dimension table. Facts are normally but not always numeric values that could be aggregated, for example, the number of products sold per quarter. A fact table is a primary table in a dimensional model, and it contains facts or measurements and foreign keys to the dimension table. Facts can be additive, non-additive, or semi-additive. Additive facts are business measures that can be aggregated across all dimensions. Non-additive facts are business measures that cannot be aggregated across any dimension. Semi-additive facts are business measures that can be aggregated across some dimensions and not across others.
- **Dimensions**: They are called contexts and are related to events or objects in the real world, and they give more information about the business facts. They

are business descriptors and qualifiers that make the facts meaningful and specify them in terms of who, where, and what. In other words, a dimension is a window to view the information or descriptive characteristics in the facts with the help of attributes. They are essentially an entry point for getting at the facts. Dimension tables are used to describe dimensions, and they contain dimension keys, values, and attributes. For example, the customer dimension will contain attributes such as customer name, customer address, and so on.

- **Attributes**: They are the various characteristics/columns of a dimension. An attribute describes a level of summary within a dimension hierarchy.

Types of schemas

A schema is a logical description of the entire data warehouse. Just as relational data models are used by databases for their logical structure; similarly, data warehouses use various types of schemas for the same purpose. The following are three main types of DW schemas:

- **Star**: It is the simplest type of schema, and it is best used for querying large data sets. It can be implemented in both simple data marts and also in large data warehouses. It is known as **star schema** as its structure looks like a star. In this schema, the center of the star represents the fact table, and the points or tips denote the various denormalized dimension tables. A simple star schema consists of one fact table, whereas a complex star schema can have more than one fact table.

  It usually has one or more large fact tables that hold the primary information and a number of smaller dimension tables or lookup tables, and each of these contains information about the entries for a particular attribute in the fact table. Usually, the fact tables are in third normal form (3NF), whereas dimensional tables are denormalized. The fact tables contain all the measurable data, whereas the dimension tables will have attributes that relate to the fact data. Every dimension in a star is represented with only one dimension table, and it contains a set of attributes. The dimension table is linked to the fact table using a foreign key, and the dimension tables are not joined to each other.

  To optimize or fine-tune star queries: A cost-based optimizer should be used, the initialization parameter should be set to true, and a bitmap index should be built on each of the foreign key columns of the fact table/s. A bitmap index is a special type of database indexing that uses bitmaps.

The main advantages of star schema are the most widely used as it is supported by a large number of BI systems and DW systems. Performance enhancement is another benefit, and it facilitates optimal disk usage. It simplifies business logic for reporting purposes. The data can be navigated easily. The main disadvantages are that it does not enforce data integrity as well as it is in a highly denormalized state. And due to this denormalized state, it is not flexible in terms of analytical needs, and there is data redundancy; there is a lack of accuracy and consistency. In the case of large dimension tables, there could be a slower response in query time.

Spotlight

A star schema store all attributes for a dimension into one flattened table, and this requires more disk space than a more normalized snowflake schema.

A star schema (refer to *figure 2.6*) is a basic schema, whereas a snowflake schema is an extended version of the star schema as it has additional dimensions.

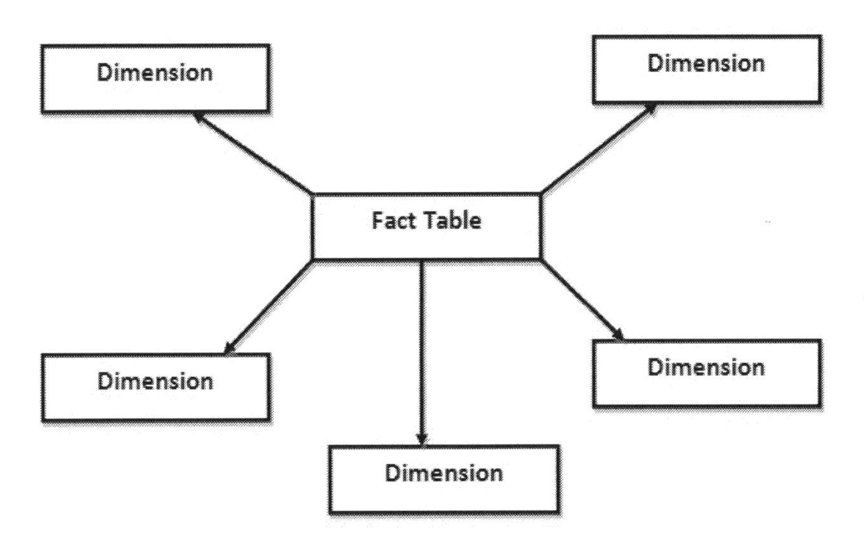

Figure 2.6: *Star Schema*

Example of star schema: In the sales (fact table), the following are the main dimensions: city, country, employees, and products (refer to *figure 2.7*). The schema contains a central fact table for sales that includes keys to each of the four dimensions and two measures of total quantity and total sales.

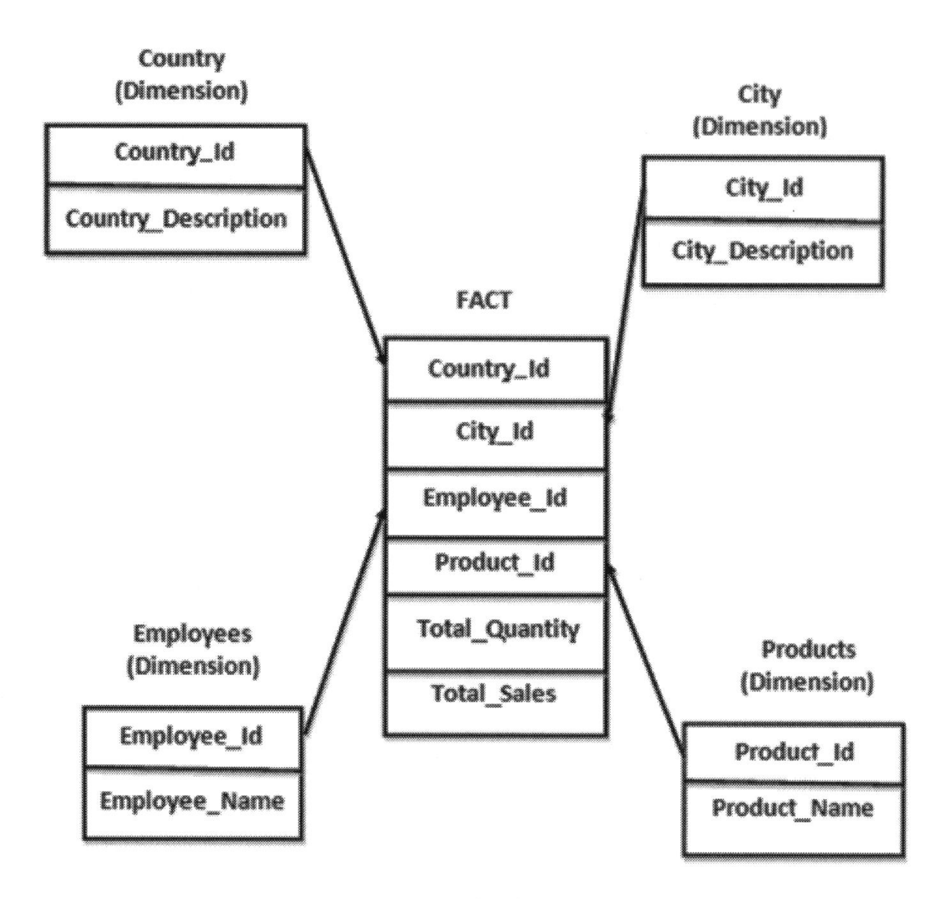

Figure 2.7: *Example of Star Schema*

- **Snowflake**: It is a variant of the star schema wherein each point or tip of the star expands or explodes into more points (refer to *figure 2.8*). In a star schema, each dimension is related to a single dimensional table, whereas in a snowflake schema, that dimensional table is normalized into multiple lookup tables, and each lookup table represents a level in the dimensional hierarchy, and this helps in reducing redundancy. For example, the product dimensions can be normalized into product table, product description table, product category table, and so on.

  This schema has each fact surrounded by its associated dimensions (as in a star schema), and then these dimensions are further related to other dimensions, branching out into a snowflake pattern.

Spotlight
The main difference between star and snowflake schema is that the dimension table in a snowflake schema is maintained in a normalized form to reduce redundancy. The benefit here is that such normalized tables are easy to maintain and save a lot of storage space. However, it also means that more joins will be needed to execute queries, and this in turn adversely affects the performance of the system.

The main benefit of snowflake schema is increased flexibility, minimized disk storage due to normalizing attributes, more accuracy and consistency, and minimized disk storage requirements. The main disadvantage is more complex queries as more tables are needed to be joined, and additional maintenance efforts are needed to increase the number of lookup tables.

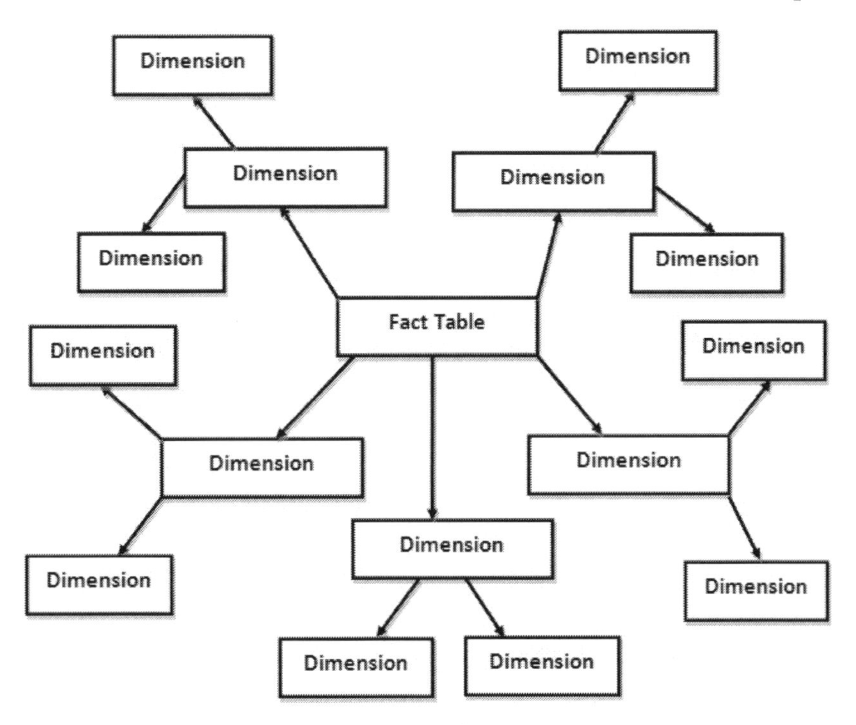

***Figure 2.8:** Snowflake Schema*

Example of snowflake schema (refer to *figure 2.9*): In the sales (fact table), these are the main dimensions: city, country, employees, and products. The schema contains a central fact table for sales that has keys to each of the four dimensions, along with two measures of total quantity and total sales. The dimension product in a star schema is now normalized to snowflake schema with two tables, products, and vendors. The products table has the attributes of **Product_Id** and **Product_Name**. The **Product_Id** is linked to the Vendors dimension table, which contains **Vendor_Name** and **Product_ID**.

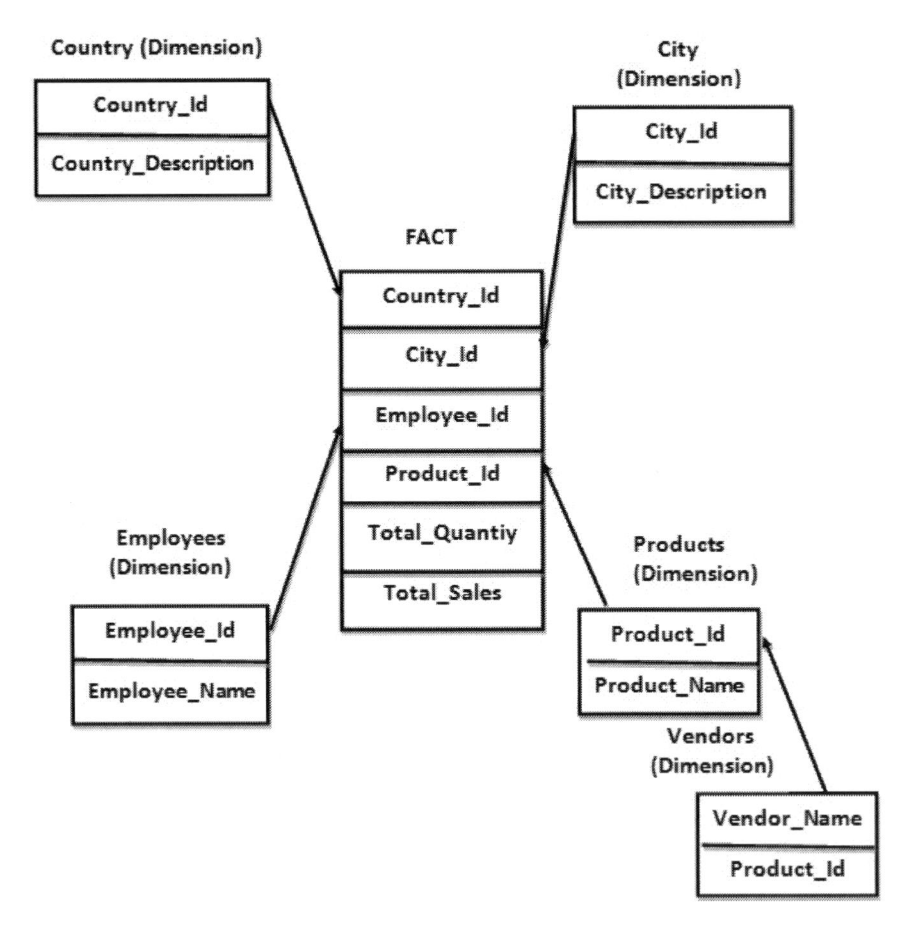

Figure 2.9: *Example of Snowflake Schema*

Table 2.2 shows the various differences between star and snowflake schemas.

Star schema	Snowflake schema
Easy to understand and design	Difficult to understand and design
The time needed for query execution is less as there are fewer joins, foreign keys involved	Comparatively more due to excessive use of join, foreign keys

Has redundant data and hence not easy to maintain	No data redundancy; and hence, easier to maintain
Denormalized data structure	Normalized data structure
A fewer number of joins	The higher number of joins
The dimension table has the hierarchies for the dimensions	The hierarchies are separated into different tables
Each of the dimensions is represented in a single table, and this schema should not have any hierarchies between dimensions	Here at least one hierarchy needs to be present between dimensions tables
Follows the top-down design approach	Follows the bottom-up design approach
Facilitates faster cube processing	Cube processing might be slower due to complex joins

Table 2.2: *Differences between Star Scheme and Snowflake Schema*

- **Fact constellation**: It is mainly used in sophisticated applications, and it is more complex than star schema and snowflake schema. For each star schema or snowflake schema, it is possible to create a fact constellation schema.

  It is a collection of multiple fact tables which share some common dimension tables. It can be viewed as a collection of several star schemas, and therefore, it is also known as **galaxy schema**.

  Figure 2.10 is a pictorial depiction of the fact constellation schema.

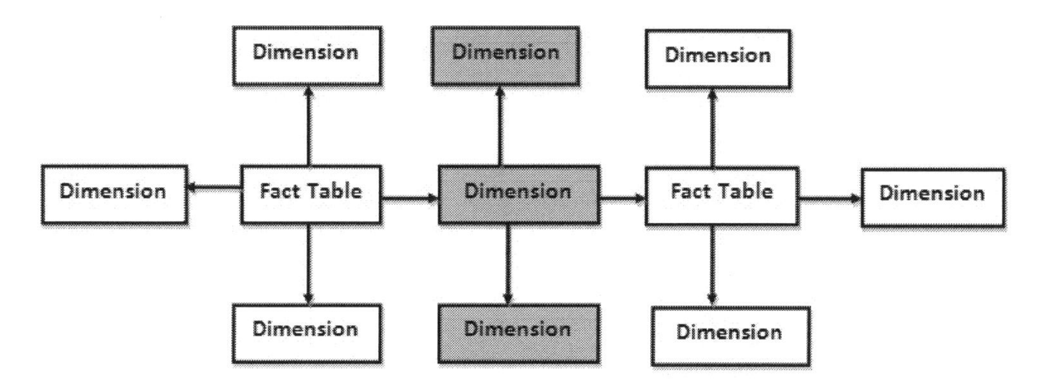

Figure 2.10*: Fact Constellation Schema*

(The Shaded Rectangles Denote Common Dimension Tables)

The main advantages of fact constellation are as follows: It is flexible, and there is no data redundancy, and moreover, low memory/space is required. The main disadvantages are the high level of complexity due to the high number of aggregations; hence, difficult to implement and maintain, and data analysis becomes difficult due to complex design.

Figure 2.11 depicts the fact constellation schema by an example.

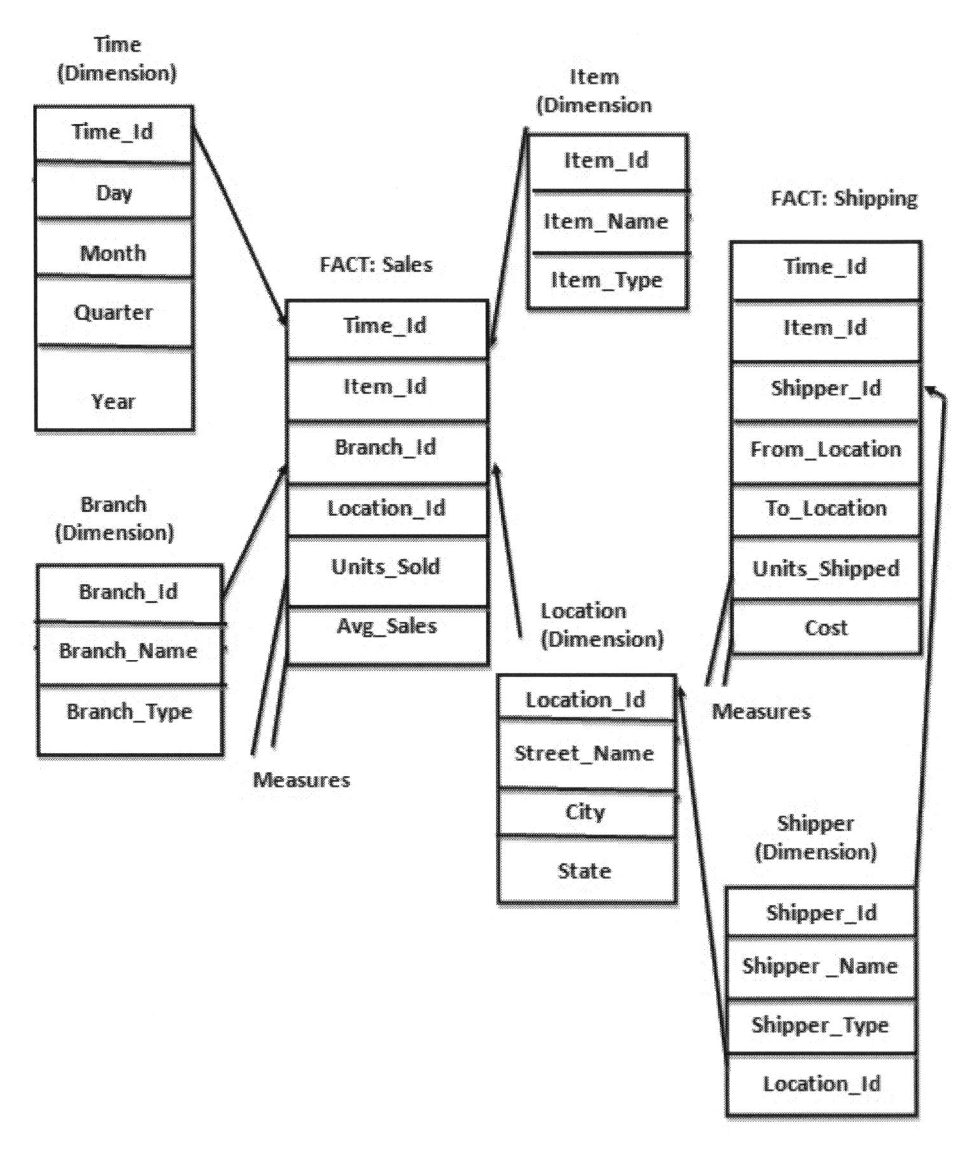

Figure 2.11: *Example of Fact Constellation Schema*

ETL and other tools sets available in market

Most organizations have their data stored in a variety of locations, right from in-house databases to external sources like cloud storage services, BI tools, and so on, and they do not want to construct and maintain a separate data pipeline; hence, they use ETL tools. **Extract, transform, and load** (**ETL**) is a data warehousing process that extracts and blends raw data from various sources, then transforms the data and eventually loads into a DW. One of the major aims of ETL is to reduce data complexity. Some of the popular ETL tools are as follows:

- **Oracle data integrator (ODI)**: ODI has great ETL capabilities that also leverage the advantages of the database. But still, it does not provide the full spectrum of ETL features. Oracle does have features that can support other ETL tools and solutions. ODI works in tandem with Oracle Warehouse Builder to handle the entire DW business workflow dynamics.
- **Skyvia**: It is an all-in-one, easy-to-use cloud data platform. It facilitates easy data integration, management, and visualization. Its data integration module allows organizations to easily integrate without the need for coding to integrate data with other cloud applications and databases like *Amazon Redshift*, *Salesforce*, *Zendesk*, *Shopify*, and so on.
- **Voracity**: It is an all-in-one, fastest, most affordable data management platform. Apart from ETL, it has other robust features like data governance and analytics.
- **Xplenty**: It is an easy-to-use, point-and-click platform. It has powerful transformation tools to transform data into an analysis-friendly form. It has excellent customer support features. It has a user-friendly graphical user interface.
- **CloverDX**: It is a fully customizable robust, lightweight, and flexible data platform. While other platforms offer low code or no code features, CloverDX goes one step further by allowing any aspect of the platform to be customizable, and this is possible using a simple built-in scripting language.
- **Amazon redshift**: It is a secure, scalable, and cost-effective cloud-based DW solution that is a part of the Amazon Web Services cloud computing platform. It can handle large-scale data storage, data migration, and so on; it is all about Big Data. It uses **massively parallel processing** (**MPP**) architecture which loads data at a super-fast speed.

Each Amazon redshift data warehouse contains a collection of computing resources called as **nodes**, which are organized in a cluster. Each cluster has its own engine and has at least one database.

Conclusion

In this chapter, we discussed the definitions of **business intelligence** (**BI**) and **data warehousing** (**DW**), main components of DW, approaches for constructing DW, online transaction processing, dimensional modeling and its components, ETL, and much more.

After reading this chapter, the readers will have gained a firm grip over the introductory concepts and topics related to BI, DW, Schemas, and much more.

And this will set the stage for the next chapter, which covers the deeper dynamics of BI and DW.

Questions

1. What is the role of metadata?
2. What is business intelligence?
3. What are the different design schemas in dimensional modeling?
4. What is an OLTP system?
5. What do dimensions and attributes denote?
6. Why is data warehousing important?
7. What are the differences between star scheme and snowflake schema?

CHAPTER 3

Business Intelligence and Its Deeper Dynamics

Successful **business intelligence** (**BI**) platforms and solutions are about agile data. Agile data is all about user-oriented focus, cohesive approach, lean and continuous delivery of value, and big picture perspective.

Business intelligence is critical for the smooth functioning of business entities, especially medium, and large-sized organizations. Today, data from various sources need to be collected and processed concurrently, and instant results need to be produced and analyzed to carry out critical customer-centric processes and operations, and this is where BI systems and solutions step in.

Structure

In this chapter, we will discuss the following topics:

- Business intelligence and its deeper dynamics
  - What is business intelligence
    - Characteristics
  - Data quality: a real challenge
    - Data quality best practices

- Structured versus unstructured data
  - Differences between structured and unstructured data
- Data lakes
  - Data lake versus data warehouse
  - Main components of a data lake
- Modern business intelligence system
  - Benefits and uses cases of modern BI

Objectives

After studying this unit, you will be able to:

- Understand the concepts of BI and its deeper dynamics in terms of what is a business intelligence and its characteristics.
- Discuss data quality and the challenges faced by it, and the main data quality best practices.
- Discuss concepts like various types of data and also deal with a data lake and its main components.
- Furthermore, understand topics like modern business intelligence systems and their benefits and use cases.

Business intelligence

Business intelligence and its framework are about turning big data into valuable insights, and it does this using a set of software solutions and services. For strategic business purposes such as business insights and business intelligence, secure, cost-effective, and scalable BI and DW solutions are needed. For example, the finance department of an organization is one of the most important operations, and BI and DW tools and solutions can be used to perform what-if scenarios, predictive analysis, and deal with complex tasks such as budgeting, reporting, and so on, in an efficient manner and with greater accuracy.

Business intelligence framework deals with the collection of data, data integration, data storage, data analysis, data distribution, and reaction/decision based on insights. This framework is responsible for linking all the elements of a business to help businesses use data in an intelligent and insightful manner. This framework also helps to implement BI strategies in an effective and efficient manner. Data warehousing is an architectural construct that supports the BI framework and facilitates data and information processing by providing a solid platform of integrated, historical data from which businesses can do analysis. BI combined with data warehousing is about applying intelligence to data.

As per the definition of Wikipedia: "*Business intelligence (BI) is a set of theories, methodologies, processes, architectures, and technologies that transform raw data into meaningful and useful information for business purposes. BI can handle large amounts of information to help identify and develop new opportunities. Making use of new opportunities and implementing an effective strategy can provide a competitive market advantage and long-term stability.*"

Business intelligence is not only an IT-driven setup but also in the larger scheme of things; it is a business-led initiative. BI is much more than a way to organize and access data; it is the information itself that helps businesses to make informed decisions. It is simply not some software application; it is a single source of information for an entire organization. It facilitates forecasting, reporting, and so on by ensuring that all these aspects are automatically updated and are kept consistent and accurate.

In other words, BI is a set of technologies, tools, and processes that convert raw data into insightful information about the nature of the business. According to industry findings, organizations that use business intelligence tools witness a five-time increase in customer experience analysis and decision-making speed. Some of the main ways of leveraging BI are reports, data visualizations, dashboards, and so on.

It starts with the process of capturing data from across an organization's departments and external sources. Thereafter, it does a lot of operations so that data can be properly contextualized. It prepares the data for analysis, runs queries against the data, and provides results in the form of graphs, reports, and so on. And all this can be achieved in a matter of minutes.

The terms BI and business analytics are often used interchangeably. But in reality, business analytics is a subset of BI. BI is to do with the overall tools and technologies that deal with who, what, where, when, why, and how, whereas business analytics is more do with a specific problem using certain methods.

As big data has become popular, so has BI. Data is being spewed at breakneck speed. But all this data is useless if we cannot make sense of it and use it to optimize business processes and operations. And this is where BI comes into play. With the help of its plethora of intelligence tools and technologies, it can cater to the needs of businesses of all types and sizes.

The top BI tools include *Dundas BI, Sisense, Tableau, Spotfire,* and many more. These tools are responsible for preparing data for analysis so that organizations can use this data to create dashboards, data visualizations, advanced statistical analysis, and so on. According to industry experts, BI tools help organizations reach a better data maturity level, going right from being data-aware to data proficient to data-savvy and finally to being data-driven.

Figure 3.1 exhibits the main components of BI:

Figure 3.1: *Main Components of BI*

BI characteristics

Business intelligence characteristics/features aim to help businesses smoothen out their operations, make data-driven decisions in real-time, understand the health of their business, and achieve business goals effectively. The main characteristics are as follows:

- **Data visualization**: It is one of the main characteristics of BI. It helps to present large volumes of data in a user-friendly manner and in a simplified format. It provides visualizations for the key performance indicators through its roll-up features. It also provides drill-down features into the details to pinpoint something which is not performing as planned. As BI provides a single source of truth, all the metrics are also found in one place, and organizations can access them easily at any time, and this eliminates the need to check multiple data sources separately.

- **Data analysis and predictive analytics**: BI platforms come with self-service features and interfaces, and this allows each and every user, both technical and non-technical, the ability to access data for analysis in a user-friendly manner.
- **Secure data access**: BI platforms, especially modern-day ones, go beyond the typical security features of multi-factor authentication and so on. They incorporate extra layers of security in the form of encryption, security certificates, security tokens, and so on.
- **Reports and dashboards**: These features allow BI to generate intuitive, insightful reports. It has the ability to extract data from all types of sources and then uses this integrated data environment to provide deep insights. Reporting of all types can be done; examples include time-series, drill-down, slice and dice analysis, and so on, operation, ad-hoc.
- **Data engineering**: It deals with data extraction, cleansing, integration, governance, and quality. A prudent choice of BI resources combined with the right human resources is needed to perform data engineering operations. Data engineering also helps to deal with several BI bottlenecks like facilitation of faster ad-hoc queries, the addition of data or transformations without any hassles, and so on.
- **Import**: BI allows organizations to import application-based data such as charts, tables, and so on in a seamless manner.
- **What-if analysis**: Using existing data with the power of BI, organizations can design strategies to undertake accurate strategic planning. BI helps organizations to study and analyze the impact and effectiveness of potential decisions before actually taking them. It helps organizations to study the risks and rewards in an objective manner.
- **Database support**: Modern-day BI platforms and tools provide adaptability and support for varied database systems and hence are able to pull data from diverse data sources.

Data quality: a real challenge

The data quality is determined by several factors such as duplication, noise, consistency, no errors, and so on. Hence, this is where data cleansing comes into play. According to industry research findings, one in five companies are reported to have lost a customer as a result of bad data quality, and more than a quarter feel that accurate data is their greatest data challenge. Poor data quality affects the business operations, processes, and objectives in a detrimental manner. Such a challenge is faced due to factors such as data inaccuracy, inconsistency, duplication, and so on.

The foundation and success of any organization is data. We can view data as the base, and on top of data, we have information (data in context), and on top of this information, we have knowledge (actionable information), and at the topmost level, we wisdom (applied knowledge). As they say, bad data quality is not very good and healthy for businesses.

According to *Gartner's* 2016 data quality market survey, the impact of poor quality data on the average annual financial costs of organizations worldwide increased by 10% in 2016. It rose from 8.8 million US dollars in 2015 to 9.8 million US dollars in 2016.

For determining the quality of data, it needs to be measured. It is all about finding out the degree of data consistency and accuracy. Apart from these two main components, other factors such as storage, accessibility, and so on also play a critical role.

If proper precautions are not taken to improve the quality of data before analyzing it, then organizations are likely to lose revenue, customers, opportunities, and above all, business goodwill. Mere automation will not improve data quality; automation will work only with clean, consistent, and complete data. Poor data quality also affects compliance requirements; the high quality of data is a must to meet the compliance requirements and objectives in an effective manner.

The complexities of managing data have increased exponentially in the last 20 years. As per industry research, 93% of organizations are actively looking for data quality problems and challenges, but the majority still say that problems and challenges come to the surface only when they are reported by customers, employees, and so on.

Duplicate data is a major challenge. Apart from this, data quality challenges can be faced when mergers occur. Such scenarios lead to inconsistencies in data.

Data quality best practices

According to the Data Warehouse Institute "*data quality problems cost US businesses more than 600 billion US dollars a year.*" And this is where data quality best practices come into play; they help to minimize the negative impact of poor data quality. Data quality best practices help in maximizing data quality by ensuring that the data is maintained in such a way that it helps organizations to meet their goals.

- **Profiling**: Also known as data assessment or data discovery, is a set of methods and tools used for collecting statistics and findings that are related to data quality. Profiling tools collect these statistics by assessing various aspects of data such as structure, content, and so on. With the help of these, organizations can pinpoint problems and challenges related to data quality. There are several profiling options such as pattern analysis, range analysis, completeness analysis, and so on that help to improve data quality.
- **Buy-in**: Getting approval and buy-in from all stakeholders is a must. Making the aspect of data quality an integral part of the corporate culture is needed to ensure each and everyone involved in the process is accountable for doing their part perfectly, and each and every one will be equally responsible for data hygiene and quality successes and failures. Such a strategy will prevent stakeholders from playing games such as finger-pointing, passing the buck, and so on.
- **Data Stewards**: A data Steward's main aim is to preserve data quality and integrity. Usually, data stewards are assigned to data sets that they maintain in terms of quality and integrity.
- **Compliance**: Using data quality monitoring tools and auditing processes can help companies meet not only compliance standards and mandates but also ensure data quality standards and safeguards against potential data leaks are put in place. Frequent, incremental audits are critical to capture data quality anomalies in a timely manner. They help to pinpoint inconsistency, incompleteness, inaccuracy, and so on in the datasets in a timely manner.
- **Eliminating duplicate data**: Duplicate data identification tools are needed to be used to bring about better consistency and accuracy of data. The concept of master data is very important in minimizing duplication of data.
- **Metrics**: There need to be clear and comprehensive metrics for evaluating the whole data quality paradigm.
- **Governance**: Data governance is a framework of policies, guidelines, and standards that needs to be made a part of the corporate culture to establish data quality standards as an integral part of the workplace DNA.
- **Training and certifications**: These aspects are important to understand the deeper dynamics of data quality in terms of tools, processes, techniques, principles, and practices.
- **Cloud computing**: It helps to integrate multiple data streams in a seamless manner, which means fewer errors in the data. By adopting a cloud-native solution and moving all data quality tools into these solutions, it becomes easier for organizations to adopt these tools and implement centralized

reusable rules management and preloaded templates across all data sources. These tools help in building integrated data pipelines so patterns, insights, trends, and so on can be got from the cloud itself. Newer hybrid cloud technologies such as cloud containers, data warehouses, and so on pinpoint, correct, and monitor data quality problems in an efficient and effective way, thereby introducing better data quality standards and practices.

Structured versus unstructured

Data comes in many forms, and the two main forms are structured and unstructured. Structured data, also called **quantitative data**, is highly specific, well-organized whereas unstructured data also called **qualitative data**, has no pre-defined format or organization. Structured data is based on a specific, pre-defined data model. Unstructured data is not based on any data model, and due to this, there are a lot of ambiguities in the data.

As structured data (refer to *figure 3.2)* is well-formatted and organized in the form of spreadsheets, relational databases, and so on (each of these has structured rows and columns that can be sorted) and this makes it easy for the users to query and analyze it. Structured data is considered the most "*traditional*" form of data storage. It is organized for machines to understand and process. It can work easily with most standard analytical models. It has revolutionized paper-based systems that organizations implemented for business intelligence decades ago.

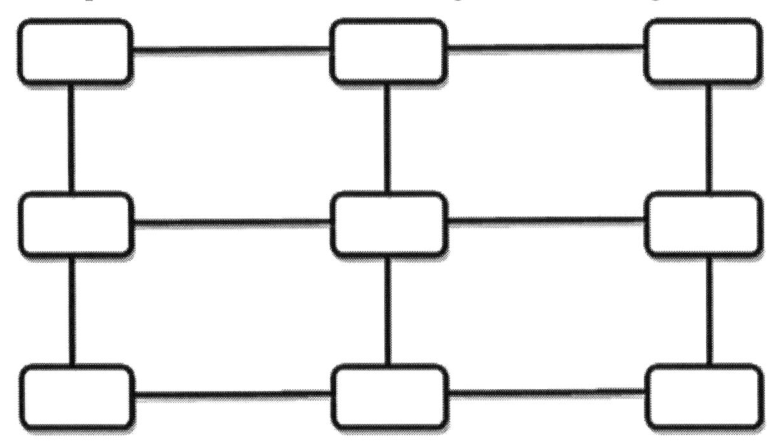

Figure 3.2: *Structured Data*

Unstructured (refer to *figure 3.3*) is exactly the opposite making it much more difficult to collect, process, deconstruct, and analyze. And it needs a lot of cleaning up before it can be processed further. It is handled using unconventional ways such as data lakes, non-relational databases, NoSQL databases, and so on. According to experts, anywhere from 80% to 90% of data is unstructured. And this percentage will continue to rise with the prominence of the internet of things.

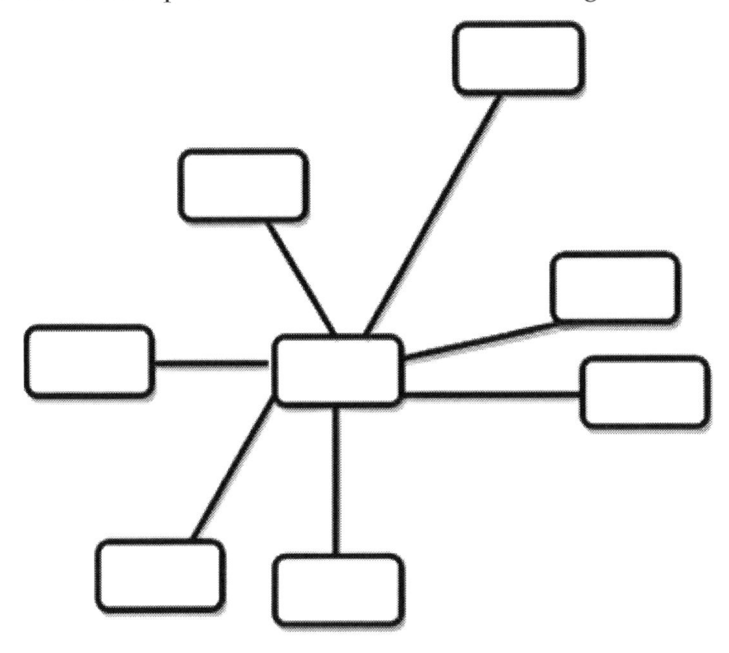

Figure 3.3: *Unstructured Data*

There are several ways in which structured data is collected. The most common one is questionnaires. Other ways included online sites, swiping a card, and so on. Unstructured can be collected through various ways such as text content in the form of news, social media, and so on, satellite imagery, videos, and so on. Until the introduction of object-based storage, most of the unstructured data was stored in file-based systems. There is significant progress happening in terms of processing specialized forms of unstructured data due to the introduction of modern-day database systems like *MongoDB*, and this kind of progress makes unstructured data one of the main fueling factors behind the rapid growth of big data. Organizations that are able to leverage the power of unstructured data are at a competitive advantage.

There is yet another data form: semi-structured data (refer to *figure 3.4*), and it does not have a fixed schema and does not adhere to any formal structure. It is a hybrid of structured and unstructured data. It is the data that does not conform to a data model but has a structure of its own in terms of semantic tags, markers, and so on (that work as classifying characteristics). It is somewhere between structured and unstructured data; it is not as well organized as structured data and also not as messy as unstructured data, but there is still some level of fluidity in this type of data. For example, in the case of emails, while the actual email content is unstructured, but it does contain some level of structured data such as names, timestamps, and so on. Other examples of semi-structured data are zipped files, binary executables, XML, and so on. Semi-structured data is organized in the form of a hierarchy using metadata instead of storing it in the form of columns and rows. Similar entities are grouped together and organized in the form of a hierarchy. Semi-structured can be broken down into predefined categories, but the information within these categories is itself unstructured.

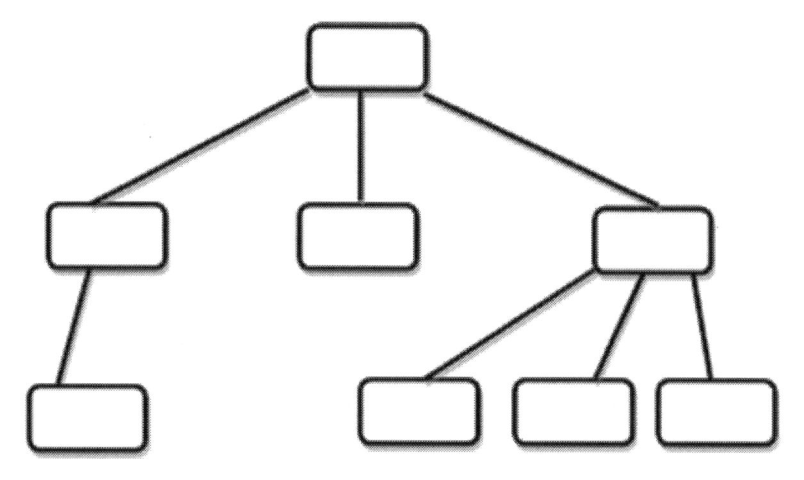

Figure 3.4: *Semi-structured Data*

The last type of data is metadata; it is data about data. It provides additional information about a specific set of data, which makes it easy to work with the instances of this specific set of data. Examples of metadata include title, description, category, and so on. For example, a digital photo is the main data, and data about this data (metadata) contains information such as filename, geolocation, timestamp, and so on. Metadata comes in handy when large amounts of unstructured or semi-structured data need to be searched, cataloged, queried, and analyzed.

Differences between structured and unstructured data

Structured data is straightforward to store, process, and analyze as it follows a pre-defined data model, whereas unstructured data is difficult to tackle as it does not follow any pre-defined data model. Here is a tabular recap (refer to *table 3.1*) of the differences between structured data and unstructured data.

Structured data	Unstructured data
Structured data is organized in a pre-defined format.	It is not organized in a pre-defined format.
Structured data is quantitative.	Unstructured data is qualitative.
It is easy to store, process and search.	It is difficult to store, process and search.
As per estimates, just 20% of data is structured.	And the remaining 80% is unstructured data.
Requires less storage.	Requires more storage.
Structured data is often stored in a data warehouse.	Unstructured data is often stored in a data lake.
Examples of structured data: databases, library catalogues, economic data, and so on.	Examples of unstructured data: text messages, sensor data, social media, audio and video files, and so on.
Structured data provides a birds-eye view of customers.	Unstructured data provides a much deeper understanding of customers.

Table 3.1: *Structured versus Unstructured Data*

Data lake

Traditional data management systems are not capable of handling big data and big data analytics, and this is where a data lake comes into the picture. A data lake is a centralized storage repository that stores structured, semi-structured, and unstructured data in a raw, granular format. It uses a flat architecture to store data. Every data element in a data lake has a unique identifier and is also tagged with metadata. According to the Aberdeen survey, organizations that implement a data lake outperform similar companies by 9% in organic revenue growth.

A data lake is a storage repository that holds a vast amount of raw data in its native format, including structured, semi-structured, and unstructured data. The data structure and requirements are not defined until the data is needed. Data stored in a data lake can be anything right from structured data in the form of relational databases to semi-structured data to unstructured data in the form of images.

A data lake and a data warehouse are used interchangeably, but in reality, they are different concepts. *James Dixon*, the CTO of *Pentaho*, uses the following analogy to describe a data mart: "*If you think of a data lake as a store of bottled water—cleansed and packaged and structured for easy consumption—the data lake is a large body of water in a more natural state. The contents of the data lake stream in from a source to fill the lake, and various users of the lake can come to examine, dive in, or take samples."*

The term data lake is often linked with Hadoop (an open-source framework that allows to store and process big data in a distributed environment) or Hadoop-related technology stacks. Here, an organization's data is first loaded into the Hadoop platform, and then business analytics and data mining tools are used on this data.

When the power of artificial intelligence, machine learning, and so on are combined with that of a data lake, organizations are able to come up with profitable predictions. A data lake is agile in nature as it can be changed and configured easily. Major initiatives around the world are being launched day in and day out to promote the use of data lakes. For example, *Informatica* (is a software development company with its main focus on *Enterprise Cloud Data Management and Data Integration*) recently joined hands with *Capgemini* (it is a French multinational corporation that provides consulting, technology, professional, and outsourcing services) and Pivotal to launch a data lake program called **business data lake**, which is a solution that aims to increase the use of data lakes across businesses.

Once the organizations identify the data sources needed for their business analytics, they then replicate the data from these data sources to the data lake with transformations if needed. Replicating the raw data helps organizations to simplify the ingestion process. Snowflake schema provides the most adaptable solution to support the data lake strategy.

There are two main types of data lakes: cloud-based and on-the-premise. In the case of cloud-based setups, scalability can be easily achieved, but in the case of on-the-premise setups, this factor is not that achievable.

Advantages of a data lake include the ability to store all types of data, provides unlimited ways to query the data, provides democratized access to data via a single, unified view, provides real-time analytics with the help of advanced algorithms, and it is faster to implement as it represents only a subset of data. Disadvantages are: combining and consolidating data from various data marts is a cumbersome task; their analysis and reporting capabilities are limited as a data lake cannot provide a holistic view of an organization's data, and at times organizations tend to create unnecessary and unrelated data lakes, and this leads to difficult maintenance of the same.

Data lake versus data warehouse

A data lake is a subset of a data warehouse, and it focuses only on a specific subject or business line. A data warehouse is a centralized repository that stores all of an organization's current and historical data. Here is a tabular recap of the differences (refer to *table 3.2*) between a data mart and a data warehouse.

Data lake	Data warehouse
A data lake can hold data derived from both traditional and non-traditional data sources.	Non-conventional sources such as images, social media activity are usually not handled by it.
It adapts to changes easily. As all data is stored in raw form, it can be easily adapted to suit the various needs of the users.	It takes longer for a data warehouse to adapt to changes. Due to the complexity of the data loading process, it takes time and resources to adapt to changes.
A data mart focuses on a single organization area or subject. It is project-oriented in nature.	A data warehouse deals with organization-wide disparate data sources. It is data-oriented in nature.
Its size is usually less than 100 GB; it is small in size.	Its minimum size is 100 GB and can go into terabytes for large organizations; it is vast in size.
It is a decentralized system.	It is a centralized system.
It follows a bottom-up model.	It follows a top-down model.
The data is highly denormalized.	The data is slightly denormalized.
It is simple to build.	It is difficult to build.
It supports all types of business users.	It supports the needs of specific business users.

Table 3.2: *Data Lake Versus Data Warehouse*

Main components of a data lake

A data lake first ingests data in raw format. Data can be ingested into the data lake through streaming or batch processing. And then, this data is stored in such a manner that it becomes easier for organizations to manage and access this large amount of data. To avoid the phenomenon of data swamp (a data swamp is a poorly designed or poorly maintained data lake), cataloging and searching are done based on metadata. Advanced algorithms are used to process the data which then can be accessed by all the stakeholders for analytics purposes. During processing, data transformation into various formats or structures occurs. Tools such as Athena, Hadoop, and so on are used to process data. And all these aspects of a data lake can function properly only when security protocols in terms of authentication, protection, access, and authorization are in place and applied to both data in transit and at rest.

Figure 3.5 is a pictorial depiction of all the main components of a data lake:

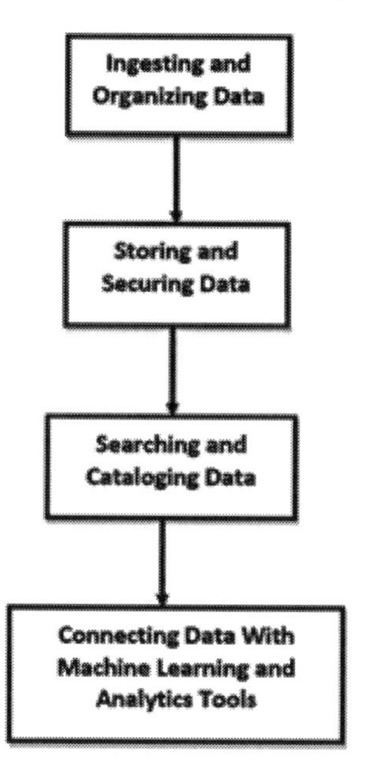

Figure 3.5: *Main Components of a Data Lake*

Modern business intelligence system

According to statista (it is a German company specializing in market and consumer data): "*The global big data market is forecasted to grow to about 103 billion US dollars by the year 2027.*" In current times, leveraging data is no longer just a competitive advantage for businesses, but it is extremely needed for long-term survival, and this is where modern-day BI systems come into play ad this is where data lakes come into play. For example, in Hadoop's distributed file system, a data lake setup offers a cost-efficient solution for storing and analyzing many types of data in its native form. A data lake solution coupled with a data warehouse is the cornerstone of the next generation of BI that deals with big data and its dynamics.

Modern BI systems offer the ability of on-the-fly self-service features and tools to meet the needs of all types of users, including non-technical and novice users. The features of reporting and dashboards are more flexible, provide an intuitive interface with auto-suggestions, and support personalization as well.

The traditional business intelligence solutions have their underlying data architecture in the form of a centralized data storage strategy called **enterprise data warehouse** (**EDW**). While EDW is great for dealing with historical data, for other data scenarios, it faces a lot of challenges. For businesses to operate well with traditional systems, a dedicated technical team is needed, which is not a feasible option in today's fast-paced environment. Traditional systems are about ad-hoc querying and prebuilt reporting, whereas modern systems are about data discovery and advanced analytics. The paradigm has shifted from hindsight to insight, and now we are venturing into the zones of foresight through the use of modern BI systems. Traditional BI only provides insights into what has happened, but to have a progressive, forward-thinking approach and to gain insights into what will happen next, modern-day setups are a must. Moreover, modern BI systems have enhanced data governance and security level.

Traditional systems are not or flexible enough to be adopted for other environments such as mobiles, whereas modern-day systems work well in any environment. Traditional systems can take weeks or even months to set up, whereas their modern counterparts can be up and running in a few hours or a few days.

According to the Gartner Report 2017, "*Technology Insight for Modern Analytics and Business Intelligence Platforms*", by 2020, smart/augmented, non-relational-, search- and visual-based data discovery capabilities will converge into a single set of next-generation data discovery capabilities as components of modern BI and analytics platforms. This is the power of modern BI systems.

Major challenges with traditional BI solutions are that they can harness and deal with only structured data. Also, they lack the presence of on-demand capability for analysis. And moreover, traditional BI solutions provide an after-the-fact approach. All these drawbacks are overcome in modern-day BI solutions.

Benefits and use cases of modern BI

Apart from the main benefit of enhanced decision-making capability, modern BI systems provide a plethora of benefits, which are as follows:

- **Rich visualization with real-time and actionable insights and intuitive reporting tools**: These systems provide a complete package that has everything right from text mining and benchmarking to predictive analytics and business performance optimization.
- **Improved organizational performance**: With an intuitive and holistic view of various performance parameters, organizations and leaders can identify areas of improvement and opportunity. BI helps organizations to understand what is working and what is not.

- **Better change management through improved visibility**: Having accurate data and improved visibility provides for better business decisions to match up to constant changes.
- **Improvement at all levels**: With the help of BI, organizations can pinpoint inefficiencies and eliminate them to improve or expand margins. And this, in turn, can improve profitability and competitiveness and reduce uncertainty. As BI systems provide a plethora of tools to make informed, data-driven decisions, they help to minimize the guesswork.
- **Insights, KPIs**: Organizations can measure KPIs and gain insights in regards to revenue, productivity, and so on, in a timely manner, respond to change in an agile manner, assess its own capabilities, compare its relative strengths and weaknesses against its competitors, and so on.
- **Data mining**: BI and its powerful tools are able to pinpoint patterns in an accurate manner; and hence, they help in identifying trends and gaining insights. Business intelligence, when coupled with areas such as enterprise reporting, online analytical processing, cloud, and so on, offers more sophisticated data mining; and hence, optimized decision-making gains better insights into customer behavior, achieves cost optimization, increases operational efficiency, and so on.
- **Enhanced understanding of customers**: BI helps organizations to acquire a deeper understanding of customers in terms of their behaviors, attitudes, preferences, and so on. Such knowledge is necessary to develop effective marketing campaigns, and such knowledge can be gained through BI systems based on various **key performance indicators** (**KPI**) related to customers. Some important KPIs are customer engagement, customer complaints, and so on.
- **Data connectors**: Modern BI systems have the capacity to be robust data connectors, and this, in turn, helps organizations to be able to get a high level of business intelligence by centralizing the disparate sources and providing a single point of view on business processes and key performance indicators.
- **Improve financial efficiency**: The finance department is the main hub / heart of any business. Without this department operating at its peak, none of the other departments can function properly. BI tools and systems are capable of providing a wealth of information in the form of comprehensive, intuitive, customizable reports, charts, graphs, and so on for improving the level of financial efficiency.

Modern BI systems entail a range of business applications, right from reporting to customer experience. And all of these fall into any of the five main uses cases, which are discussed as follows:

- **Self-service analytics**: Through its interactive, intuitive user interface, self-service analytics platforms provide both technical and non-technical users the ability to connect to a number of data sources so that they can extract data, drill down data, analyze data, query data, and generate data visualizations in various formats.
- **Embedded analytics**: It provides analytics (reporting, interactive dashboards, and so on) functionality within an existing business application. Some of the self-service BI platforms have the ability to embed analytic dashboards into commonly used applications to make data analysis more accessible and convenient. Embedding analytics into existing workflows and processes helps organizations to gain access to the data and insights without accessing external systems and applications. Embedded analytics are available both through web-based and cloud-based setups. Embedded analytics differs from traditional BI; traditional BI is mainly a standalone application, whereas embedded analytics embeds all the capabilities of business intelligence systems directly within the existing applications.
- **Augmented analytics**: It uses artificial intelligence and machine learning to enhance the entire data analytics cycle. It automates all the processes involved in the cycle. It is exactly the opposite of traditional systems. It is about transforming big data into smaller, usable datasets, which helps decision-makers to act on data quickly and accurately.
- **Cloud analytics (also called cloud analytics as a service model or software as a service model)**: It is all about providing BI solutions through the cloud, and this setup provides a single and secure access point to all the data. As more and more organizations adopt cloud technologies, cloud analytics will grow in popularity. It is about analyzing data on demand. Some organizations adopt a hybrid approach where a combination of on-the-premise and the cloud is involved in their BI solution. Its advantages: provides a unified approach for gathering, integrating, and analyzing data; scalability in terms of the volume of data and users; and faster intelligent and actionable insights in real-time.
- **Advanced analytics**: it is exactly the opposite of basic traditional systems. Traditional systems are about using historical data to make more informed decisions in the future, whereas advanced analytics is an autonomous or semi-autonomous system that focuses on forecasting future events by providing various capabilities such as discover patterns, provide semantic analysis, giving recommendations, provide forecasting, and so on., in a really quick response time and it also operates in real-time.

Conclusion

In this chapter, we dealt with the deeper dynamics of **business intelligence (BI)** in terms of what is BI and its characteristics, data quality challenges and data quality best practices, structured versus unstructured data, data lake and its main components, and modern BI system and its benefits and uses cases. After reading this chapter, the readers will have gained a firm grip over the advanced dynamics of BI, and this will set the stage for the next chapter, which covers data visualization.

Questions

1. Define BI and its framework.
2. What do you mean by data quality, and what are the real challenges you see in today's industry related to data quality?
3. Define structured versus unstructured data.
4. What are data lakes?

Further readings

1. Hands-On Data Visualization with Polybase by Pablo Alejandro, BPB Publications [**https://in.bpbonline.com/products/hands-on-data-virtualization-with-polybase**].
2. RDBMS in depth by Dr. Madhavi Vaidya, BPB Publications [**https://in.bpbonline.com/products/rdbms-in-depth**].
3. Mastering PL/SQ Through Illustrations by Dr. B.Chandra, BPB Publication [**https://in.bpbonline.com/products/mastering-pl-sql-through-illustrations**].

Chapter 4
Introducing Data Visualization

In the previous chapter, we have been introduced to the dynamics of **business intelligence** (**BI**) by following its characteristics, data quality challenges, and data quality best practices. In this chapter, we will be introduced to various tools/ components that deal with data visualization. Data visualization demands are growing at a rapid rate in this era, where the use of data is vital in many different fields. Data visualization techniques allow people to use their perception to better understand this data. The end goal of this chapter is data visualization, including both the principles and techniques. The audience will learn the value of visualization, specific techniques in information visualization and scientific visualization, and how to understand best leverage visualization methods.

We are literally drowning in a never-ending sea of data. In the current time, the corporate world is trying to remain afloat in the vast virtual ocean of data, and this is where the life jacket of data analytics and business intelligence comes into play. They help to derive value out of this vast virtual ocean of data. But what keeps this life jacket functional is data visualization. Data visualization is the presentation of quantitative data and information in a graphical or pictorial format such as maps, graphs, charts, and so on. In other words, creating visual representations of data helps to distill large datasets into visual aids to provide bite-sized pieces of information that are easily digestible, facilitate easier identification of new patterns, communicate complex concepts using metaphors and symbols, and so on.

Both data visualization and analytics deal with data. Data visualization helps data analytics to get better insights. An end-to-end BI solution consists not only of the front-end dashboards and tools (data visualization), which transform data into a visual context but also algorithms and tools at the back-end for data mining and evaluation (data analytics). Data analytics deals with data at a much deeper level in comparison to visualization. Data visualization is only as effective as the data used to prepare various data visualizations. Data analysis is an exploratory process, whereas data visualization is about the visual representation of data. Data analytics offers the bigger, complete picture, whereas data visualization summarizes the data in the best possible way.

Structure

This chapter will highlight the following topics:

- Presenting data visualization
- Types of data visualization
- Visualization dashboard
- Introduction to reporting tools

Objective

The aim of this chapter is to understand and highlight the importance of data visualization, its components, and reporting tools.

A balanced approach in data visualization and data analytics is the key factor in formulating an effective data management strategy.

At the end of this chapter, one will be able to.

- Understand the introduction to data visualization, its main aims, and its importance as well.
- Apply the various types of data visualization such as hierarchical, temporal network, and multi-dimensional.
- Apprehend topics like visualization dashboards and introduction of different reporting tools.

Presenting data visualization

In simple words, one can define data visualization as:

To present the data in a viewable manner using various graphs, charts and so on.

This means that data visualization is a way or technique that helps us to represent data graphically. The data can be visualized using graphical elements such as charts, graphs, and maps. These elements provide us accessibility so that we can view and understand the trends and patterns of the data.

To understand data visualization, imagine we have an imaginary publishing house (call it OWL Publishing House) and need to analyze their sales data.

The following are a few things about this imaginary publishing house:

- The *OWL Publishing House* was established in 2018 to encourage technical education in the country.
- The publication house deal in every type of edition, namely Paperback edition, eBook, and others (consider remaining in this category).
- Management needs a sales vision picture for the year 2020 to develop a new strategy to achieve new goals and boost sales.

In view of all these points, we collected the sales data compiled and let us start to analyze the same.

To bypass any complexity and for easy understanding, I used MS Excel. You can use any spreadsheet software like Open Excel, Google Spreadsheet, or anyone of your choice.

Table 4.1 provides us with the sales data for the year 2020:

	Jan	**Feb**	**Mar**	**Apr**	**May**	**Jun**	**Jul**	**Aug**	**Sep**	**Oct**	**Nov**	**Dec**
Paper back	5800	6670	7671	8822	10,145	8623	9916	13,387	15,395	17,704	20,360	23,414
Ebook	8410	9672	11,123	12,792	14,710	12,503	14,378	19,411	22,323	25,671	29,522	33,950
Others	290	334	384	441	507	431	496	669	770	885	1018	1171
Total sales	14,500	16,676	19,178	22,055	25,362	21,557	24,790	33,467	38,488	44,260	50,900	58,535
Total copies old	58	158	215	320	335	115	385	395	415	435	445	515

Table 4.1: *Sales data in 2020*

Imagine you presented the same table to management and asked them to take this for all the strategies. Do you think it will work for them where they have less time to analyze to check the various factors such as trends, patterns, and so on? In the preceding tabular form, one cannot deduce the sales patterns or trends unless he / she has complete and thorough analytical data. Here, the data visualization comes into the picture. With the help of visuals, one can identify the specific area, points and / or trends. The short version of this discussion is—that it is very difficult to identify data-pointers and analyze them on the various aspects. If we need to do the analysis between sales of paper back and eBook editions or paper back versus eBook versus other editions. Then it might take a couple of minutes or hours to calculate the same. But with the help of visual elements which can be drawn programmatically or can be created manually. However, the manual job may take stipulated time.

The following visual diagrams will help us to solve the preceding problem:

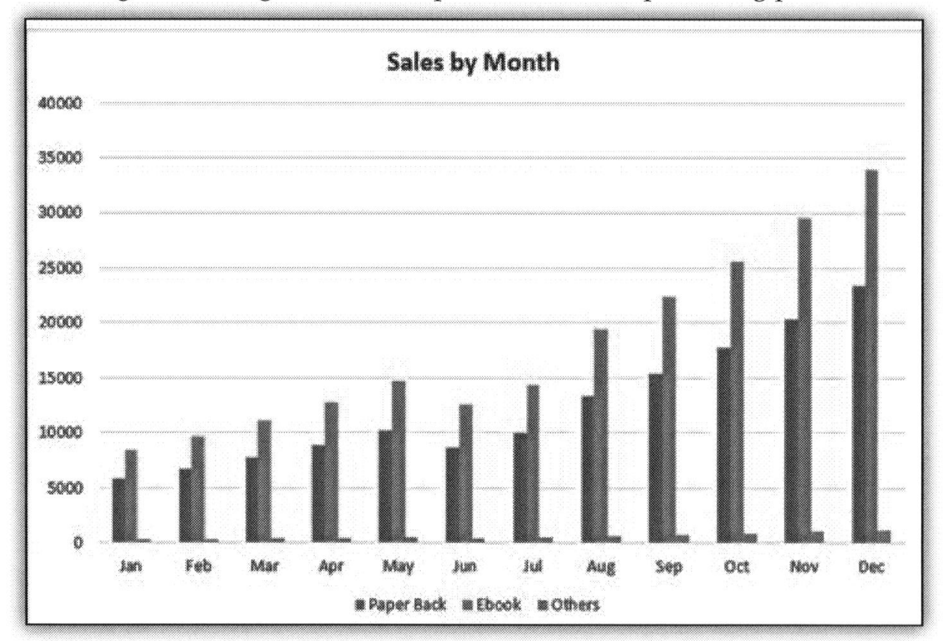

Figure 4.1: *Chart on the monthly sales data Paper Back vs eBook vs Others*

The chart shown in *figure 4.1* is a visual representation of the monthly sales data paper back versus eBook versus others. The previous chart provides us a much clearer picture and gives us a presentation of the data pointers for every month.

Similarly, the chart in *figure 4.2* provides us with the sales trend month-wise. We can immediately identify the sales data pointer of a specific period as soon as we look into this chart.

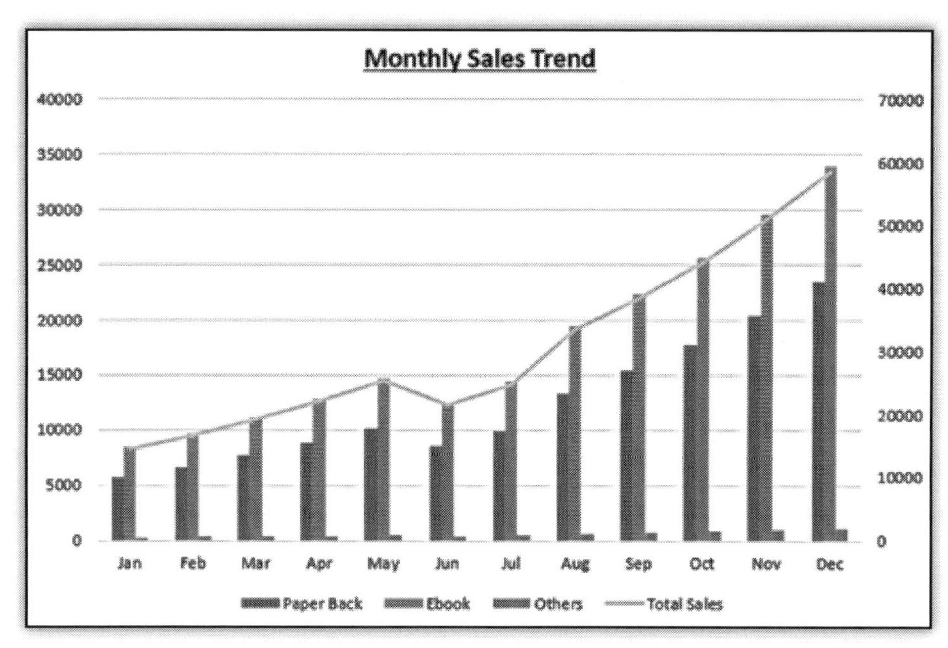

Figure 4.2: *The month-wise Sales Trend*

There are more graphical/visual elements that can be used to represent data. In the coming sections, we will discuss more basic visual elements and see how these elements are helpful to make analyses and strategies.

Aims of data visualization

The main aims of data visualization are to be helpful, scalable, and accurate. It helps users to analyze data for exploration and explanation purposes. It provides accurate data and hence clarity of analysis and insights. Moreover, it is able to scale and adapt to user needs to be based on various factors such as depth, modality, device size, and so on.

Without context, the visualization is not that effective. This context is a sort of storytelling that fulfills a business purpose, and it helps the eyes of the users to recognize and their brain to comprehend in an effective and efficient manner and to perceive patterns that may have been missed previously. Skill sets are changing to accommodate a data-driven world, and to support these skills, data visualization is critical. Once the data is collected and processed, it can be further simplified and analyzed through data visualization aids such as maps, dashboards, tables, graphs, and so on.

Techopedia (it is your go-to tech source for professional IT insight and inspiration) defines data visualization as: *"the process of displaying data/information in graphical charts, figures, and bars."* The definition by *Wikipedia* (it is a free online encyclopedia, created and edited by volunteers around the world and hosted by the Wikimedia Foundation) states that data visualization *"is the graphic representation of data. It involves producing images that communicate relationships among the represented data to viewers of the images"*.

The minimum requirements for a data visualization tool is that it should facilitate visual creation, allow combining of various data sources, hide unwanted details, auto refresh data to reflect the most recent data, export visuals, provide categories of large data with drill-down option, etc.

Popular visualization software tools such as *Qlik, Google Charts, Tableau,* and so on, have set the stage for the rest of the vendor community to follow their path. Some are freely available, while others come with a paid subscription.

History at a glance

In prehistoric times, the carvings on cave walls could be a strong case of data visualization. In Roman times, maps were used as a means of formulating competitive strategies. In 1570, the first recognizable map of the world was released by *Abraham Ortelius,* a Brabantian cartographer, and geographer.

In the 18th century, lines were introduced. In *Joseph Priestley's* chart of biography, the timeline of events it has covered has several centuries of history. Lines were used to show the duration of life of prominent people, the rise and fall of empires, and so on.

Data visualization has been around for centuries and the concept of data storytelling is as old as time.

The earliest recorded instance of data visualization tools in current times is that of maps, and the most famous example is that of *Charles Minard's* 1861 map of *Napoleon's* invasion of Russia. In 1805, a pie chart was created by *William Playfair,* the inventor of statistical graphs, and this pie chart was used to show the then-proportions of the states, territories, and provinces of the United States. The line and bar charts we use so often today were invented in this period.

The period of 1850–1900 is considered the golden age of data graphics as there was rapid growth in visualization due to various aspects such as industrial growth, social factors, and so on. In 1967, *Jacques Bertin,* a French cartographer, published the Semiologie Graphique, which is considered the foundation of data visualization.

Thereafter, during 1900–1950, there were not too many developments in this field. Post-1950s, there was renewed interest, and data visualization began to come out of its dormant state as computers began to explore the deeper dynamics of data visualization.

The Spanish papers *"El Mundo"* and *"El País"* became the international defacto standard. In 1999, *Leland Wilkinson,* a statistician and computer scientist, wrote *"Grammar of Graphics."* It is a comprehensive book of grammatical rules for data and graphics. Later on from the 1990s, with the advent of the Internet and new technologies, and more free flow of information and data, and subsequently with the onset of the big data age, has resulted in the introduction of a plethora of visual aids and tools, multi-dimensional and interactive in nature, and which provides detailed advanced analysis, and all these factors have led to the democratization of data visualization.

Importance of data visualization

Data is only as good as it is presented. As per experts, in the year 2020, there will be approximately 40 zettabytes (which is equal to 40 trillion gigabytes) of data in existence, and according to research studies, 53% of business leaders say that too much data is being left unanalyzed, and this where the importance of data visualization comes into play. For example, comparing numbers in a flat table is a cumbersome task, and this can be made easier through data visualization widgets or aids. Data visualization tools are integrated into most business applications such as CRM, marketing, analytics, and so on.

As the saying goes, a picture is worth a thousand words—data visualization not only helps to pinpoint patterns, outliers, correlations, and trends but also makes data more accessible and less confusing. Moreover, it facilitates quick decision-making. When organizations feed accurate data visualization into their decision-making tools, they are bound to make better decisions. The main aspect for this process to be effective is that the data that is fed is unbiased, as biased data can result in skewed or faulty decisions. The accuracy of the data minimizes any distortion in the insights generated through data visualization. It helps to identify areas that need more attention for improvement.

Data visualization and its tools help to consolidate all the data and present it in the form of visuals. This facilitates easy understanding and saves a lot of time. It also helps a layman to understand the business processes and does not require the expertise of data experts. It has the ability to put isolated pieces of data into a bigger context.

Data visualization helps to develop a new and enhanced business language. It always provides various options to cater to the various needs of the business users, right from annotation to color consideration. Businesses can create the most complex and yet accurate insights and forecasts possible. Still, for these to work, they have to be made available through multiple delivery channels, and data visualization is the answer to this. Data visualization reveals the story behind the business; hence, it helps to develop better business goals and strategies.

Every day, 2.5 quintillion bytes of data are created. And this is what we call "*Big Data.*" Big data refers to data sets that are very complex and large, and traditional applications are not in a position to capture, analyze, search, and so on these data sets. This is where data visualization comes into play. Well-designed visual aids provide the simplest yet most powerful way to deal with huge amounts of data. As big data looks at the bigger picture, showing insights, findings patterns, conducting research, and so on with visual aids will make it easier to grasp and evaluate for all stakeholders. It helps businesses to utilize data, right from the minute details to the broad overview level. It helps to make the data shareable across teams.

Visualization of any kind has a more powerful impact on its target audience than the written word. It allows organizations to get their message across in clear and crisp terms; it helps them to amplify their message and corporate brand story. Visual interpretation of data helps to retain the attention for more than they would normally do for written interpretation/presentation.

Data visualization facilitates the quick detection of errors in data; hence, erroneous data can be removed quickly from the analysis and decision-making processes. It can help to identify factors that control and influence consumer behaviors and attitudes.

Types of data visualization

There are two basic types of data visualization: explanation is about telling a story to the audience, i.e., communicating data to the end-users, and exploration helps find a story the data is telling you, i.e., researching and analyzing data for yourself.

These two basic types can be presented in various visual ways. This further can be categorized into four main types: hierarchical, temporal, network, and multi-dimensional. There is a story behind all the numbers, and visualizing them in the form of various charts, graphs, and so on brings them to life. The right kind of data visualization tool offers key insights, and we will discuss these tools and when to use which tools in this section.

Hierarchical

In hierarchical data visualization, data is arranged in the form of a tree. The following are the main types in this category:

Tree diagram

Tree diagram is also called a **hierarchy diagram**. Its tree structure represents a hierarchy. It consists of the root node that has no parent. Then there are nodes, which are linked together with lines called branches that represent the relationships between the members. Finally, there are leaf nodes that have no child nodes. It resembles a tree with a trunk and multiple branches.

It takes the users from generalities to specifics by breaking broad categories into a finer level of details. A common use is to display an organizational chart. It is also used in probability calculations and strategic decision-making scenarios. Several tools provide visualization of hierarchical data in a collapsible tree diagram that can be minimized or expanded in real-time. Here is how a tree diagram looks (refer to *figure 4.3*).

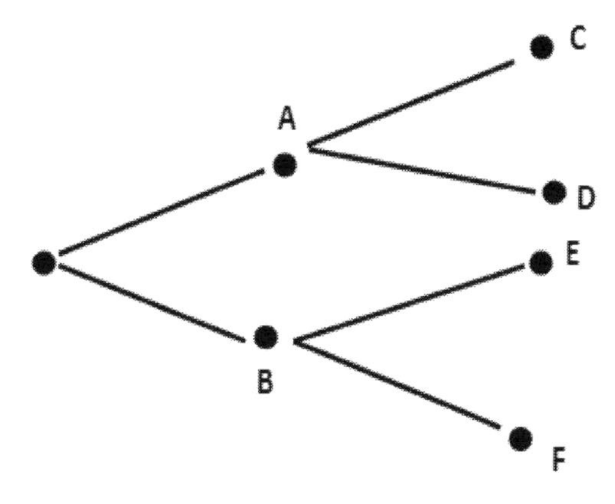

Figure 4.3: *Representation of Tree Diagram*

Tree map

Tree map or the rectangular tree diagram is an alternative way of viewing the hierarchical structure of a tree diagram. It can show a large amount of hierarchical data using nested rectangles of varying sizes and colors. Each branch of the tree is represented by a rectangle, which is then tiled with smaller rectangles representing sub-branches. To create a tree map, we need to have a tiling algorithm in place.

As compared with the traditional tree diagram, tree map makes more efficient use of space and performs the function of showing the proportion.

To understand it better, consider following trending books data of trending books during the year-2020:

Edition	Title	Price
Paper back	Microservices by Examples Using .NET Core	399
Paper back	Learning Elasticsearch 7.x	839
Paper back	Mastering Azure Serverless Computing	599
Paper back	MongoDB Complete Guide	1149
eBook	JavaScript for Gurus	599
eBook	Docker Demystified	399
eBook	Cloud Computing Simplified	519
eBook	Blockchain in e-Governance	560
Others	Smart Contract Development with Solidity and Ethereum	319
Others	Intelligent Reliability Analysis Using MATLAB and AI	720
Others	Hands-On MuleSoft Anypoint platform	749
Others	Getting started with RPA using Automation Anywhere	1273

***Table 4.2**: Book Price Data*

The preceding data can be represented in visualization form of tree map as follows:

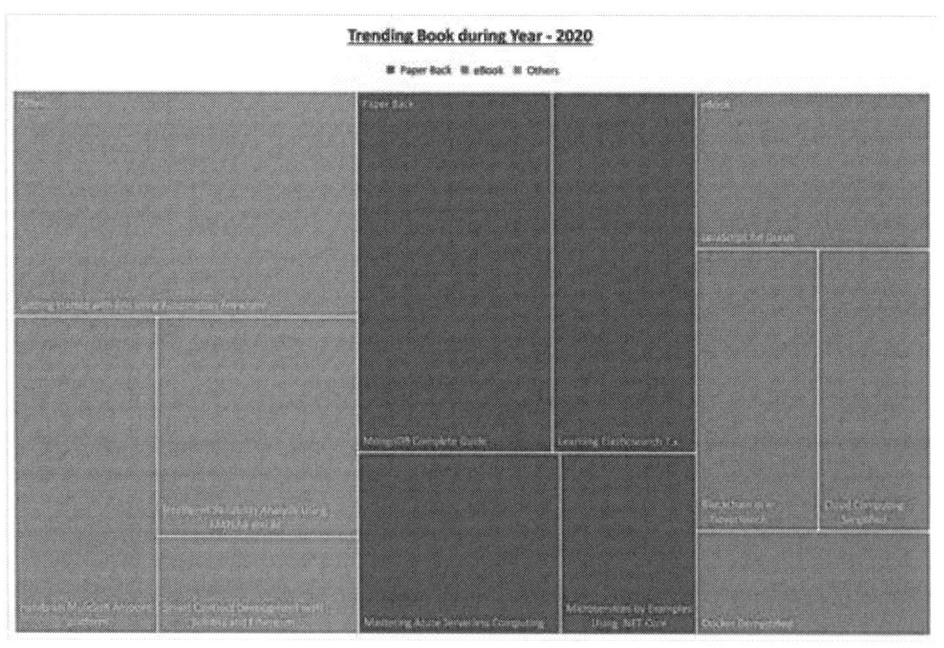

***Figure 4.4**: Tree Map—Book-wise price*

Note: The chart in *figure 4.4* is based on the tiling algorithm. The explanation of the algorithm is beyond the scope of this book. If you want to know more about the algorithm and want to create your own implementation of tree map graphs you can refer to this documentation: http://gavrog.org/TCS.pdf.

Ring chart

A ring or sunburst chart is a multilevel pie chart that visualizes hierarchical data with concentric circles (refer to *figure 4.5*). It consists of an inner circle surrounded by rings of deeper hierarchy levels. The angle of each segment is either proportional to a value or divided equally under its parent node. It depicts hierarchy through a series of rings.

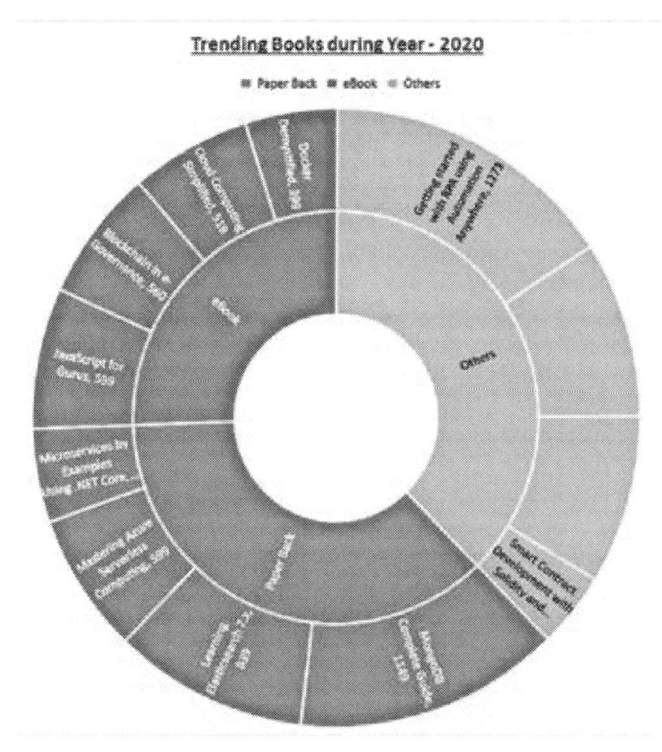

Figure 4.5: *Trending book in 2020*

Thissunburst chart represents the same data set which we used in the previous section for tree map for data visualization.

Dendrogram

It is based on hierarchical clustering. It is a useful tool in analyzing qualitative data. The key to interpreting a dendrogram is to focus on the height at which any two objects are joined together. They are used to represent grouped data. One of the most common uses is in biology to show clustering between samples or genes.

For example, consider the following sales data for year-2020:

Month	Paper Book	Ebook
Jan	5800	6670
Feb	6670	9672
Mar	7671	9672
Apr	8822	12,792
May	10,145	14,710
Jun	8623	12,503
Jul	9916	14,378
Aug	13,387	19,411
Sep	15,395	22,323
Oct	17,704	25,671
Nov	20,360	29,522
Dec	23,414	33,950

Table 4.3: *Sales Data for Year-2020*

A dendrogram can be a row graph or a column graph. The main components are: the clade corresponds to the branch, and each clade has one or more leaves. The more the number of leaves, the harder the graph will be to read and comprehend. Clades are usually labeled with Greek alphabets.

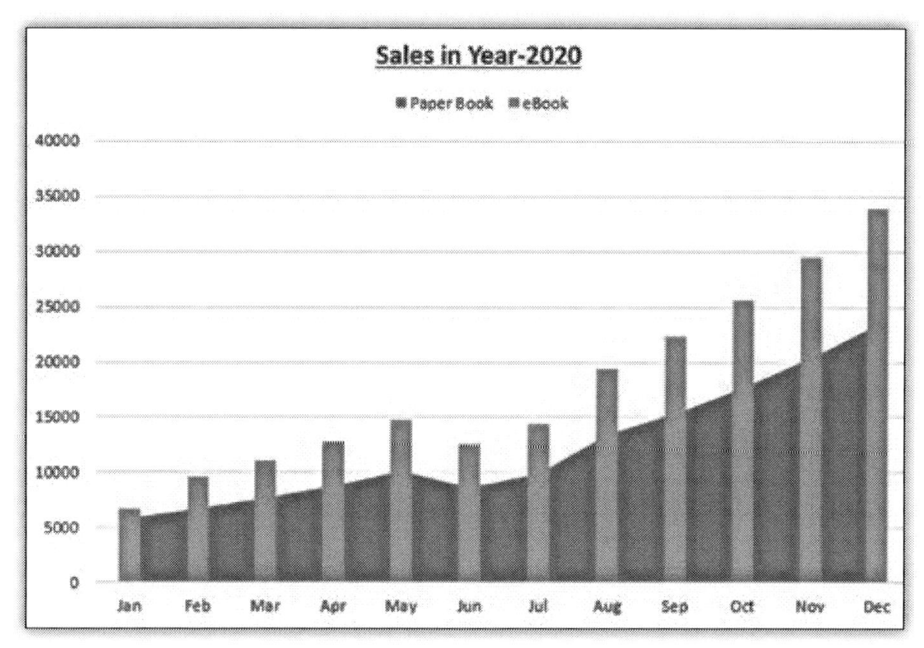

Figure 4.6: *Visualization of Sales in 2020*

The chart in *figure 4.6* is a simpler representation of the dendrogram with column and stacked graph. The data is a group based on the Month (Jan–Dec).

Temporal

Temporal tools deal with timelines. They are related to all events before, after, or during some time period or moment. Several popular tools for temporal data visualization are in the market;examples include, Provotis, TimeFlo, and so on. Temporal data visualization is widely used in historical presentation, project management, and so on.

In the coming sections, we will check the main temporal data visualization representation by using the sales data of our imaginary *OWL Publishing House*.

Bar chart

It represents data as horizontal or vertical bars. It helps to compare variables, compare items between different groups, or how they moved over time. It displays and compares the number, frequency or any other measure. It displays data using bars of different heights. It is useful for reports and presentations. It is popular because it allows the users to identify trends and patterns far more easily than looking at a table filled with numerical data (refer to *figure 4.7*).

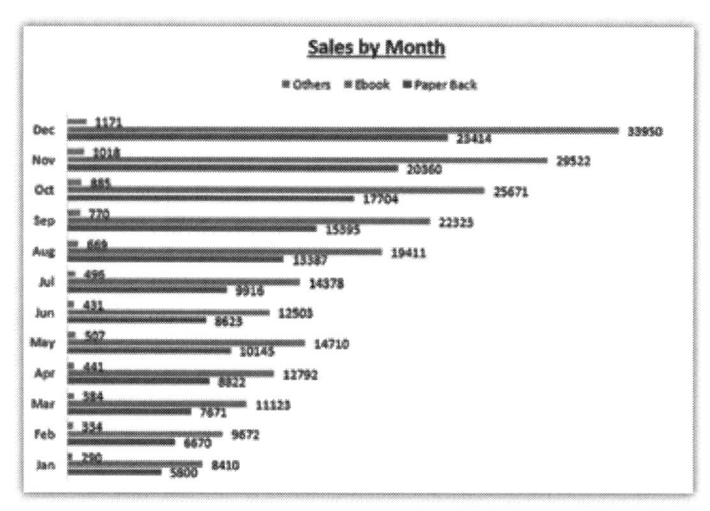

Figure 4.7: Visualization of monthly Sales

Line chart or line graph

It is a series of data points joined by a line, also called a trend line. It shows the time as a progression from left to right along a horizontal line. The element of time is usually mapped on the horizontal axis, and the quantitative variable is mapped along the vertical axis. It is one of the most popular data visualization techniques.

One should not represent more than four variables on a line graph. With many variables, the axis scales can become difficult to understand.

It is ideal for depicting trends over time. It gives the user a quick sense of how something has changed over time. Time is always the independent variable and is plotted on the horizontal axis. Then the dependent variable is plotted on the vertical axis.

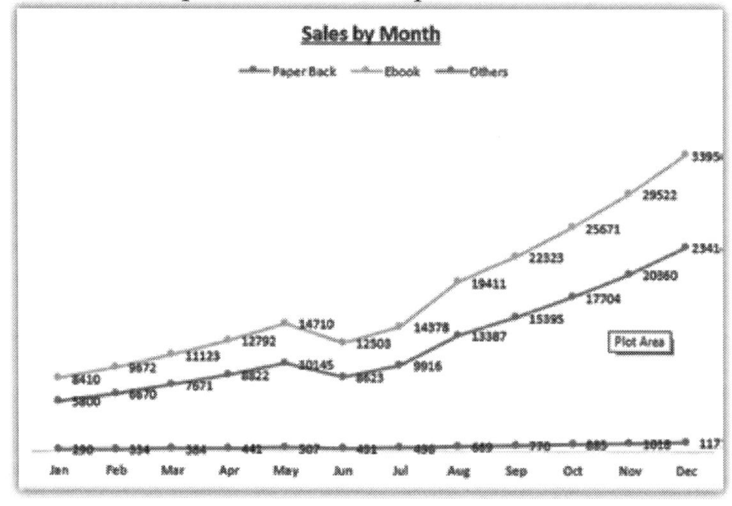

Figure 4.8: Visualization of monthly Sales

Stacked bar chart or stacked graph

It helps to observe changes in multiple variables and how they affect the cumulative total. It is used to break down and compare parts of a whole. Each bar depicts the whole, and segments in the bar show different categories or parts of that whole (refer to *figure 4.9*).

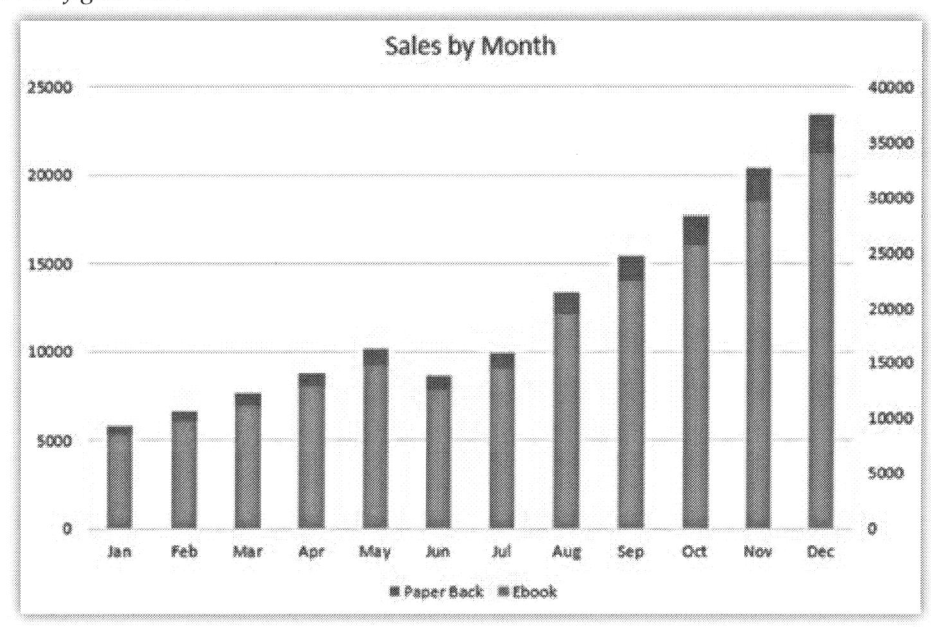

Figure 4.9: *Month-wise Sales*

It is called "*stacked*" because all legends' values are stacked in a single bar for each row in a given dataset. However, they can become hard to read when a large number of variables are introduced.

Gantt chart

It is also called **harmonogram**. It is mostly used in project management. It is one of the most popular ways of showing tasks or activities displayed against time. In other words, it shows what has to be done (the activities) and when it needs to be done (the schedule). It captures the details like the start and end date of a project, when each activity begins and ends, the overlap between activities, and so on.

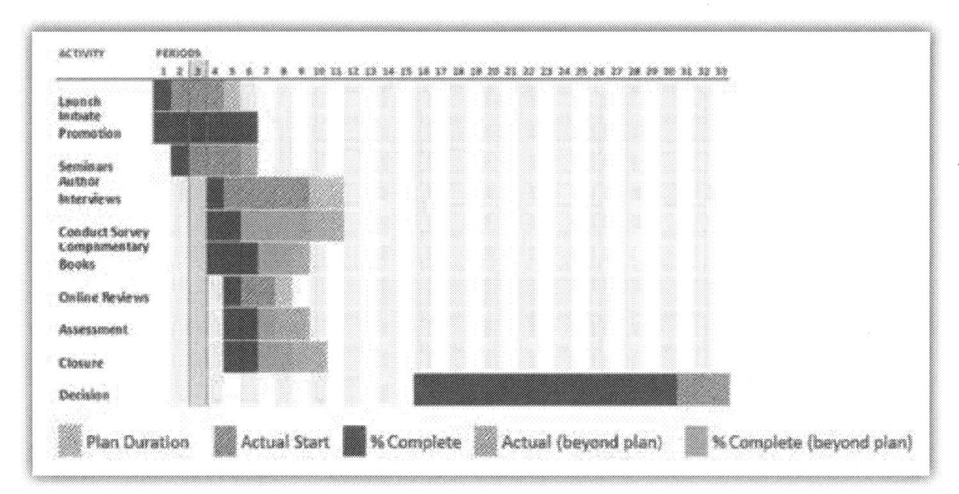

Figure 4.10: *Activity plan*

On the left side, a list of the activities is displayed, and along the top, there is a time scale. Each activity is represented by a bar, and the position and length of the bar show the start date, duration and end date of that particular activity.

Scatter plot

It is also known as a **scatter graph,** and it shows the relationship between two sets of data. The main types of correlations that can be depicted in a scatter plot are: positive: values increase together and negative: one value decreases as the other increases, linear, exponential, u-shaped and null.

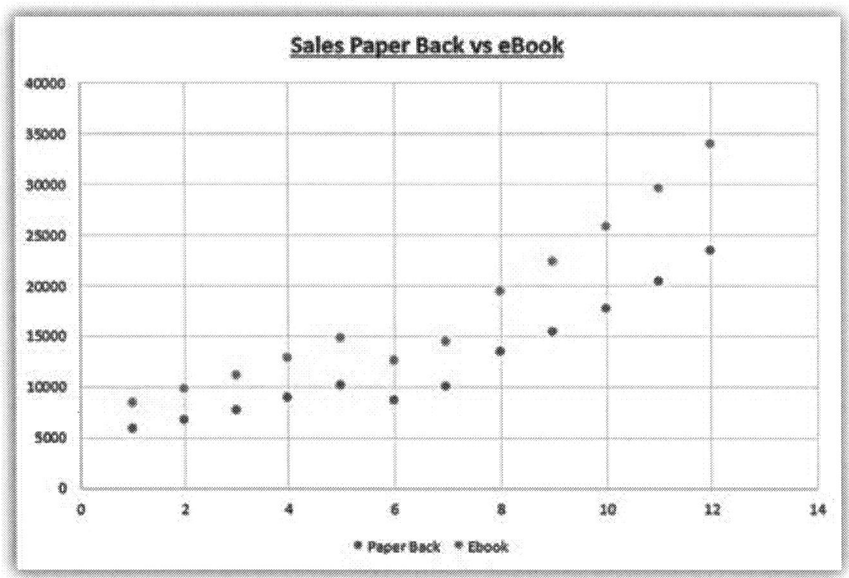

Figure 4.11: *Sales—Paper back vs eBook*

Stacked area chart

It is the extension of a basic area chart and is useful for comparing multiple variables changing over an interval. The values of each group are displayed on top of each other. They show multiple data series that start off each point from the point left by the previous data series. It is helpful for studying the evolution of the whole and the relative proportions of each group. Typical examples include the decrease or increase of the value of investments in a stock portfolio over time, profits made by the various branches of a large departmental store over time, and so on.

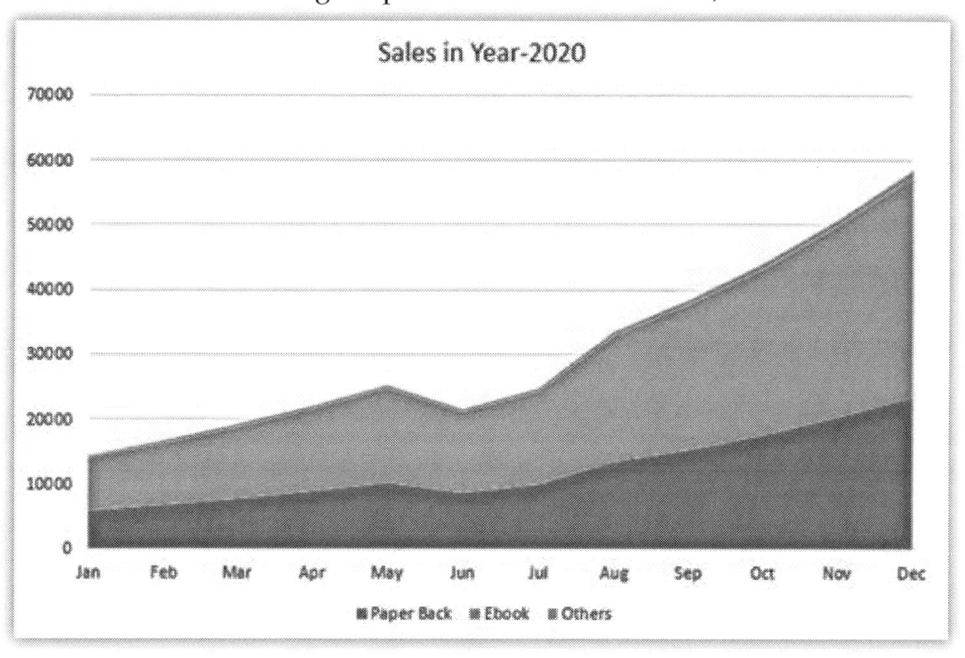

Figure 4.12: Visualization of Sales

Sparkline

It is a lightweight chart that is used for showing many trends at once, and they provide a quick context without taking up too much space. They can be easily embedded in dashboards because of their compact size. It is mainly used to depict stock market price, temperature, and so on.

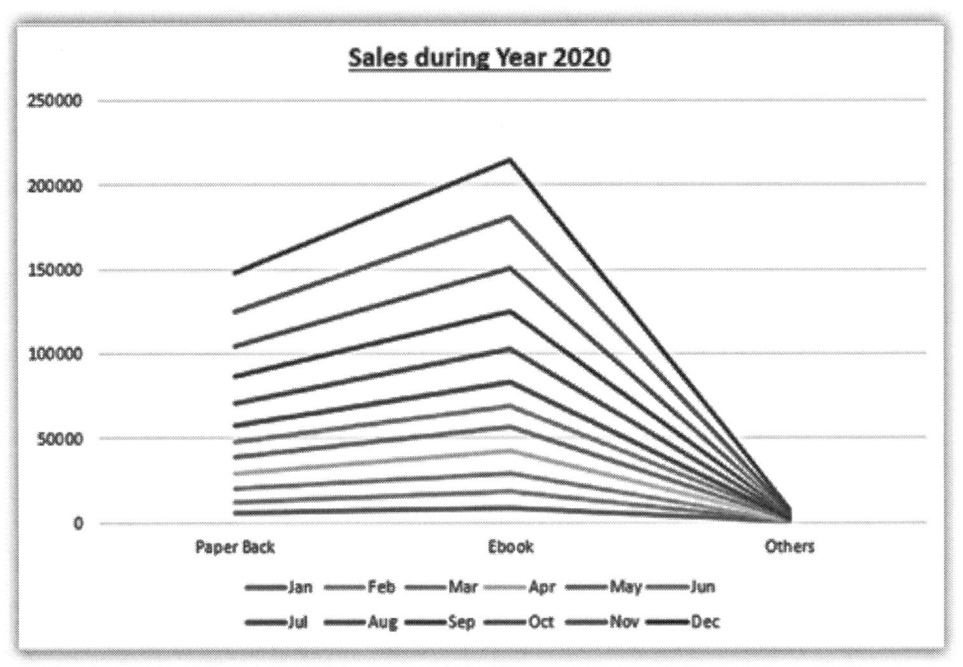

Figure 4.13: *Representation of Sales data of Year 2020*

Network

In the network data visualization, complex relationships between a large number of elements are depicted. The following are the main network data visualization tools:

Word cloud

It is also known as **tag cloud** or **text cloud**. It displays how frequently words appear in a given body of text and this is done by making the size of each word proportional to its frequency. The more a particular word appears, it is shown bigger and bolder in the word cloud. The words are arranged usually in a cloud or cluster, also at times, they can be arranged in columns, horizontal lines, or any other shape.

It can be used in identifying new SEO terms, pinpointing customer opportunities, analyzing text from online surveys, and so on. A word cloud is engaging and shows the essentials. But if there are more words in the word cloud, the analytical ability of this tool is affected.

Matrix chart

Shows relationships between two or more variables in a data set in a grid format. It helps to visualize complex, many-to-many relationships.

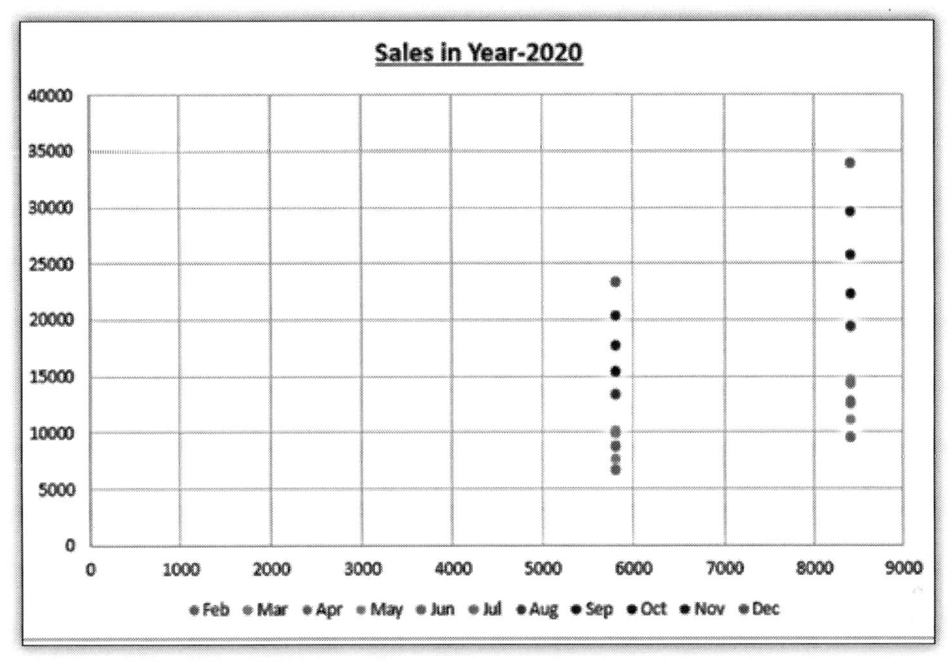

Figure 4.14: Sales during Year 2020

Node link diagram

It is also called a network map or network graph. Data is interconnected through the use of vertices or nodes, and link lines are used to represent their connections.

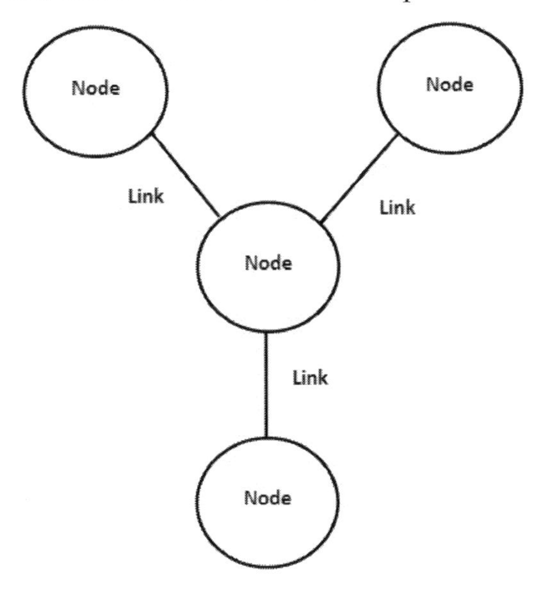

Figure 4.15: Node-link diagram

It is mainly used to depict any kind of network of relationships such as corporate structure, social network, and so on. The main elements are in the form of data variable and visual variable: a node corresponds to a dot, a link corresponds to a line segment, a node label corresponds to text near a dot, a qualitative attribute corresponds to dot color, and a quantitative attribute corresponds to dot size.

Multi-dimensional

Multi-dimensional tools are used for dealing with very complex data due to their high dimensionality, large volume, and diversity of data types. The following are the main types of multi-dimensional tools:

Pie chart

It is useful for showing the share of each value that makes up the whole; for displaying proportions and percentages between categories by dividing a circle into proportional segments. It is a statistical graph in a circular shape. Every 1% contribution that a category contributes to the total corresponds to a slice with an angle of 3.6 degrees.

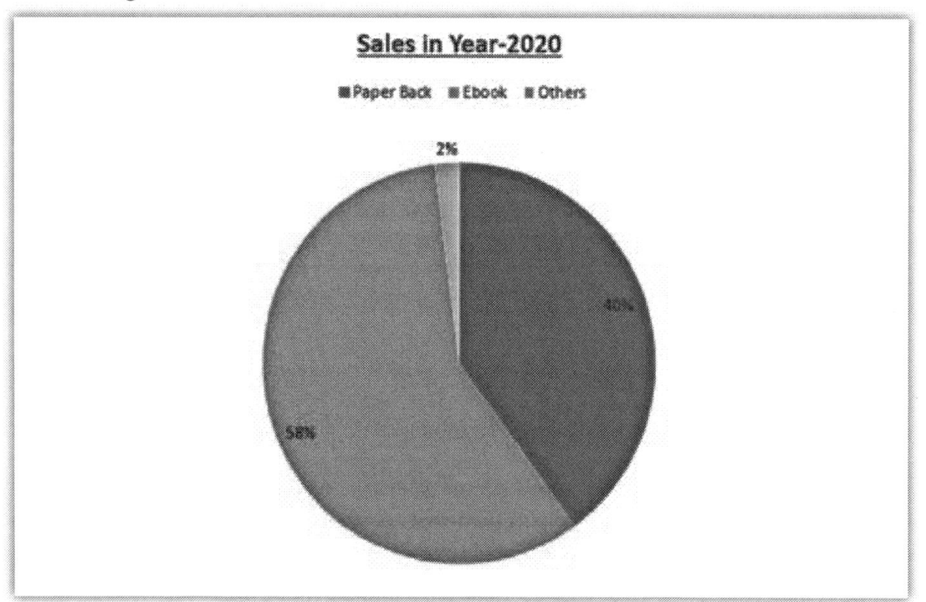

Figure 4.16: Pie Chart of Sales in 2020

They are good for showing a maximum of six categories, and anything beyond six categories becomes difficult to read and comprehend. They show proportional data or percentages, and usually, the proportion/percentage represented by each category is provided next to the corresponding slice of pie. Normally the different slices are shaded, and they grade from dark to light tones as one moves from the first towards the last slice.

Histogram

It is a graphical display where data is depicted using bars of different heights. It groups numbers into ranges (called **bins**); it shows numerical data by showing the number of data points that fall within a specified range of values. The height of each bar shows how many fall into each range. Taller bars show that more data falls in that range.

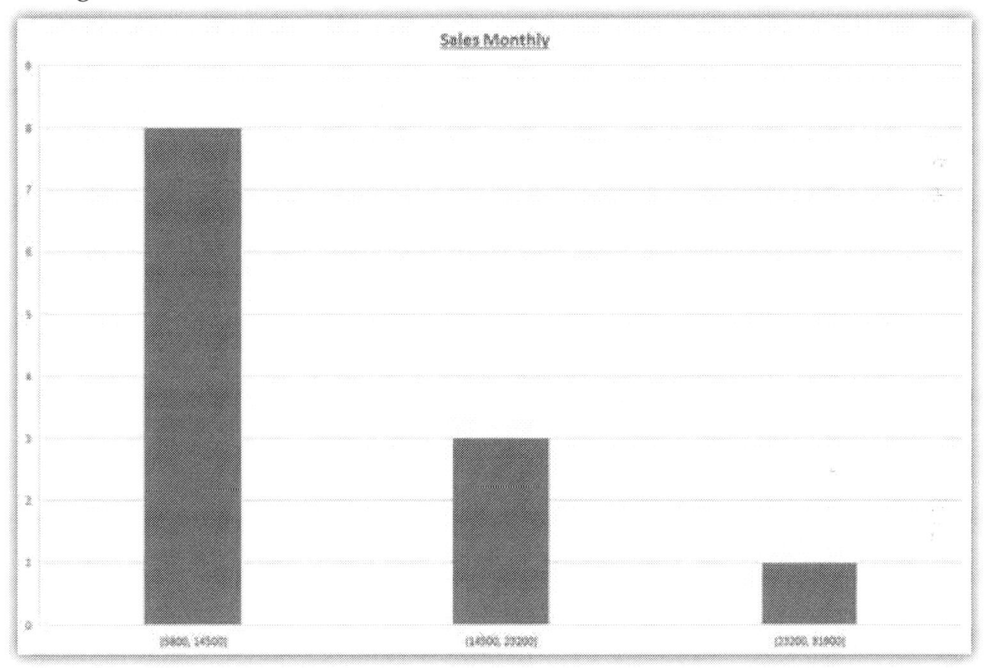

Figure 4.17: *Histogram of Monthly Sales*

It consists of bars wherein the width of the bar shows the interval that is covered, whereas the height of the bar shows the number of times the values occurred within that interval. The *X*-axis or the horizontal axis shows the possible range of the data values, and the *Y*-axis or the vertical axis represents the number of times that the values occurred within the intervals set by the *X*-axis.

Visualization dashboard

Visualization dashboards, also commonly known as **business intelligence dashboards**, provide a graphical snapshot or see-at-a-glance summary representation of the data, and they have the capability of answering several questions related to business through visual and intuitive means. They are the most common type of data visualization that helps to track, analyze and display data in the form of key performance indicators and actionable analytics that helps answer the most burning business questions. As KPIs, benchmarks, and so on became more popular during the 1990s, digital dashboards became more and more popular, and with the introduction of Microsoft's digital nervous system, their use became rampant in all sectors.

Otherwise, without dashboards, organizations would not be able to make any sense of the deluge of data and would be shooting in the dark. Moreover, dashboards are easy to build and customize. Dashboards are not only visual and interactive in nature but also intuitive too; they present a comprehensive view of an organization's goals, processes, strategies, departments, and so on.

The history dashboards can be traced back to almost 40 years ago. In the early 1970s, dashboards were mainly based on manufacturing parameters and decision support systems, and they were all simple charts and graphs, anything, unlike their modern-day counterparts. These were the first-generation dashboards. The second-generation dashboards became more functional in nature as they focused more on functionality than mere appearance. The growth of second-generation dashboards got a further boost due to **executive information systems (EIS)**; EIS was the early predecessor of modern-day dashboards.

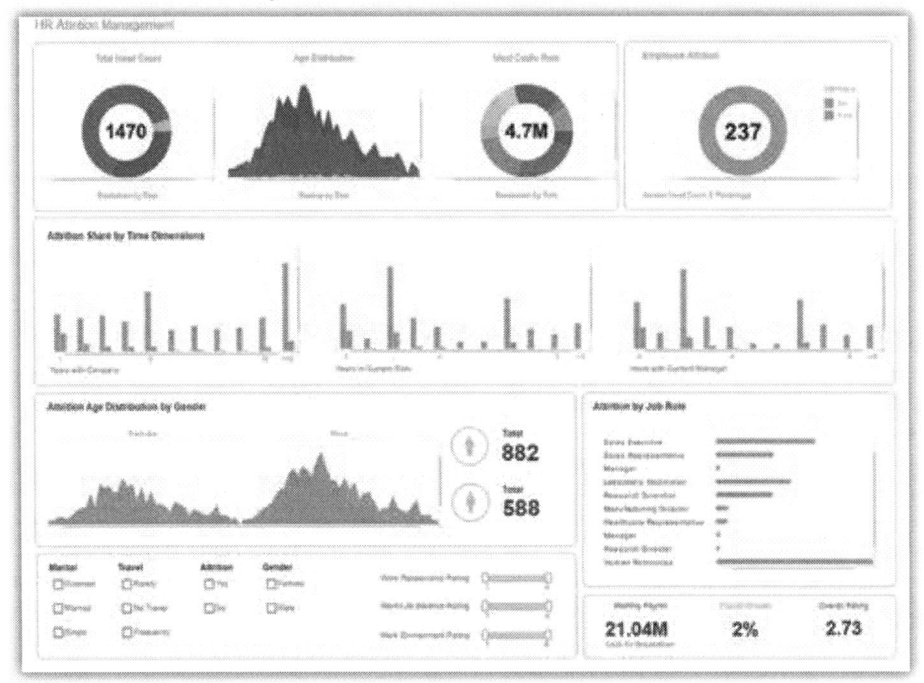

Figure 4.18: *A sample Dashboard (adapted from* http://intellspot.com/wp-content/uploads/2018/10/InetSofts-dashboard-screen-shot.png*)*

In the 1990s, as the information age picked up the pace, this progress added momentum to the process of developing better dashboard systems. Dashboards have come a long way, indeed, right from hand-written ledgers to their modern-day interactive avatar. Monitoring of key aspects of a business is now more advanced than ever before. The modern-day digital dashboards have three main flavors: standalone software applications, desktop applications, and web-browser-based applications.

Modern-day dashboards allow total visibility of all business operations and systems, and they have the ability to provide detailed reports showing outliers, patterns and trends. This self-service software is prompt in its delivery, and it generates a visual presentation of performance measures and much more in no time. With the proper understanding that the data provides, organizations are able to know their users in terms of feedback, behavioral patterns, and so on; and this where dashboards help.

Introduction to reporting tools

Reporting tools provide data visualization developers and designers with an easier method to design and develop visual representations of large data sets. We will have a look at some of the major reporting tools in this section.

Pentaho

Pentaho provides a plethora of services related to business intelligence, right from ETL capabilities to reporting. It can handle any kind of data and integrate data from multiple sources in an agile, seamless way. Its main aim is to improve communication, integration, and automation of data flows between data managers and consumers in a seamless manner. It accelerates this entire process in a cost-effective manner. It supports the big data analytics process right from big data aggregation, preparation, and integration to interactive visualization, analysis, and prediction. It also has features that provide integrated dashboard widgets and an enhanced graphical user interface. The self-service dashboard designer has extensive built-in dashboard templates, and this helps users to build personalized dashboards with little or no training required, and there is no complex coding needed.

It can be deployed in the cloud, on the premises, through custom applications and hybrid models. It comes in the form of open-source, professional standards, professional premium, and enterprise. The presentation layer deals with reporting, analysis, dashboards, and process management. The business intelligence platform deals with administration security, business logic, and repository. This tool has great data mining features, and it has simplified embedded analytics. It has a comprehensive set of machine learning algorithms to identify patterns, trends and outliers.

Pentaho not only provides ad-hoc reporting but also helps in fine-tuning reporting. It provides scheduled and on-demand reporting. It provides connectivity between the reporting tools and the BI server, and this allows for publishing the content directly to the BI server.

Sisense

It is an easy to navigate self-service, agile reporting tool, which helps organizations to make use of all of their data across their whole data landscape—no matter where it is. It has strong mash up features to connect and analyze data from multiple data sources. It can be deployed on the premises, on the cloud or in a hybrid setup. Because it does not require technical expertise or complex coding, it has a low learning curve.

It has in-built connectors, and it is the only tool on the market that provides users with a drag-and-drop interface to data combine large data sets. With this tool, staying up-to-date on the latest business analytics has never been easier. It has advanced monitoring capabilities that show the data in real-time, and it has great slicing and dicing features to tackle complete complex data sets.

Business objects

It is an SAP product that has reporting tools meant for using data from SAP BW and SAP HANA for reporting and analysis. The main tools are: crystal reports, QaaWS, design studio, lumira, analysis office, and dashboard designer.

SAP **Business Objects (BO)** business intelligence offers different tools for reporting and analysis purposes. These tools provide a full suite of business intelligence reporting solutions. These reporting tools are purposely designed for different levels of the user according to their business role and interactivity with the business data.

Crystal reports provide better solution than its counterparts. It is easy and flexible reporting because crystal report focuses on formatting as well as report development features, whereas other reporting tools mainly focus on only report analysis. QaaWS is a client-side tool used for creating the web services and publishing them on web. The design studio is a dashboard design tool that helps application designers and developers to create analysis applications and dashboards.

Tableau

It is a dynamic tool with hundreds of data input and output options that can be handled easily with its drag and drop interface. It also has video tutorials to help new-comers with detailed walkthroughs on how to use this tool. Its data blending ability, data discovery and exploration, and real-time analysis are Tableau's strong points. And these strong points help to bring about yet another important benefit of speed of analysis. And this speed of analysis provides answers to critical questions within seconds.

It has ready data connectors that allow its users to connect to any database. Then the data extracted can be accessed by users on their desktop, laptop, and so on through Tableau's server. It has various options and features to present a complete picture of the data through data-driven stories. Tableau is architecture-independent and the organizations and users need not worry about any software and/or hardware requirements.

Domo

It is an all-inclusive cloud-based dashboard BI tool. It facilitates the integration of data from a variety of sources. It is capable of providing automatically updated real-time metrics. It provides a seamless experience on mobile phones.

It has great speed when it comes to pulling together dashboards and reports. It provides answers in an intuitive way so that organizations are able to make prudent decisions. It also has great alerting features. And it does all this on the go.

Tibco Jaspersoft

It is a Java-based open-source, modular, scalable, flexible, and cost-effective BI tool for AWS, and it can be embedded in applications, or it can run in standalone mode. It can run 100% on any architecture; its architecture is agnostic. It supports a development community consisting of more than 400,000 registered members who regularly participate in Jaspersoft's open-source BI projects.

Jaspersoft helps developers and users to build intuitive data experiences into their applications and leverage big data and its dynamics to the fullest. Its robust reporting component allows users to discover trends in an easy and effective manner. The latest version works with the Visualize.js JavaScript framework for its dashboards. It lets the users build better dashboards within the web applications by using JavaScript in an easier manner.

High charts

It is a JavaScript-based charting library that provides a wide variety of charts through its simple, interactive charting capability. It supports all types of charts, right from line charts to scatter charts.

Conclusion

In this chapter, we dealt with data visualization and its various dimensions in terms of main aims, history, importance, types, and much more. After reading this chapter, the readers will have gained a firm grip over data visualization and its dynamics. We have covered all basic versions/functioning of the data visualization tools. This chapter sets the stage for the next chapter.

In the upcoming chapter, we will excel our knowledge with advanced visualization tools. We will also learn the implementation with the help of various tools.

Questions

You may be interesting to revise your readings of this chapter:

1. Why do graphs, maps, and so on, communicate better?
2. Why is data visualization so important?
3. How can organizations create a data-driven culture?
4. What are some of the common data quality issues?
5. How can we visualize more than three dimensions?
6. Which tools are used for big data visualization?
7. Who are the end-users of the data visualization tools?
8. How data visualization helps you make decisions?

CHAPTER 5
Advanced Data Visualization

In the previous chapter, we have been introducedthatdata visualization techniques that allow people to use their perception to better understand this data. The endgoal of this chapter is data visualization, including both the principles and techniques. We have also discussed basic concepts and visual elements.

In this chapter, we will extend our learning with advanced data visualization concepts and their elements. Advanced data visualization software also offers new ways to view data through visuals such as bubble charts, word clouds and geospatial heat maps. Correctly used visualization technology can deliver business insights to users faster than they can get it with traditional BI tools, and visualizing data can also simplify the process of analyzing big data sets. Once data processing is completed, it demands rich visuals to reflect those trends; and hence, advanced data visualization plays a vital role there. However, advanced visualization tools are somehow complex to deploy and use, requiring support from outside consultants or the services of internal data scientists.

Structure

This chapter will highlight the following topics:

- Types of advanced data visualization charts
- Data visualization trends

- Introduction to visualization tools
- Data visualization best practices

Objective

The aim of this chapter is to understand and adhere to the advanced techniques of data visualization.

An advanced tool provides a big visualized picture at micro level.

At the end of this chapter, one should be able to.

- Understand the various types of advanced visualization charts.
- Get to know about the various data visualization trends.
- Discuss different data visualization tools such as*Tableau, Power BI, QlikView,* and so on.
- Furthermore, implement the various best practices in the field of data visualization.

Types of advanced data visualization

Advanced visualization provides out of the box capabilities, offers new ways to view data, and uses graphs and charts to visualize large volumes of complex data (thousands of dimensions, billions of rows). The following are the main advanced ways of viewing data:

Bubble chart

A bubble chart or bubble plot is mainly used to show relationships between numeric variables; it is used for identifying and showing industry clusters. It is a variation of scatter charts wherein data points are replaced with bubbles. Bubbles in one series are all of the same color, and there may be more than one series of bubbles on a chart.

Most of the commonly used charts are capable of visualizing one or two dimensions, whereas a bubble can illustrate three and over three dimensions. It is a multi-layer, dynamic chart that displays bubbles in a two-dimensional plot. Each dot relates to a single data point, and the variables' values for each point are shown by horizontal position, vertical position and dot size. A bubble chart is used to visualize a data set with two to four dimensions. The first two dimensions are visualized as coordinates, and the third as color and the fourth as size.

A bubble chart is often used to display medical data, social data, financial data, and so on. This chart type is often used to show correlations and patterns between numeric variables. The number of data points should not be too high; only then a readable bubble chart is possible. It is always advisable to include a legend to show how different bubble sizes correspond with the values of the third variable.

To understand the bubble chart with more ease, let us take the sales data of our imaginary company *own* publishing house. We have the following sales data of a paperback book for the month of January. The sales are showing in comparison with previous month sales (Dec-2019).

Total copies sold	Total sale	Percentage increase in sale
68	7820	3%
38	4370	6%
45	5175	4%
55	6325	16%
40	4600	21%

***Table 5.1:** Monthly Sales data*

The monthly sales data mentioned in *table 5.1* shows the increase in sales; this data is readable because we have very few data points. Now, imagine if we have more data, let us say thousands of data points. In that case, will it be easily readable and can be analyzed easily? The answer is no.

Here, visualization charts come into the picture, as we are going to analyse monthly sales data, so we picked the bubble chart to visualize the data. *Figure 5.1* represents the visualization of our monthly sales data.

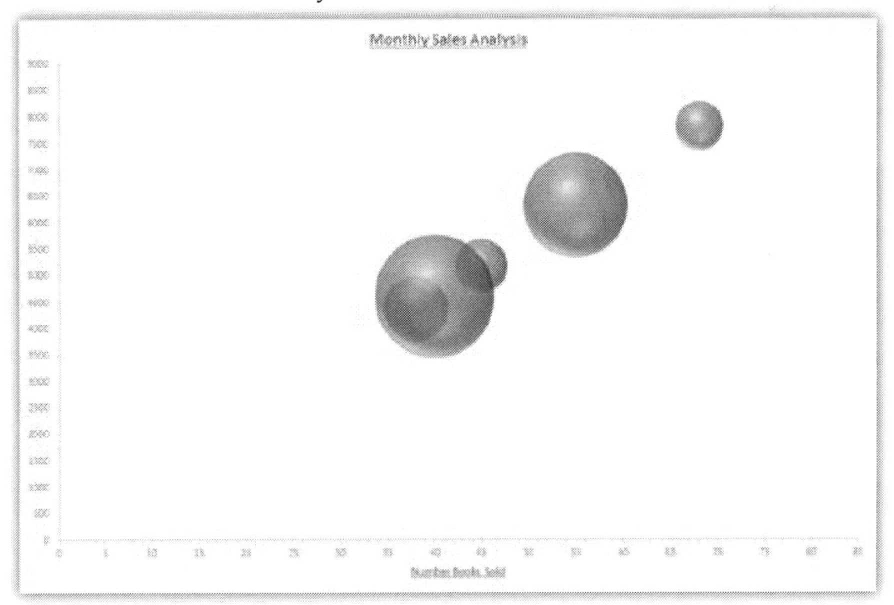

***Figure 5.1:** Bubble Chart: Monthly sales analysis*

Word cloud

Word cloud is also known as a tag cloud, word collage, or text cloud, which is a cluster of words shown in different sizes. The bolder and bigger a word appears, the more frequently it is mentioned in a text. It helps us to quickly pinpoint the most prominent terms and for locating a term alphabetically to determine its relative prominence. Many variations are there in terms of font, size, shape, text orientation, and so on.

It displays how frequently words appear in a given body of text, and this is done by making the size of each word proportional to its frequency. The more a particular word appears, it is shown bigger and bolder the word cloud. The words are arranged usually in a cloud or cluster, and also, at times, they can be arranged in columns, horizontal lines, or any other shape.

It can be used in polling, identifying new SEO terms (SEO stands Search Engine Optimization; it is the process of optimizing websites and pages so that they can achieve higher rankings and reach in search engines' organic results) , pinpointing customer opportunities, analyzing text from online surveys, analyzing speeches such as election campaigns, and so on. A word cloud is engaging and shows the essentials. It can also be used to compare two different sets of text together.

There are also examples of live word clouds that can be shared through software in settings such as training, event, meeting, and so on.

If there is no proper context or it is lacking, then word clouds do not work or add any value at all. Optimized data sets/contexts are needed to be able to use word clouds in an effective manner. The simpler the design, the easier it is to deliver effective and engaging insights.

A word cloud is engaging, fast, easy to create, and engaging in impact. But if there are more words in the word cloud, the analytical ability of this tool is affected. Word clouds are a cost-effective way of performing visualization. There is a variety of word cloud generators freely available on the internet. Word clouds can take up a lot of space, so avoid using too many words.

There are a lot of tools available online (free or paid) that can help you to build the WordCloud that represent your targeted words. Just to showcase, the free online version of MonkeyLearn has been used to draw the word cloud. You can find a sample set of words in the repository folder (file: **wordcloud.txt**). To build the WordCloud from MonkeLearn (**https://monkeylearn.com/word-cloud**), you just need to upload the text file or type your words and click to generate. The output would be similar as shown in *figure 5.2*:

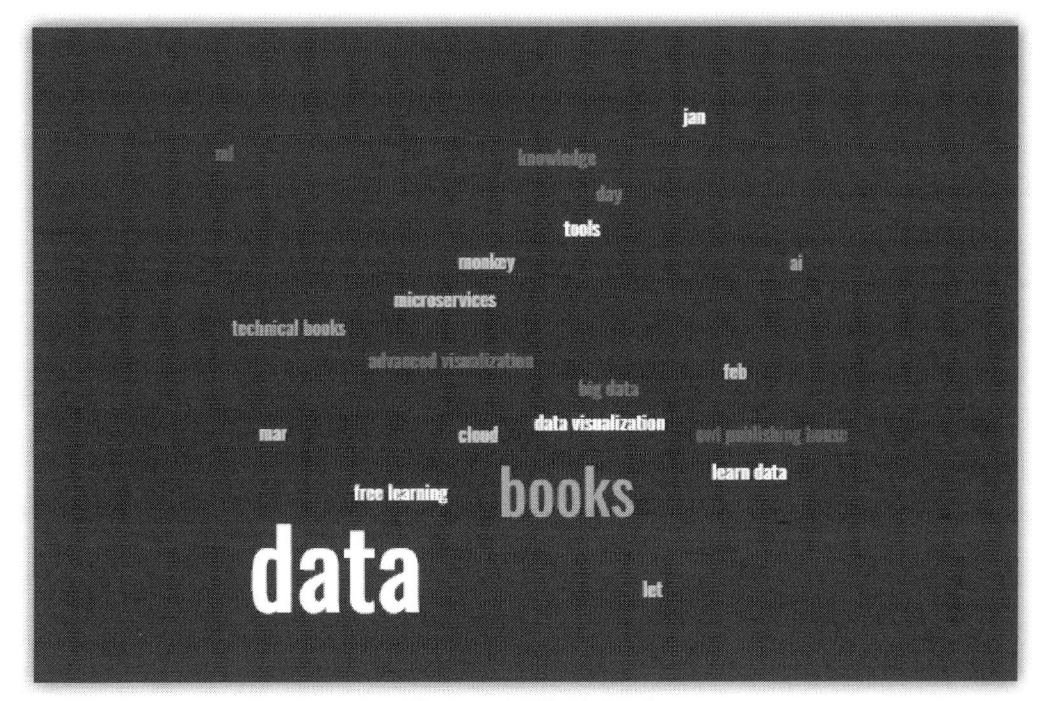

Figure 5.2: Word cloud

Geospatial heat map/hot spot mapping

This chart represents the density of a variable, and it is more effective when used in conjunction with another visualization type like a time series chart. It is a way of geographically visualizing locations so that patterns of higher-than-average occurrence of things can be identified; in other words, it has the power to define the aspect of "*where*".

It is usually used for pinpointing patterns like hotspots or regions of high density/concentration of a variable. It is used to represent large sets of continuous data on a map using a color spectrum, and the color spectrum is normally red-to-green or red-to-blue. Heat maps are so named because of their color scheme.

Generating heat maps usually involves extrapolation logic to create a continuous fill of color. Hence, the data at any particularpoint cannot be 100% accurate and reliable.

Heat mapping, from a geographic point of view, is a technique of showing the geographic clustering of an event. It is good to identify where something occurs and show areas of high and low density.

Consider the sales data of the top five selling books during the past 5 years (refer to *table 5.2*):

Av. Sales Data of Top 5 Books												
	Jan	Feb	Mar	Apr	May	Jun	Jul	Aug	Sep	Oct	Nov	Dec
2016	5800	6670	7671	8822	10,145	8623	9916	13,387	15,395	17,704	20,360	23,414
2017	8410	9672	11,123	12,792	14,710	12,503	14,378	19,411	22,323	25,671	29,522	33,950
2018	290	334	384	441	507	431	496	669	770	885	1018	1171
2019	14,500	16,676	19,178	22,055	25,362	21,557	24,790	33,467	38,488	44,260	50,900	58,535
2020	58	158	215	320	335	115	385	395	415	435	445	515

Table 5.2: *Sales data from past 5 years*

We need a visual snapshot of the past 5-year sales data, so we are picking the Heatmap to visualize the sales analysis as shown in *figure 5.3*.

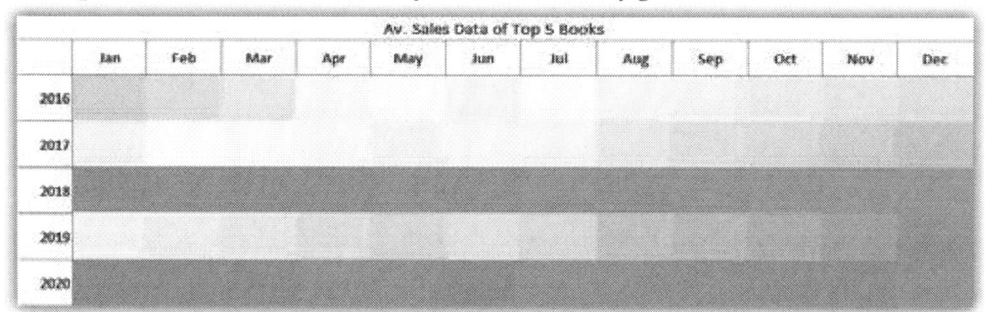

Figure 5.3: *Heat-map: Sale Analysis*

Data visualization trends

Data visualization is growing by leaps and bounds and opening up new horizons, especially with big data in the picture. The various data visualization trends indicate that it is going to get better and better, right from accurate decision-making to effective storytelling.

This section is meant to introduce the visualization tools;the complete explanation of these tools is beyond the scope of this book.

There will be a lot of cross-pollination of ideas from various fields. This interdisciplinary and cross-pollination nature of data visualization is what opens the door to new opportunities and the latest trends, which we are about to discuss in the following points:

- **Data literacy**

  By the year 2020, 80% of organizations will introduce initiatives to bring about data skills, deliberate competency development and analytics certifications in the field of data literacy. It is all about introducing digital-first work setups.

  The main aim of data literacy is to demystify data and to make learning the deeper dynamics more enjoyable. Along with this, there will also be a rise in visual literacy. Data literacy is to do with understanding the data itself, whereas visual literacy is doing with the presentation of the data.

  As time goes by, the learning curve to become a data literate and finally a data expert would be shortened.

- **Free tools**

  For small to medium companies, the door to data visualization needs to be opened up with free tools so that they can level up. And this trend is already picking up pace.

- **More adoption of data visualization tools**

  According to industry findings, the global data visualization market, which was valued at 4.51 US billion dollars in 2017, is expected to increase to 7.76 US billion dollars by 2023.

  These tools are going to fuel the data-driven culture and its dynamics. Without these tools, making data-driven decisions will not be possible. Implementing this data-driven culture will become the norm in the coming days.

- **Data journalism**

  It is the science of telling a story in new ways, which are driven by large amounts of digital data. It helps to cut through the clutter of a complex story to get straight to the point.

  Big data is transforming the world of journalism. According to industry findings and research, data journalism is going to go mainstream in the coming years. For example, the Guardian (it is a popular British daily newspaper) is a big example of this trend using big data to present big data stories.

  According to the *University of Minnesota*, visual data is processed by human brains 60,000 times faster than written data. And such figures definitely reinforce the importance of data journalism.

- **Rise in the demand for data engineers and data scientists**

  IBM predicts a 39% increase in demand for these roles in the next 3 years. Data engineers and data scientists are the key resources for unlocking the hidden value of data.

According to the findings of the Dice report: data engineer is the fastest-growing job market in technology in 2019, with a 50% year-over-year growth in the number of open positions. These findings also show that the demand for data scientists will also increase manifold over the next decade.

- **Social media is a big trend**

  We will get to see more and more data visualizations on various social media hubs and platforms. For example, there is already a growing presence of data visualizations such as GIFs, images, looping animations, and so on.

- **On the-go visualization**

  The future is mobile. At present, there is a combination of multiple devices, which include tablets, desktops, and mobiles. A technology that cannot serve all its features and benefits on various platforms is good for nothing. Data visualization is developing capabilities to deliver mobile users the same experience that it has been offering to desktop users. Data visualization will become more mobile-friendly.

- **Data quality and security**

  These two aspects are gaining more and more importance, and now with big data, having these two aspects in place is of utmost importance. With a proper framework of practices and protocols to control and secure the democratization and access of data, organizations can strike a balance between having huge amounts of data and using visualization tools to access this data.

- **Volume, variety, and velocity**

  These aspects are needed for helping organizations to make quick decisions based on advanced analytics, and due to this, there will be more and more focus on the volume, variety and velocity of data.

  Going forward, there will be more demand for designing and deploying self-servicing visualization and analytics packages that combine a simple user interface with advanced algorithms that, in turn, will take care of the volume, variety, and velocity of data.

- **Adoption of machine learning, virtual reality, and artificial intelligence**

  To tackle outrageous volumes of data, the various stakeholders have begun to look at machine learning, and artificial intelligence algorithms and this trend is picking up pace and will be useful in extracting data out of complex data sources and sophisticated data configurations, and then help in deriving useful patterns and insights.

2D data visualization is slowly and steadily being replaced with 3D data visualization and all thanks to virtual reality or also called **virtualitics**. VR (it is the use of technology to create a computer-simulated environment which can be explored and interacted with by people) tools and headsets shift the paradigm by placing the users in the middle of all the data floating around them and by presenting data to them in novel and collaborative ways.

Introducing data visualization tools

According to research, 90% of the world's data was generated in the past 2 years alone. Data visualization tools are about the visual representation of large data sets. No matter what data you want to study and analyze, performing data visualization is an inevitable step. Data visualization tools help to transform or map the dynamics from data space to graphic space.

We will discuss some of the main tools that can handle multiple sets of data in a single visualization and also offer several ways of presenting it. Data visualization tools provide a plethora of features that help create visual data models. And these models help to transform big boring data into an interactive, intuitive storytelling framework, which then can be used by businesses and users to stay ahead in the race.

- **Power BI**

  Power BI is a Microsoft data visualization tool that produces compelling visualizations to close the gaps between data and decisions. It has three main parts: Power BI service that is an online Software-as-a-Service, Power BI desktop, and Power BI mobile apps for Windows, Android, iOS platforms. It offers a secure environment and quick deployment.

  With the help of artificial intelligence, Power BI can implement features like text analytics and image recognition using machine learning models and algorithms. It also has the ability to embed reports directly in web pages. It has a calculation language, data analysis expression, which returns aggregates and calculations based on very large datasets (string, numeric or object data) in a quick manner. DAX (DAX stands for Data Analysis Expressions and it is a collection of functions, operators and constants that can can be used in BI and visualization tools) reports are easy to build and comprehend using a library of over 200 operators, constructors, and functions.

Power BI has advanced features based on AI algorithms, and it is called Quick Insights. It uses sophisticated algorithms on a specific subset of data to help organizations to unearth important patterns, insights and trends.

It is an **extract, transform, and load** (**ETL**) tool and is very efficient. It can combine and transform data from multiple data sources in just a few clicks. It also provides a plethora of metrics that help organizations to keep a tab on anomalies and correct them in a timely manner. Also, Power BI has features that help to integrate machine learning and stream analytics, and this allows business entities to take proactive action based on powerful predictive analytics.

It has a great library of data connectors that keeps growing day by day. It lets users to connect directly to hundreds of in-the-clouds and on-the-premises data sources such as SharePoint, Salesforce, and so on. It has features that can help users to design and develop personalized dashboards featuring a 360-degree view of living and streaming data.

- **QlikView**

  QlikView is suitable for organizations that need a high degree of customizability factor. It is the forerunner in the BI landscape as it has revolutionized how data is visualized based on intuitive visual discovery. It is an end-to-end ETL solution.

  Its in-memory data processing feature provides super-fast results. As data is stored in-memory, aggregations, and calculations are done on the fly. Users need not pre-configure the relationship between data entities as QlikView automatically recognizes the relationship between data. Because of its next-generation in-memory architecture, QlikView can provide real-time analysis with a few clicks as all data is already loaded in memory.

  The main component is the QlikView associative engine,and this game-changing augmented intelligence component has revolutionized the way organizations use data with the help of intuitive visual discovery. With its sister package, QlikSense, it provides great data exploration and discovery features. The modern analytics period truly began with the launch of QlikView.

  QlikView provides most likely trends and patterns automatically, which in turn help organizations to make better decisions. Unlike traditional tools where users and developers need to have coding skills, QlikView users and developers do not need to have technical skills, as it has integrated both back-end and front-end, which makes personalization easy.

- **Tibco Spotfire**

  Tibco Spotfire is a very powerful and interactive analytical platform for deriving actionable business insights; it provides several powerful features such as location analytics, predictive analytics, and so on. It focuses on data discovery and visualization, big data analytics, content analytics, and predictive analytics.

It can be deployed on-premise or in the cloud. It comes in three flavors: desktop, cloud, and platform. It democratizes data access, helps to make decisions in real-time, and provides interactive visual analytics dashboards.

It is designed to grow with the needs of any business, and it explores data from multiple angles quickly with the help of point-and-click data exploration. Features such asvisual data exploration, automatic data filtering, a simple merging of multiple data sets, and more provide a highly interactive and visual way to explore and interact with data. It can also be integrated with a number of third-party applications and databases, and tools. It provides smart, AI-driven analytics which takes data discovery to the next level.

With its advanced contextual collaboration tools, Tibco Spotfire can help organizations to either have formalized workflow or free-flowing brainstorming to bring about a natural decision-making process.

Spotfire also offers rich APIs to develop powerful apps. Spotfire performs well under all scenarios, irrespective of its scale of usage, right from small to large enterprises, and it provides cutting-edge value and performance.

- **MATLAB (matrix laboratory)**

  It is useful for people with less or no technical knowledge. Algorithms can be modified with minimal changes to find the right analysis and mathematical models. It is heavily used in areas like algorithm development.

  With the built-in integrated development environment, programs can be easily developed and modified. It has several features to present data in 2D, 3D formats, in the form of animations and so on, and provide multimodal data representations that are accessible to everyone. It has several customizable and flexible interfaces for visualization.

- **Zoho analytics**

  Zoho analytics, previously known as **Zoho reports**, is a BI and analytics platform, and it is cloud-based. It allows users to create dashboards and analyze any form of data. It features an AI-powered assistant that allows users to ask questions and get intelligent answers in the form of meaningful reports.

  It helps to bring together data from various sources such as vendors, leads, and so on. It provides a variety of predefined templates, and it is user-friendly as one need not be a technical person. It provides a bird's eye view of an organization and based on this aspect, users can use the data to drill down reports, and these reports can be easily published and shared. Data alerts are used to notify in real-time all users involved. Graphs, themes, and so on provide with endless opportunitiesto design multifaceted dashboards adapted to different audiences

It allows organizations to slice and dice data the way they want. It also provides several export options for the reports, and scheduled emails can be also sent at a set time containing the reports. It also allows embedding dashboards, reports, and so on in a blog, website, and so on, with a secured login or a private permalink or with public access.

Zoho analytics Zia is an AI-powered analytical assistant. It provides powerful insights quickly by leveraging AI, machine learning and natural language processing. It helps to generate business metrics without querying and also optimizes data. It also provides smart suggestions to help the audience ask the right questions. It provides an alert panel where predictions and suggestions are shown. Zia also keeps track of your targets and uses the alert panel to warn you when it looks like you will notmeet your expectations. It also gives contextual suggestions relevant to keywords used in text or voice commands. It is able to understand data from any business lingo or domain.

- **Dundas BI**

  It is an end-to-end flexible business intelligence and data visualization platform that has a host of features, right from reporting tools to integrated dashboards.

  It simplifies the whole data analytics process and provides users with the ability to create interactive, customizable dashboards, run ad-hoc queries, and so on through its touch-based interface.

- **Xplenty**

  It is a cloud-based, customizable and expandable data integration platform that pulls in, integrates, analyzes, and transforms data. It has the ability of pulling in data from more than 100 data sources right from data warehouses to the public cloud through its rich connectivity library.

  It offers out-of-the-box data transformations and data integration use cases that do not need much coding or technical knowledge. It provides a simple visualized data pipeline for the users to allow them to optimize and customize the platform as per their business requirements.

- **Adaptive insights**

  Formerly called **adaptive planning**, it resembles somewhat like *Microsoft Excel*. The system's visual similarity to spreadsheets is intended to lessen the learning curve for new users.

- **Domo**

  It is a cloud-based, easy-to-use, intuitive dashboard tool, which provides micro-level and macro-level data analytics. It provides tailor-made solutions based on various parameters such astitles, industries, roles, and so on. It has great features that help to automate reporting, build a dream dashboard, and so on. It organizes mini visualizations / presentations in the form of cards of existing data.

  It has a sleek user interface that is available on a variety of devices, right from personal computers to mobiles. It provides real-time data in a single dashboard. Its users do not have to install Domo as data can be published to the web or emailed.

- **Plotly**

  With the help of its integration features with analytics-oriented programming languages such as MATLAB, R, and so on, it can bring about more sophisticated data visualization. It is built on top of the open-source **d3.js** (d3 stands for data-driven documents) visualization libraries for JavaScript. It is a data visualization library with a brilliant, user-friendly interface designed to build custom APIs.

Data visualization best practices

A human brain is more receptive to interactive images than mere written words. An effective data visualization strategy should be able to leverage this fact of the human brain and how it processes visual inputs. And this is where the various data visualization best practices come into play.

The following are the best practices that are needed as they can tackle the factor of misleading users; it can be done away with:

- **Customization based on audience type**

  Knowing the audience and their requirements are critical. Data visualization is a form of storytelling. Organizations need to tailor their data visualization story to their audience; only then they can make a strong connection with their audience. Several factors such as technical knowledge, data literacy on the analytics spectrum, objective, role, and so on of the audience will determine how the story around data needs to be told in terms of specificity, engagement, transparency, and presentation.

  Based on questions like who will be consuming the data, what additional information does the audience have, who is the visualization for, which metrics will matter to the audience, what is the end-result/decision that will be derived from the visualization, etc., the right set of data visualizations need to be chosen.

Visualization is used to reveal patterns, provide context, and describe relationships within data. While a designer holds no influence over the patterns and relationships within a given set of data, she/he can choose how much data to display and what context to provide based on the needs of the audience. After all, just like with any other product, visualization is meaningless if its viewers cannot use it. Visualizations for novices should be customized in a clear and engaging manner.

- **Storytelling**

  One of the main aims of visualization is to engage the audience at the right level of compelling storytelling by showing data in an interactive and intuitive manner, right from the minutest detail to the broader overview. Keep it simple and clear so as to retain the attention of the audience, and the best way of achieving this is by providing context for the storytelling aspect so that a more effective story emerges from the deluge of data and provides the right frame of reference. Context can be made clear and effective through various ways such as proper metrics, proper color scheme, and so on.

  To a layman, it may seem that data visualization is all about numbers. But in reality, that is not true, as a compelling story cannot be told without words. Clear the clutter to develop compelling stories. Clear and easy to understand analytics bring about immense value-addition. This aspect of storytelling should be able to provide clear answers to questions such as what does the data show, what questions are you trying to answer, and so on.

  The elements used in the visualization need to be kept simple and should be used in such a way that they advance the aspect of clarity. This is a must to avoid any kind of cognitive overload on the audience.

  Storytelling and all its aspects need to finally be able to answer and fulfill the purpose of this whole process of data visualization. The two types of narratives of data visualization narrative and story narrative need to work hand-in-hand. The data visualization narrative deals with what the chart, report, and so on is going to mean, whereas the story narrative deals with the whole story from beginning to end. The context and purpose provide the glue to hold these two narratives together.

- **Choosing the right colors, labels, and more**

  It is critical to think through the color choices to present the data in the best possible manner and highlight the main points of a graph or chart to make it easy for viewers to correctly figure out the meaning of the color choices. While creating the visualizations, it is important to keep the contrasts high so even if there is low-level light on the screen, the audience is able to read the visualization in a clear manner.

Also, ensure to label data points and add clear titles on visualizations, and name the color combination depicting a particular data point is maintained throughout. To ensure that the colors are correctly interpreted by the audience, we need to encode them properly using a color key. Label the *X* and *Y* axes with proper words. There are two types of labels: the name label and the value/category label.

The more colors in a visualization, the harder it becomes to read it effectively; hence, more than six colors should be avoided.

- **Focus on the essence and substance of data**

  The users of the data need to be able to focus on the essence and substance of the data and not the background process of how data is handled. Use the visual features effectively and ensure that they form an integral part of the visualization; all this has to be a part of a deliberate design. And this design can be maintained only when the complexity of the visualization is in direct proportion to the complexity of the data. Everything has to be in balance. Too much simplification can dilute the essence and substance of data. Too much complication can make the audience lose interest.

  While creating visualizations, one should strive for a balance between style and substance. Though this balance may be difficult to achieve, the main focus should be to strike a balance between aesthetics and functionality. It is always wise, to begin with focusing on functionality and then add any embellishment.

- **Design in an iterative manner, and the design should be minimalist**

  As these factors let the users and businesses to focus on the visualizations rather than being distracted by other factors. Take feedback from the customers, users, audiences, stakeholders, and so on from time to time and then improve in an iterative manner to avoid the aspect of analysis paralysis.

- **Proper methodology in place**

  A proper methodology in regards to various aspects such as how to design visuals, how to carry out dashboard development, what ways will be used to gather data, and so on needs to be in place.

- **The right visual tool to fulfill the purpose**

  For example, to show or track trends, the best option for doing so is a line chart. For visualizing quantitative data, a scatter plot is a great choice. In the case of comparing quantities of different categories, then a bar chart is the most effective way of doing so.

- **Balance**

  Use the appropriate number of relationships per chart, report, and so on. The ideal number is six, as anything beyond this number defeats the very purpose of data visualization. Other factors such as texture, color, and so on also need to be used in balance and spread equally across the visualization.

  According to Gestalt principles (it is a group of visual perception principles developed by German psychologists in the 1920s): "*to create orderly and recognizable experience/image so that humans can gain meaningful perceptions amidst disorders.*" The same principles when applied to visualization, this order can be achieved using symmetrical, asymmetrical and radial types of balance. In symmetrical balance, visualization has all design elements equally on all sides. In asymmetrical balance, both sides are unique/different but carry a similar visual weight. In radial balance, visual elements are placed around a central anchor object, and here, the attention of the audience is drawn towards the center focal point.

- **Classification**

  Each type of visualization has a different purpose of serving. Define the purpose and goals of the visualization strategy and then classify tools accordingly to be able to serve these purposes and goals.

- **Rhythm**

  Visualization has an effective rhythm when the design elements create a movement that is pleasant to the eye. Another related element maintaining the aspect of rhythm is unity. Unity makes sure all the elements of the visualization are in sync and are congruent with each other.

- **Static and live data**

  Understanding the key difference between static and live data is a must for creating value-add visualizations.

  Static data is data that does not change after being recorded, and it represents a fixed data set. Static visualization is commonly used in infographics posted on the web or printed as handouts. As it normally focuses on a specific data story, users cannot go beyond a single view to explore additional stories beyond what is in front of them. The story is specifically captured in a single page layout and displays data that is not expected to change.

  Live or interactive visualization is commonly seen on the web only as an application. Users can select specific data points to build a visualized story of their choice. Better known as data visualization apps, and these visualizations allow the user to be a part of the data visualization process by building a story of their choice. An interactive graphic tells a different story each time new data is inserted. It helps the users to view data in real-time through various reports, dashboards, and so on. These help users to compare live data to historical data or to a specific date and time in the past, and all this happens seamlessly.

Static visualizations have a lower degree of engagement than interactive visualizations. Interactive visualizations are becoming more popular, and they are a part of most BI suites. Interactive visualizations optimize the way information is displayed.

Some target audiences may prefer static over dynamics and vice versa. The target customer, data story and ROI are three important indicators that can help figure out which is the best option. The complexity determines what kind of visualization might be used. For example, for simple stories, static visualization can be used, but for complex stories involving larger data sets, interactive visualization is the best option. Slowly and steadily, static reports are becoming outdated.

- **Understand the type of data**

  This aspect is needed to create the visualization in an effective manner. There are three types of data you may encounter while building visualizations, and knowing which data type you will need to helps to build effective visualization. The main types are: ordinal, categorical, and quantitative.

- **Feedback**

  Seek feedback from the audience on a regular basis. As what may seem meaningful and appealing to you could be confusing to your audience. It is also wise to seek inputs from teammates and colleagues and then fine-tune the visualizations based on all these inputs.

  One should get feedback early and often. By seeking and incorporating feedback from the audience right from day one, things tend to go smoother when the audience has some say and stake in data visualizations. They will tend to less criticize any faults as they too are a part of the ownership dynamics.

- **Classify the dashboard**

  Depending on the business requirements, organizations need to identify what type/s of dashboards they need. There are three main types: operational, analytical, and strategic. The operational dashboard is the most common type of dashboard. It is a tool used to provide a comprehensive snapshot of day-to-day performance and to keep track of the current performance of key metrics.

The analytical dashboard is highly interactive and more complex than the other two types of dashboards. They are used by analysts to perform data analysis and gain deeper insights, which then they can share with the executive tier and higher-ups. A strategic dashboard is typically used by executives for making strategic and high-level decisions.

- **Future changes and developments**

  Anticipating future changes, trends, and developments area must so as to ensure that visualizations reflect them in an effective manner. They need to be updated to keep in sync with the emerging technologies.

  Social-first visualizations are picking up pace; and hence, visualizations need to be created to suit these new audiences. As the attention span on social media is low, the visualizations need to be created in such a way that they are able to make the required impact in that short span.

Conclusion

In this chapter, we covered advanced aspects of data visualization in terms of types of visualization charts, visualization trends, the introduction of different data visualization tools such as *Tableau*, *Power BI*, *QlikView*, and so on, and the various data visualization best practices. After reading this chapter, the readers will have gained a further understanding of data visualization and its dynamics. This chapter sets the stage for the next chapter that covers an introduction to big data and its related technologies, which can be used and analyzed for insights that lead to better and timely decisions.

Questions

You may be interesting to revise your readings of this chapter:

1. What are the advantages of Tableau?
2. Why do companies use data visualization tools?
3. What is the significance of data visualization best practices?
4. What are the various types of dashboards?
5. What are the top three trends in data visualization?
6. How can we visualize more than three dimensions?
7. Which tools are used for big data visualization?

CHAPTER 6

Introduction to Big Data and Hadoop—Too Huge to Avoid

In the previous chapter, we were introduced to advanced data visualization software. We have also gone through new ways to view data through visuals such as bubble charts, word clouds, and geospatial heat maps.

The explosion of social media and the computerization of every aspect of social and economic activity has resulted in the creation of large volumes of mostly unstructured data: web logs, videos, speech recordings, photographs, e-mails, tweets, and alike. Accordingly, computer technology too kept evolving, and now we have access to systems and technology that are more powerful and affordable. Today, we have the ability to reliably and easily store huge volumes of data efficiently at very nominal rates. There is also a provision to analyze huge chunks of stored data to extract relevant information that can aid in making informed decisions and strategic moves for business growth.

Such data—both structured and unstructured that is huge (exceeding terabytes in size) and that keeps growing exponentially with time is termed as big data. It is so large, fast, and complex that the deployment of traditional methods for processing desired information would prove futile. The key objective of this course is to familiarize students with the most important information technologies used in manipulating, storing, and analyzing big data. Big data is not just about storing and extracting data, but much more than that. Big data encompasses so many technologies that to zero down anyone to begin learning with is a tough task. Some of the top technologies used to store and analyze big data are *Hadoop, MapReduce, Apache, Pig, Hive, Flume, Sqoop, Zookeeper, Oozie, Spark, Cassandra*, and *Mongo DB*.

Structure

This chapter will highlight the following topics:

- Introduction and need of big data
- Characteristics of big data
- Introduction of *Hadoop* and HDFS system
- Integration and processing of big data
- Understand and implement *Hive* and *Pig*
- Understand and implement *Hbase, Flume, Sqoop,* and *Oozie*
- Sample big data scripts

Objective

Here, we aim to understand and highlight the importance of big data, followed by its various properties and implementation of *Hive* and *Pig*.

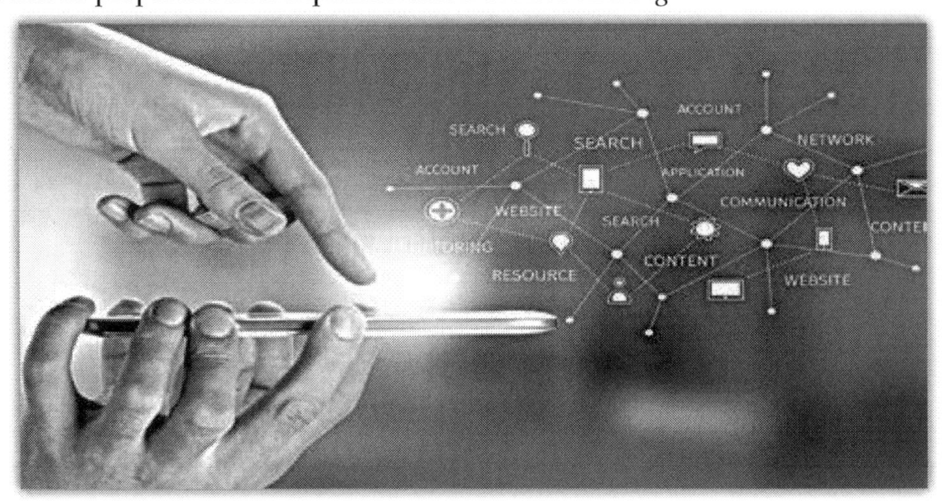

Figure 6.1: *Big Data* (source: CCY3.0)

Introduction and need of big data

Data is growing continuously and at a fast rate. Big data and business analytics have a great impact on businesses today. And, companies; therefore, would want faster insights into growing volumes of data. Organizations get flooded with data on a daily basis. This enormous data can be as follows:

- **Structured**: Data in a fixed, predictable format is called **structured data**. It has a defined length and format. Numbers, dates, excel files, and SQL databases are examples of structured data. It usually has structured rows and columns that can be sorted. It follows a pre-defined data model and is easy to analyze. The clearly defined patterns and the existence of mature analytics tools make it easily searchable. **Relational databases** (**RDBMS**) applications such as airline reservations systems, inventory control, sales transactions, CRM systems, and ERP systems usually have structured data.

An 'Employee' table in a database is an example of Structured Data

Employee_ID	Employee_Name	Gender	Department	Salary_In_lacs
2365	Rajesh Kulkarni	Male	Finance	650000
3398	Pratibha Joshi	Female	Admin	650000
7465	Shushil Roy	Male	Admin	500000
7500	Shubhojit Das	Male	Finance	500000
7699	Priya Sane	Female	Finance	550000

Figure 6.2: *Structured Data*

- **Unstructured**: Data with an unpredictable structure is called **unstructured data**. It does not have a pre-defined data model and is not organized in a pre-defined manner. Examples of unstructured data include pictures, videos, blogs, e-mails, mobile data, social media, and pdf documents, and so on. Such irregularities in format and ambiguity in style make its analysis difficult as compared to structured data. The majority of data on a company's premises as well as in online private and public sources such as *Instagram*, *Twitter*, *Linkedin*, and *Facebook* is unstructured data. In the past, comprehending results from unstructured data was not easy. Companies lacked tools to easily study and analyze data to make informed decisions. The ability to unsheathe value from such data is one of the prime drivers behind the speedy growth of big data.

Figure 6.3: *Unstructured Data*

- **Semi-structured**: Semi-structured data is that which contains both forms of data—structured and unstructured. It is structured in form but is not actually defined. It contains tags or markers that separate semantic elements and enables information on grouping and hierarchies. With the evolution of the internet and technology, data can be represented in many forms and not just full-text documents and databases, which has led to the increased occurrence of semi-structured data. Data represented in an XML file, Open standard **JavaScript object notation (JSON)** and NoSQL are a few examples of semi-structured data. This type of data forms only 5–10% of the data type pie but has critical business usage.

```
SELECT [CustomerID],
[CustomerName],
[CustomerCategoryName],
[PrimaryContact],
[AlternateContact],
[PhoneNumber],
[FaxNumber],
[BuyingGroupName],
[WebsiteURL],
[DeliveryMethod]
FROM [WideWorldImporters].[Website].[Customers]
WHERE CustomerID< 3 FOR XML PATH;
```

Figure 6.4 shows the data formats in big data.

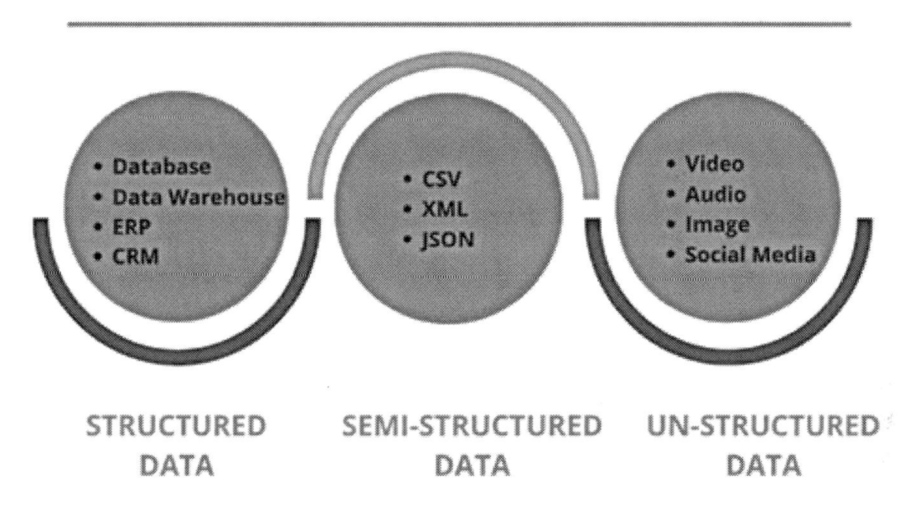

Figure 6.4: *Data formats in Big Data*

How big data extraction works

The term big data gives an impression only of the data size. This is partly correct but is not exactly what big data is all about. Big data refers to the use of multiple technologies to extract relevant and meaningful information from a huge pile of structured, semi-structured, and unstructured data. It involves the deployment of **terabytes** (**TB**), **petabytes** (**PB**), and even **exabytes** (**EB**) of data captured over time. The volume of data keeps adding up with every information exchange over the internet. A simple act of attending a phone call or commenting over social media, or switching on the CCTV can generate a data chain. As per IBM's study, businesses around the world generate nearly 2.5 quintillion bytes of data daily! Nearly 90% of the worldwide data has been produced in the past 2 years.

The sources that generate data are many. It is produced through social media networks, weather forecasts, business informatics, social media, genomics, search engines, weather forecasts, and many other sources. As per Statista report on smartphone users worldwide 2016–2021, worldwide smartphone users have surpassed three billion as of February 2020, and the number is estimated to only grow further by several hundred million in the upcoming years. These smartphones and apps contribute every minute to the ever-growing data pool. It is quite evident that enormous data is now being generated all around us—through smartphones, apps, social media, and so on. Facebook statistics on data show that it generates 4 petabytes of data per day! That is close to a million gigabytes.

Big data is getting bigger every second in almost all sectors. As per *Google* search statics, *Google* processes over 40,000 search queries every second on average. It is reported that *Twitter* gains 319 users every minute, *Youtube* users upload 500 hours of videos every minute. With the increasing number of internet users, approximate output data is estimated to be 2.5 quintillion bytes per day; these numbers will only go uphill in the years ahead. In the eighth edition of Domo's *Data Never Sleeps* report on how much data is generated every minute, the numbers are quite surprising. Have a look at the following figure:

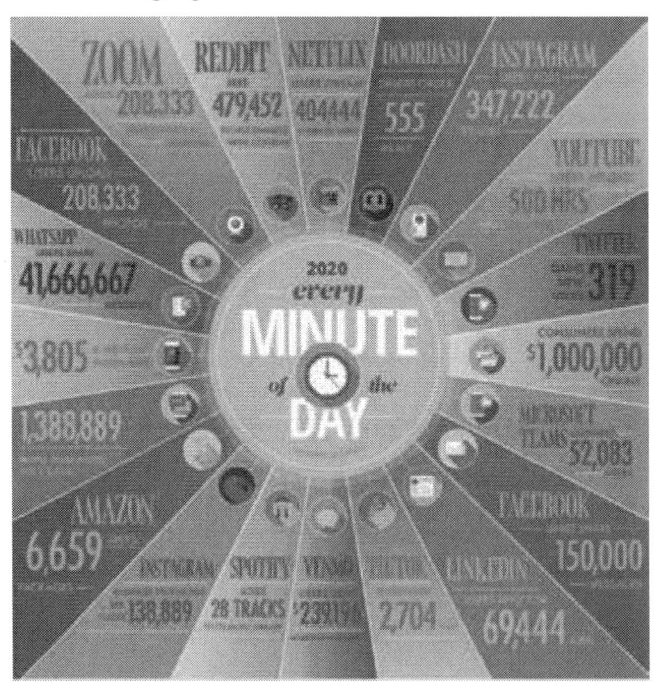

Figure 6.5: *Big Data is getting bigger every second in almost all the sectors*

These data sets contain a billion records of millions in the form of images, audio, web social media, and so on and are too voluminous to be processed by conventional data processing software. But it contains vital information that can benefit companies in many ways. Now, if a company wants to use this massive data, it needs to put in place special data processing processes. This colossal volume of data can be put to use in addressing key business problems and exploring effective strategies. Traditional tools used to organize data are incapable of processing such variety and volume. Therefore, we can put it this way that big data actually refers to the data that cannot be analyzed by traditional tools and techniques that are usually used to process structured or semi-structured data.

Big data—the combination of structured, unstructured, and semi-structured data can be collected and mined by organizations to improve their marketing approaches. Now businesses can leverage technology to make informed decisions that are based on signals generated by actual customers. It allows companies to hear the voice of each consumer and use this information to customize their communications which aid in the better mapping of customer expectations and generating happier customers. Through publicly accessible, plentiful consumer-generated information, companies can garner knowledge on their purchase history, purchase patterns, what consumers searched for, their likes, dislikes, what they watched, and so on that can be used in designing personalized marketing campaigns, sentiment analysis, and connecting with the right customer.

Uses of big data in business

It can be of great use to various businesses; we will have a look at a few. It is imperative that businesses thoroughly understand their consumer's collective behavior if they wish to capture the ever-changing landscape. Many big data products facilitate this by developing models to capture user behavior and aid businesses to target the right audiences for their product or identify and develop new products altogether for uncharted territories. Cinema owners can use the data to understand what time slots are popular, sell out the most, and may line up more food stalls during those hours.

Tremendous benefits have been brought about by big data to businesses in developed countries. These benefits can be replicated by indigenous organizations to improve their decision-making. Big data has vital applications in various areas such as the healthcare system, business decision-making, educational development, network optimization, travel estimation, and financial services. Owing to this, several studies and reviews have been published in big data analytics, implementations, and related technologies in recent times.

Uses of big data in healthcare

Big data, when used correctly, can help improve the healthcare sector. Having data-centric tools allows customer-facing employees to focus their service when dealing with patients. Also, the service provided would be more informed, analyzed, and accurate. Hospitals can deploy historical data to determine their pharma inventory based on the previous usage, assist patients more quickly with access to their full medical histories. By providing more personalized service through processed data, healthcare companies can provide optimal customer service to improve the overall experience and plummet their overall costs.

One can analyze and assess production, client feedback, and other factors that can reduce outages and predict future demands using big data. It can improve decision-making in line with current market demand; thus, improving operational efficiency.

One of the largest growing big data types is Genomics data. It is estimated that between 100 million and 2 billion genomes could be sequenced by the year 2025. Analysis of such massive volumes of sequence data will be expensive and would take up to 10,000 trillion CPU hours. One of the biomedical applications that this much data is providing is personalized medicine.

In summary, big data has a massive potential to enable models with higher precision in many application areas and ultimately amplify profitability.

Characteristics of big data

As with all the big things, to have a better understanding, we usually characterize them. Similarly, big data can be explained through its characteristics. These characteristics help to decipher big data as a concept and also give insight on how to deal with massive and diversified data at a manageable speed within a reasonable time frame so that we can extract value out of it and do some real-time analysis. The 3 "V"s of big data—*Variety, Velocity, and Volume* were listed by *Gartner* analyst *Doug Laney* back in 2001. Refer to the following in-depth description of these characteristics, which isolated, is enough to know what big data is.

- **Variety**

  Variety is one of the significant characteristics of big data. It refers to the types of data. It throws light on how diverse the data formats are. Variety implies the heterogeneous sources and the nature of data, both structured and unstructured. In the past, data could only be collected from spreadsheets and databases nut; today, data comes in a variety of formats such as e-mails, PDFs, images, videos, social media, and much more.

- **Volume**

  Volume refers to the size of exploding data from the computing world. It throws light on the quantity of data. We, by now, have clarity that big data indicates huge "volumes" of data that are being generated from a myriad of sources—social media, business processes, machines, networks, human interactions, and so on. The size of data plays a very critical role in determining the value out of data. Storing this massive data would have been a problem in the past—but not now anymore; new technologies (such as Hadoop) have relaxed this burden.

- **Velocity**

  Velocity points to the processing speed. It includes the rate of change, linking of incoming data sets at varying speeds. The flow of data is huge and continuous from sources such as business processes, application logs, networks, and social media sites, sensors, mobile devices, and so on. Data comes in at high speed and must be dealt with in a timely manner; this will also offer strategic competitive advantages.

  It is quite possible that the size of the data is comparatively small but many-hued and complicated, or it is also possible that the data be simple but huge in terms of volume. Basis this, we can also add another characteristic, Veracity, in addition to the aforementioned characteristics.

- **Veracity**

  Veracity refers to the abnormality in data. It is important to establish the accuracy and relevance of the data to the business value we want to extract before we sit to analyze. More the accuracy, the higher the chance of getting valuable information.

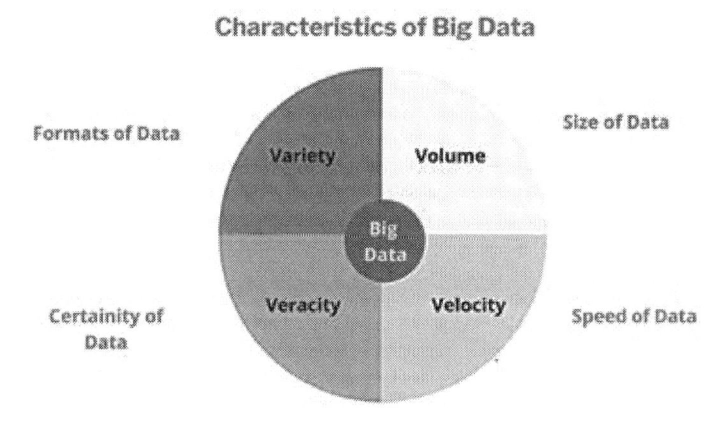

Figure 6.6: *Characteristics of big data*

Big data has provided new avenues for data harvesting and extracting value out of it, which otherwise were lying waste. It is not possible to capture, manage, and analyze big data with the help of traditional tools. The big data platform offers tools to extract insight out of the voluminous, diverse, fast-growing data. These piles of data now have a viable context to be used for various purposes in the business process of a company. Therefore, to zero down what type of data we need, we must understand it and its characteristics as the primary step.

Challenges of big data and business analytics

Like any resource, big data also has its own potential challenges in case it is not handled properly. It is required to comprehend the imperfection level in the collected data to calibrate and understand the meaning of the outputs with respect to the quality of the data. Some of these challenges are outlined as follows:

- **False sense of security**

  False security is given by big data. It may not capture the right information that a business may need for solving a specific query. At times smaller data is better. A huge amount of data does not necessarily mean it will all be relevant for the business.

- **Physical challenges**

  The challenges posed by big data are beyond volumes, velocity, and variety. It poses challenges for the present IT architecture, servers, networks, and softwares. Infrastructures of data centers that support big data and its storage are a problem to deal with.

- **May waste resource**

  Computer resources, money, and time should not be committed to big data if it is not required. If the required insights can be extracted from a small volume of data, spending time on big data would be sheer wastage.

- **Management challenges**

  Big data can prove very destructive if it lands up in the wrong hands. Security, privacy compliance challenges may shape up if the people handling big data do not have the correct intentions. Big data demands complete attention to detail and to new tool offerings to ensure complete compliance.

Applications of big data and business analytics

Many areas of business and industries have immensely benefitted from big data analytics technologies. The following are a few:

- **Education sector** Big data helps in predicting the learner's performance and achievements. It also plays a vital role in managing course content and designing personalized modules.
- **Crowdsourcing and sensing:** Smartphones can be deployed to source opinion data from the public and then make informed decisions basis the responses received.

- **Energy consumption analysis:** The analysis of energy consumption data using big data technologies provides usage patterns that can be used to promote green energy.

Introducing Hadoop and HDFS system

Given the huge size, diversity in formats, and fast-paced growth of data, we need many technologies and analytical tools to derive relevant information. For analyzing and processing this massive data, we need exceptional technologies; which ones are used would depend on the data type and the value that is being attempted to be derived. To handle, visualize, manipulate, and analyze big data, many solutions have been made available, but Hadoop is the most widely deployed technology. It is the key technology used to handle big data and its analysis.

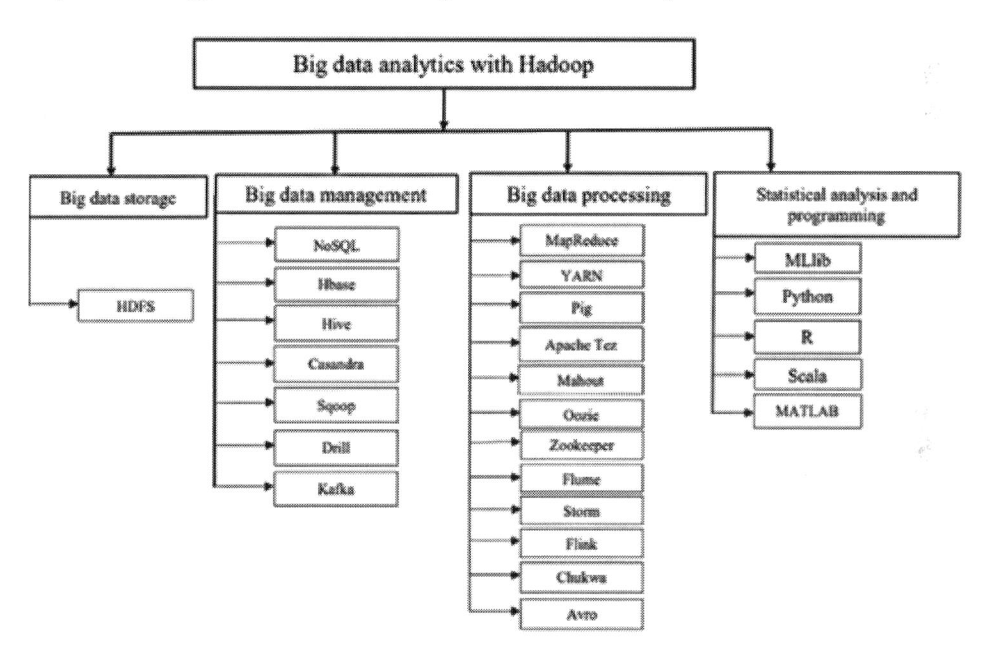

***Figure 6.7:** Managing big data and its analysis*

In simple terms, Hadoop is a collection of open-source and robust programs that deal with big data analysis. By open-source, we mean—it is freely available for use for anyone who is interested. It can be reused and modified (with some restrictions). It is often referred to as the backbone of operations by big data scientists.

The innovation of brilliant software engineers at Apache Software Foundation—*Doug Cutting* and *Mike Cafarella*, gave birth to *Hadoop*. The first version of the *Apache Hadoop* framework was made available in 2005, and since then, it has helped to chalk the way for better and efficient big data analytics. It was named after the toy elephant of one of the key developers' son. These engineers realized it was easier to read data from multiple small storage devices working simultaneously than reading data from bulk storage devices. Also, this made data available to multiple users spread across a network. Scaling up to multiple machines with local storage and computations from single servers is one of the major advantages that *Hadoop* offers.

Hadoop with huge data handling

We will now talk about how *Hadoop* favors the fortune companies. Because *Hadoop* is meant for big data analytics, its primary users are corporations with huge chunks of data to be analyzed and interpreted across multiple geographical locations. The *International Data Corporation's* report shows that at least 32% of the organizations already have *Hadoop* in place, and another 36% are preparing to use it within the next year. Another report by Gartner, Inc. also forecasted 30% of enterprises to have already invested in *Hadoop*.

Because *Hadoop* is flexible, additional data can be inserted, edited, or even deleted as per business process requirements. It offers cost-effective and practical solutions, and adding more storage units is hassle-free; readily—available storage from IT vendors can be easily procured. Off-shelf software systems are rigid and complex to customize, whereas *Hadoop* being open source, provides sufficient flexibility for organizations to tailor it the way they deem perfect. Also, the easy availability of commercial versions in the market simplifies the installation process of the *Hadoop* framework. All these reasons are strong enough to make *Hadoop* popular amongst organizations.

The *Apache Hadoop framework* comprises the following main modules:

- Hadoop common
- Hadoop distributed file system (HDFS)
- Hadoop YARN
- Hadoop MapReduce

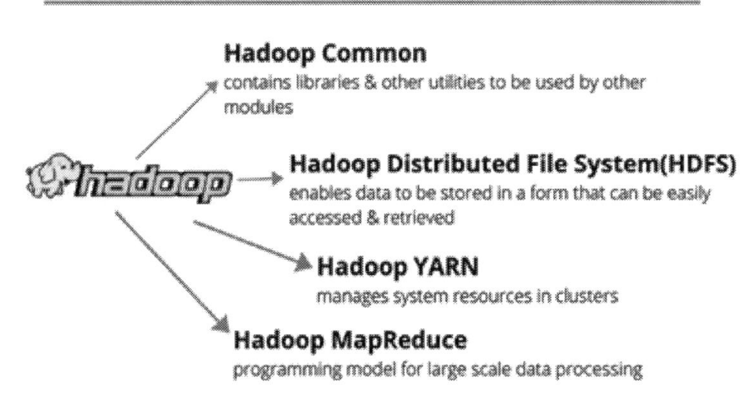
Hadoop Core Modules
Hadoop Common
contains libraries & other utilities to be used by other modules
Hadoop Distributed File System(HDFS)
enables data to be stored in a form that can be easily accessed & retrieved
Hadoop YARN
manages system resources in clusters
Hadoop MapReduce
programming model for large scale data processing

Figure 6.8: *Hadoop Framework*

- **Hadoop common**

  It refers to the collection of libraries and other common tools that support other Hadoop modules. *Hadoop common* forms an integral part of the Apache Hadoop framework, along with the other modules—**Hadoop distributed file system** (**HDFS**), Hadoop YARN, and *Hadoop MapReduce*. It works with the assumption that hardware failures are pretty common and that these failures should be handled by default by Hadoop framework software. It contains the basic and essential **Java archive** (**JAR**) files and scripts that are required to start *Hadoop*. The set of utilities supports *Hadoop* subprojects and includes filesystem, RPC, and serialization libraries.

- **Hadoop distributed file system (HDFS)**

  It is the pillar of *Hadoop* and maintains the distributed file system. It provides storage and replication of data across multiple servers. The data is stored across various interconnected devices that can be accessed using MapReduce. HDFS is used to scale a single *Apache Hadoop* cluster to thousands of nodes. It offers very high aggregate bandwidth across the cluster.

The goals of HDFS

- Quick recovery from hardware failures: HDFS has been designed to detect faults and quickly recover.
- Access to streaming data: Emphasis in the design of HDFS has been for high data throughput rates, which provide streaming access to data sets.

Accommodation of large data sets—HDFS has been built to store zillion files, each larger than hundreds of gigabytes and filesystems of tens of petabytes.

Portability—HDFS is portable across multiple hardware platforms and compatible with various operating systems.

Term	Meaning
Cluster	Set of computers which consist of DataNodes and NameNode.
NameNode	It acts as a monitor and supervises the operation performed by DataNodes. This single computer usually has best-in-class hardware.
DataNode	It is a computer with commodity hardware. It stores and processes the files.
Mapper	If we are to find a particular file from the multiple DataNodes that are already on operation, Mapper goes to each DataNode and runs certain code to find out where actually the required data is.
Reducer	It gets the result from each Mapper.
Job tracker	It schedules the jobs and tracks the jobs assigned to the task tracker.
Task tracker	It tracks the task and reports the status to Job tracker.
Block	It is the smallest size in which files split. In Hadoop 1, the block size by default is 64 MB.

Table 6.1: *Few Terminologies of HDFS*

The Hadoop distributed file system

The HDFS is a distributed, scalable, and portable file system is written in Java. Each node in Hadoop has a single NameNode and a cluster of DataNodes. Every DataNode serves blocks of data (is the smallest size in which files split. In Hadoop 1, the block size by default is 64 MB) to the network using block protocol which is specific to HDFS. A remote procedure call is used by clients to communicate with each other.

Hadoop distributed file system stores files of the size ranging from gigabytes to terabytes across many machines. To ensure no data is lost, it replicates the data across multiple hosts. It has the default replication value of 3, and it stores the data on three nodes: two on the same rack and one on a different node. Data nodes communicate with each other and rebalance data, move data copies around, keep data replication on high priority.

Secondary NameNode in the HDFS file system can mislead some into thinking that it comes into action on the failure of primary NameNode. It rather connects with primary NameNode regularly and compiles snapshots of primary NameNode's directory information. This information is then saved on local or remote directories. These images are used to restart a primary NameNode that has failed. The entire replay of file system actions can thus be skipped.

Data awareness between job tracker and task tracker offers a great advantage while using HDFS. Job tracker schedules the jobs and tracks the jobs assigned to the task tracker with an awareness of data location. Let us consider that node A contains data (m, n, o), and node B contains data (a, b, c). The job tracker appoints node B to perform map or reduce tasks on (a, b, c), and node A would be assigned to perform map or reduce tasks on (m, n, o). This way amount of traffic that would go over the entire network plummets.

Industry examples of HDFS

Hadoop distributed file system has many industry usages in multiple fields. All sectors such as marketing, healthcare, media, and research use the HDFS to handle their huge amount of data.

- **Marketing**: The success of personalized marketing campaigns is dependent on how well a marketer knows his target audience. There are many sources through which this can be accomplished. Off-line sources such as POS systems, CRMs, direct mail responses, coupon redemptions, and online sources such as *Facebook*, *Twitter*, online ad CTRs can help marketers procure the relevant information. But the person will have to sift through a mountain of data to find any desired information. That is where HDFS can help. Because the majority of the data is unstructured, the HDFS cluster will be the most cost-effective staging area before analytics.
- **Healthcare:** Through HIPAA and HITECH Acts, which encourage the use of **electronic data interchange (EDI)** and interoperable **electronic healthcare record (HER)**, health organizations have been accumulating high volumes of structured data. Along with it, image and video files from X-rays, ultrasound, CT scans, endoscopies have too been piling up massive data. Online data in the form of forum discussions on symptoms, blogs, and social media form

the pool of unstructured data. All this, if processed over *Hadoop* will provide useful insights for improving patient healthcare.

- **Media and entertainment:** HDFS cluster can prove useful in the storage and processing of data to interpret people's reactions on social media. It can help spell the difference between a blockbuster and a flop.
- **Research**: Data analysis forms an essential part of any research. A single experiment can generate a million petabytes of raw data per year. Since research labs are not as financially rich as business units, it is all the more important that they invest in an inexpensive but highly effective infrastructure. HDFS clusters can help researchers cost-effectively perform data analysis.
- **Electric power:** The power industry deploys **phasor measurement units (PMUs)** to monitor the health of smart grids. PMUs record voltage, current, frequency, location, and other physical quantities. The collected data can be analyzed to detect any faults. Because PMU networks record thousands of records per second, power companies can benefit hugely from inexpensive, highly efficient file systems like HDFS.

Hadoop YARN

Apache Hadoop **yet another resource negotiator (YARN)** refers to the resource management aspect of Hadoop. It manages the system resources when analytics are being conducted on the data stored in linked devices. It allows various data processing engines, such as graph processing, interactive processing, stream processing, and batch processing, to run and process data stored in the HDFS. This way, it increases the efficiency of the system. The processing of the application in YARN is scheduled through its different components. YARN aids in the proper usage of available resources, which is essential for processing a high volume of data. In addition to resource management, YARN also performs job scheduling. It helps other evolving technologies by extending them the power of Hadoop so that they can also benefit from HDFS.

The following listed features of YARN make it very popular:

- **Multi-tenancy:** YARN gives access to multiple data processing engines such as batch processing engine, stream processing engine, interactive processing engine, graph processing engine, and many more. This offers multi-tenancy to the organization.
- **Cluster utilization:** Clusters are used in a dynamic manner in Hadoop with the help of YARN.
- **Compatibility:** YARN is compatible with Hadoop 1.0 as well.

- **Scalability:** The resource manager component of YARN allows thousands of clusters and nodes to be managed and extended by Hadoop.

Hadoop MapReduce

MapReduce is a programming model that works on the basis of two functions—Map and reduce that dissects the data in a quick and efficient manner. It first reads data from various databases and then aligns them in a format that would support the analysis of big data. It then breaks down the data into relevant and meaningful information that can be used for interpretation. The Map function groups, filters, and sorts multiple data sets in parallel to generate tuples (key, value pairs), and then the reduce function aggregates the data from the tuples to generate the desired result. This model was first used by *Google* for indexing its search operations.

In a nutshell, Hadoop is an open-source, flexible, and robust framework for the analysis of big data and is made up of the aforementioned four major modules, and more are being added to it for diverse applications.

Integration and processing of big data

Data integration refers to the technical and business processes used to combine data from multiple sources to provide a unified and single view of the data.

Big data integration

It is an essential step in any big data project. It refers to the advanced data integration processes devised to manage the massive volume, variety, and velocity of *big data* and combining data that originates from a variety of sources and software such as web data, social-media, machine-generated data into a single framework and then providing users a translated and unified view of accumulated data.

Generally, in the data integration process, the client sends a request to the master server for data. The master server then finds the needed data from internal and external sources. The required data is extracted from the sources, then consolidated into a single, cohesive data set. This is served back to the client for use.

Data integration software programs and data integration platforms developed by data integration architects provide an automated data integration process for connecting and directing data from source systems to target systems. The following are the various data integration techniques that help achieve this:

- **Extract, transform, and load:** In this, copies of datasets from various sources are collected, coordinated, and loaded into a data warehouse.

- **Extract, load, and transform:** In this technique, data is first loaded into a big data system and then transformed later for a particular analytics issue.
- **Change data capture:** This technique identifies the real-time data changes in a database and then applies those to the data warehouse.
- **Data replication:** By using this technique, data in one database is replicated to other databases for backup and to also keep the information in sync for operational users.
- **Data virtualization:** In this method, to create an integrated view, data from a variety of systems are virtually combined.
- **Streaming data integration:** In this method, different streams of data are continuously integrated in real-time and entered into analytics systems and data stores.

In the integration of data from different applications, data is taken from the source data environment and sent to the target data environment. Big data integration services use real-time integration techniques that adjuncts the traditional extract, transform, and load (ETL) technologies and add dynamic context to continuously streaming data. The conventional ETL technologies have evolved and continue to evolve to work with big data environments.

Tools supporting batch integration processes with real-time integration across several sources are very useful while working with big data. We will take the example of a pharmaceutical company to understand this better. A pharma company would want to merge data stored in its master data management system and big data from various sources showcasing the outcomes of prescription drug usage. This would help the company in the collection, aggregation, consolidation, and delivery of reliable data that can be used while formulating business strategies. New tools like *Scribe* and *Sqoop* also support big data integration.

The process of integrating massive data sets is quite complex and can pose several challenges. We will discuss a few as follows:

- **Finding the right staff:** Though the number of data scientists is continuously growing, there still are not enough people to fill in the positions in the big data industry.
- **Extracting data:** It is necessary to have data extraction skills to analyze and process big data.
- **Synchronization:** The traditional data management systems promote data desynchronization through their conventional process of data extraction, migration, and transformation. Also, data quickly becomes desynchronized

from its originating source as it comes from a wide range of sources at different rates.

- **Data management tools:** Incompatibility between big data management tools is bound to create issues. The selection of appropriate tools is extremely important.
- **Choosing a strategy:** A clear and true data integration strategy should be devised to meet the goals and to avoid leaping from one project to another without an organizational plan.

Big data processing

Big data processing can be explained as the process of handling large volumes of information—information that is complex in nature, huge in terms of volume, and in a variety of formats. We have already talked about how traditional methods will prove futile if assigned the task of handling this chunk of information. The handling of data includes data processing, data visualization, and data analysis.

To be able to extract valuable information from big data, it first needs to be processed. We will now study how it can be done. There are numerous open-source solutions and enterprise solutions available for processing big data. Few data processing frameworks have wide usage while others are more specific in their usage; these have still carved out respectable shares in the market.

We will discuss the top five open-source frameworks for big data processing as follows:

- **Hadoop:** It is one of the top frameworks that is used for big data processing. Because of its vast prevalence, *Hadoop* has become almost synonymous with big data. *Hadoop,* with its ecosystem of tools and technologies such as *Pig, Hive, Flume,* and HDFS has gained widespread adoption in the industry. Though it processes complex *big data* and has a large group of tools, it is actually quite simple. *Hadoop* will work just fine for you if your data can be processed in batches and then be split into smaller processing jobs that are spread across a cluster and can be recombined.
- **Spark:** Spark, developed at the *University of California* at Berkeley, is now becoming another popular system for big data processing and was designed to improve the performance of earlier systems. It is compatible with *Hadoop* and helps it to work faster, and it can even work as a standalone big data processing framework. Hadoop's software replaces the *MapReduce* section to work with *Spark's* processing engine. Big data powerhouse *Cloudera* is an example of a business that replaces *MapReduce* with *Spark* for processing

big data. This type of approach also gives rise to a variety of alternative processing scenarios with a mixture of algorithms and tools from two systems. *Spark* does not include its own distributed storage layer and uses Hadoop's distributed file system. It has superior memory, which speeds up the processing time and makes it different from the *Hadoop* and *Google's MapReduce* models. Its ability to perform in-memory computations makes it unique.

- **Flink:** It is an engine that processes streaming data and provides facilities for distributed computation over streams of data. *Flink* treats the batch process as a special case of streaming data, which makes it an effective framework for both real-time and batch processing but clearly gives priority to the streaming data. If you want to process streaming data in real-time, you should use *Flink*. It can very effectively handle large volumes of data streams with low processing latency. A number of APIs, like a streaming API for *Java* and Scala, a static data API for *Python, Scala* and *Java* are provided by *Flink*. It has its own machine learning library and also graph processing library. *Flink's* set of impressive additional features are listed as follows:
    - Fault tolerance through lightweight distributed snapshots.
    - Continuous streaming model with backpressure.
    - High performance and low latency.
    - Support for event time and out-of-order events.
    - User-friendly, customizable windowing component.
- **Storm:** This was designed to process unbounded streams of data in an easy and uninterrupted manner and can be used with any programming language. It is a free and open-source distributed real-time computation system. *Apache Storm* can process over one million tuples per second per node. It is written in *Clojure*, a dialect of *Lisp*, and is predominantly a functional programming language. It can be used for real-time analytics, distributed machine learning, and in situations where high-velocity data is to be processed. *Storm* is *Hadoop* compatible and can be run with YARN. It comes with Trident, a highly functional abstraction layer, and is functionally similar to *Spark* as it also processes mini-batches. The below listed five characteristics make *Storm* ideal for real-time data processing:
    - **Fast**: A benchmark clocked it at over a million tuples processed per second per node.

    - **Scalable**: With parallel calculations across a cluster of machines.
    - **Fault-tolerant**: It will automatically restart when a worker (*Apache Storm* processes that run on predefined ports on the machine that hosts storm are called **workers**) fails, and the worker gets restarted on another node in case a node dies.
    - **Reliable**: It guarantees that each unit of data, which is also called a tuple, will be processed at least once or exactly once. Messages get relayed only in case of any failures.
    - **Easy to operate**: It is easy to operate once the standard configurations are set up.
- **Samza:** It also processes distributed streams of data. It allows building stateful applications that process real-time data from a variety of sources, including *Apache Kafka* (an open-source distributed event streaming platform that is used for streaming analytics and data integration). It uses *Kafka* for messaging as it guarantees that the received messages and the processed messages are in the same order and does not ensure that no message is lost. *Apache Samza* uses YARN for cluster resource management. When a system in the cluster drops out, YARN comes into action and moves the task to another computer. In addition to *Kafka* and YARN, *Samza* also has a pluggable API that allows it to work with other messaging systems. *Linkedin* uses *Samza* for sending notifications and e-mails to its members. All e-mails are sent through a central *Samza* e-mail distribution system. After combining and organizing e-mail requests, summarized e-mails are sent to the member based on the windowing criteria and specific policies.

Various big data processing frameworks have a fair degree of compatibility, which offers an exploration of mix and match options to generate desired results. There are multiple solutions for big data processing, and organizations can compare each of them to find what meets their specific needs the best.

Understanding and implementing Hive and Pig

Hadoop technology is a popular word these days, but many technology professionals are not yet familiar with the key components that constitute the Hadoop ecosystem. *Pig* and *Hadoop* are two main components of the Hadoop ecosystem.

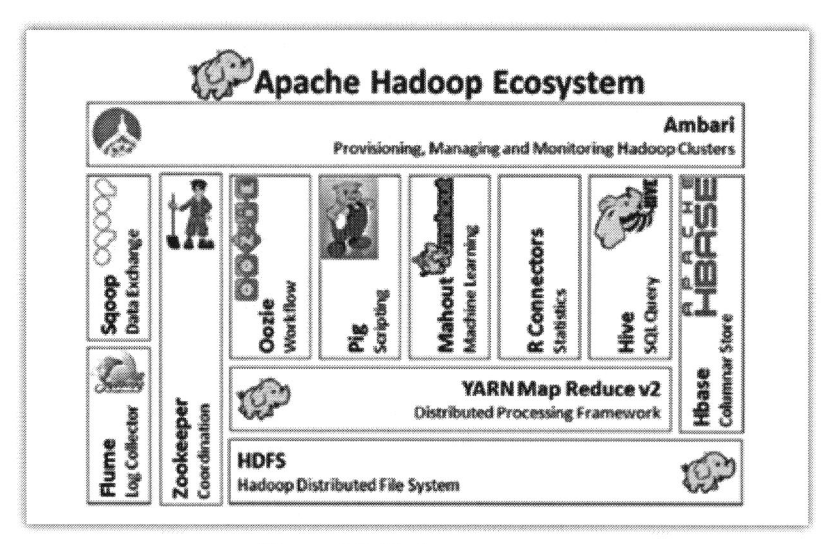

Figure 6.9: *Hadoop ecosystem*

Hive Hadoop was founded by *Jeff Hammerbacher* of *Facebook*. Because *Facebook* receives huge loads of data every minute, Jeff realized the need for a mechanism that can store, mine, and analyze this data. This led to the development of the *Hive*. Using *Hive*, *Facebook* now deals with 10's Terabytes of data on a daily basis with great ease.

Hive is a type of data warehouse infrastructure tool to process structured data in *Hadoop*. It makes the task of analysis easy by summarizing the big data. The three main important functionalities for which *Hive* is deployed are as follows:

- Data summarization
- Data analysis
- Data query

HiveQL—the query language that *Hive* exclusively supports, suits the specific demands of analytics. It is based around SQL; thus, making it easier to learn for those who are familiar with SQL. For developers, who are not well versed with the *MapReduce* framework for writing data queries, *Hive* is of great use. Hive can be used by anyone who is not even familiar with *Java* programming and *Hadoop* API's. *HiveQL* translates SQL-like queries to *MapReduce* jobs that are further deployed on *Hadoop*. *Hive* improves schema design flexibility, data serialization, and deserialization.

Key features:

- Hive provides the users with strong, robust, and powerful statistics functions.
- It provides tools that enable easy access to data via SQL; thus, allowing data warehousing tasks such as ETL, reporting, and analysis of data.

- It provides a mechanism to impose structure on a variety of data formats.
- The learning curve for SQL developers will be almost negligible because *Hive Hadoop* is quite similar to SQL.
- Hive Hadoop can be integrated with HBase for data querying.
- It can start an optional thrift-based server that can send queries directly to the *Hive* server from any nook and corner.
- There is not any single specific format in which data must be stored in Hive. It has inbuilt **commas and tab-separated values (CSV/TSV)** text files, *Apache ORC*, and other formats. *Hive* can be extended to other formats with connectors. The most important file systems supported by Hive are as follows:
- Flat files or text files.
- Sequence files consist of binary key-value pairs.
- RCF files that store columns of a table in a columnar database.

Hive is best suited for batch jobs; it works best for traditional data warehousing tasks and cannot work with an online transaction processing system as it does not provide real-time querying for row-level updates.

As mentioned earlier, *Apache Hive* is used for data querying, analysis, and summarization. It helps improve developers' productivity considerably, which generally comes at the cost of increasing latency. *Hive* is a very good variant of SQL. Its many user-defined functions enable effective ways of solving problems. Connecting *Hive* queries to various *Hadoop* packages such as *RHive*, *RHipe*, and so on is quite easy. Hive has proven to help the developer community working with complex analytical processes and challenging data formats in a significant way.

Hive enables users to simultaneously access data and increase the response time (which is the time which a system or a functional unit takes to react to a given input). Hive generally has a very fast response time and is also highly flexible as many commodities can be easily added in the response of adding more data clusters without compromising the performance.

Pig Hadoop

Pig Hadoop was developed in 2006 by *Yahoo* with the main motive to cut down on time required for development through its multi-query approach. *Yahoo* developed *Pig Hadoop* so that it can have an ad-hoc method for creating and executing *MapReduce* jobs on large data sets. *Pig* is a high-level data flow system that uses Pig Latin—a simple language platform for manipulating data and queries.

Microsoft, *Google*, and *Yahoo* deploy *Pig* to collect and store large data sets in the form of web crawls, clickstreams, and search logs. At times, *Pig* is also used in ad-hoc analysis and processing of information.

Key features

Pig Hadoop provides the users with nested data types such as maps, tuples, and bags that are absent in *MapReduce*, along with major data operations such as orders, filters, and joins.

- It has a multi-query approach that cuts down on the number of times data is scanned.
- It is very easy to learn for SQL familiar users.
- It enables naive Java data workers to write complicated data transformations.
- *Pig* is complete in itself; and hence, one can do all required data manipulations in *Hadoop* with *Pig*.
- *Apache Pig* provides a good set of operators for performing data operations such as sort, join, filter, and so on.
- Automatic optimization in *Pig* enables programmers to concentrate only on the semantics of the language.
- It can analyze both structured and unstructured data and store the results in HDFS.
- Pig Hadoop component provides users with sample data for each scenario and each step through its "*Illustrate*" function.

Difference between Pig and Hive

Is that the *Pig* and *Hive* have the same advantages and disadvantages while processing the massive amount of data? The answer is a clear no. There is not any *Hive* versus *Pig* in the real world. One just needs to conclude which out of the two would suit the requirements the best. *Hive* query language supports better the specific demands of analytics, and *Pig* supports huge data operation better. *Pig Hadoop* was developed to avoid the complicated syntax of *Java* programming for *MapReduce*, whereas *HiveQL* is based on SQL, which makes it easier to learn for SQL developers. Serialization is faster in *Pig* because it supports AVRO. Each component of the given business logic must be carefully considered before taking any decision on deploying a *Hive* or *Pig*.

Characteristic	Pig Hadoop	Hive Hadoop
Language name	Pig Latin	HiveQL
Type of language	Dataflow	Declarative (SQL Dialect)
Developed by	Yahoo	Facebook
Data structures supported	Nested and complex	
Relational complete	Yes	Yes
Schema optional	Yes	No
Turing complete	Yes, when you extend it with Java user-defined functions.	Yes, when you extend it with Java user-defined functions.

Table 6.2: *Deploying Hive Hadoop versus Pig Hadoop*

Figure 6.10 also shows the difference between Hive Hadoop versus Pig Hadoop:

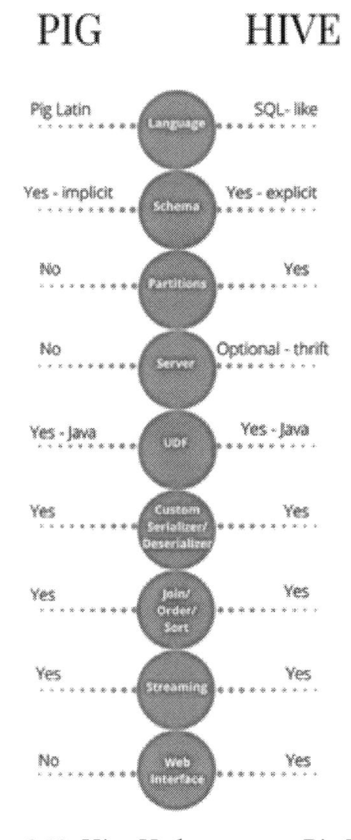

Figure 6.10: *Hive Hadoop versus Pig Hadoop*

Many high-quality codes make *Apache Pig* more efficient than *Apache Hive*. Join operation is slow in *Hive* as it creates many objects while implementing joins. IBM conducted a *Pig* versus *Hive* performance benchmarking survey, and the results were as follows:

IBM Pig versus Hive performance benchmarking survey results	
Join operations on the database.	Apache Pig is 36% faster than Apache Hive.
Arithmetic operations.	Apache Pig is 46% faster than Apache Hive.
Filtering 10% of the data.	Apache Pig is 10% faster than Apache Hive.
Filtering 90% of the data.	Apache Pig is 18% faster than Apache Hive.

Table 6.3: *IBM Pig versus Hive Performance Benchmarking Survey Results*

From *table 6.3*, we can conclude that *Pig* has consistently outperformed *Hive* for most of the operations, barring the grouping of data. *Hive* and *Pig* both have almost the same number of committers in each project and likely in the near future, and we can imagine the great advancements in Hive and Pig on the development front.

Understanding and implementing HBase, Flume, Sqoop, and Oozie

The next step forward is to understand Hadoop ecosystem.

HBase

Apache HBase is an integral part of the *Apache software foundation*. It is a database that is column-oriented and built on top of the HDFS, and provides fast lookups for larger tables. It is an open-source and non-relational distributed project, which is horizontally scalable and provides the capabilities of *Google Bigtable* for the *Hadoop* framework to store large volumes of unstructured data at high speed to derive meaningful insights from it.

HBase has a highly fault-tolerant way of storing data and is great for storing sparse data. An example of sparse data could be finding out that one person who has spent over INR 1,00,00,000 in a single transaction on *eBay* among the tens of millions of transactions that happen on any given week.

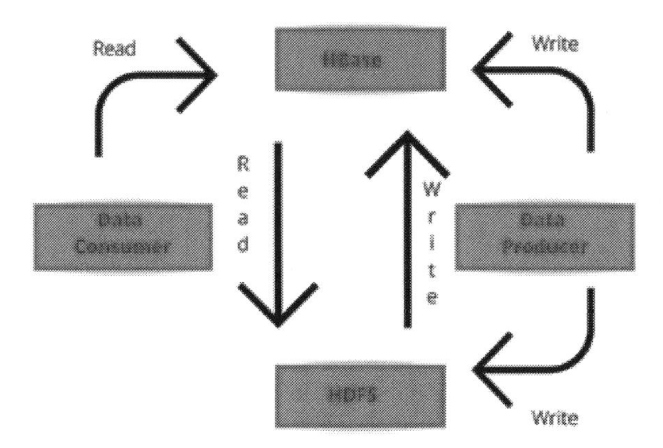

Figure 6.11: *HBase transaction*

HBase provides random real-time read/write access to data in HDFS. Data can be stored in HDFS either directly or through *HBase*. A data consumer can read or access data in HDFS randomly using *HBase*, which sits on top of HDFS and offers read and write access.

HBase is one of the important components of the *Hadoop* ecosystem along with HDFS and *MapReduce*. Few key features of *HBase* that make it one of the most sought after message storing systems are as follows:

- It can be used for both structured and semi-structured data types.
- It offers high security and easy management of data.
- *HBase* works efficiently for extremely random read and writes operations.
- It can work on extremely large-scale data with its completely distributed architecture.
- Scaling up is real quick and seamless in the event of additional requirements.
- It has modular and linear scalability features.
- The data reads and writes highly consistent.
- Automatic failure support is provided to various servers.
- *HBase* tables back up *MapReduce* jobs.
- Java APIs provide seamless client access.
- *HBase* offers unprecedented high write throughput.
- *HBase* provides data replication across clusters.

One of the most salient features of *HBase* is that it can handle data sets with billions of rows and millions of columns. It combines a wide variety of data types, structures, and schemas from various sources in an efficient manner. It can be integrated with

Hadoop to provide a seamless fit. It also works well with YARN. It provides very low latency access over a fast-changing and enormous amount of data.

HBase—a progressive NoSQL database, is now being used increasingly in today's world, which is overwhelmed with big data. A lot of businesses look exclusively for sparse data, meeting certain criteria within data fields, which are in billions. Extreme fault tolerance, resilience, and the ability to work on multiple types of data make it highly useful for varied business scenarios.

The column-oriented table makes looking for the right data among billions of data fields very easy. With the right configuration and automatization, data can be easily sharded into tables. Distributed storage helps in the analytical processing of huge amounts of data which can exceed the limits on a single server. The read/write capacity of *HBase* can be scaled up to even millions/second, which gives it an unprecedented advantage. *Facebook* leverages this feature extensively for real-time messaging applications.

Flume

Apache Flume can be explained as an agent for data collection. It takes data from various sources such as Avro, Syslog's, and delivers it to various destinations like Hadoop HDFS and HBase. It is responsible for collecting and transporting massive amounts of data such as events, log files, and so on from a variety of sources to one central data store. It is a unique tool in a sense, and it copies log data or streaming data from different web servers to HDFS.

Each unit data in *Flume* is considered as an event. The data source is the source of various sets of events. *Flume* system, since it is configured to a specific data source, consumes the event and passes it to the destination as soon as any data is written by the configured source. It is also referred to as a real-time data transfer distributed system to prevent any loss of data.

To understand *Flume* better, let us take this example where logs of various web servers have to be analyzed. The logs would get stored in the configured server. For analysis, these files have to be transferred to HDFS using *Hadoop*. One way is to transfer the huge files over the network (this can lead to data loss), and the other way is to transfer the logs as soon as they are created and then store them in the required file system, i.e., through *Apache Flume*—it takes the data from the source and writes it into the configured destination. It is highly useful and important when a data file is to be written in multiple locations or data from multiple sources is to be written in a single destination.

Following listed are the advantages of using *Flume*:

- *Flume* is highly reliable, fault-tolerant, scalable, manageable, and customizable.
- It guarantees reliable message delivery since the transactions are channel-based, and two transactions are made for each message.
- Data can be stored in any of the centralized stores such as *HBase*, HDFS using *Apache Flume*.
- It acts as a mediator between data producers and the centralized stores and provides a steady flow of data between them when the rate of incoming data far exceeds the rate to which data should be written to the destination.

Sqoop

Apache Sqoop is a tool that was designed for transferring bulk data between *Apache Hadoop* and structured databases such as relational databases, *MySQL*, *Oracle*, *Teradata* to *Hadoop* HDFS, and export from Hadoop file system to relational databases. *Sqoop* transfers bulk data between Hadoop and external data stores such as enterprise data warehouses, relational databases, and so on quite efficiently. That is how *Sqoop* got its name—"*SQL to Hadoop and Hadoop to SQL*". In addition to this, *Sqoop* is also used to import data from external datastores into the *Hadoop* ecosystem's tools like *Hive* and *HBase*.

***Figure 6.12**: Sqoop tool*

Once the data is converted from relational databases into the form supported by HDFS, that is when the developers begin to derive valuable insights. Custom coding or scripts for transferring data to and from *Hadoop* can be written as well, but *Apache Sqoop* provides an alternative to performing the same task in a simple yet efficient manner. Through the *MapReduce* framework, *Sqoop* works on importing and exporting data and provides a parallel fault-tolerant mechanism. Following are the advantages of *Apache Sqoop* that makes it so popular:

- It transfers data from a variety of structured data sources such as *Oracle*, *Postgres*, and so on.
- Automation of a lot of processes brings in a high level of efficiency.

- Kerberos security authentication can be integrated.
- Data can be loaded directly from *Hive* and *HBase*.
- Because of the continuous contribution and development, regular updations keep happening.
- With a huge support community, it is a very robust and efficient tool.

Apache Sqoop is a powerful tool to transfer data from different sources in a variety of formats onto *Hadoop* and then put back the processed data to the relational database systems. The importance of *Apache Sqoop* will only go uphill with the advent of its latest versions.

Oozie

Apache Oozie can be defined as a scheduler system that is used to run and manage *Hadoop* jobs in a distributed environment. *Oozie* works towards supporting the combination of multiple complicated jobs that run in a specific order for the accomplishment of a more significant task. It enables the programming of two or more jobs to run in parallel within a specific set of tasks. It is nicely integrated with *Hadoop* stack that supports many *Hadoop* jobs such as *Pig*, *Sqoop*, and *Hive*, along with other system-specific tasks like *Java* and *Shell*. For this reason, *Oozie* has this wide usage. Workflow actions that use the *Hadoop* execution engine for executing various tasks are triggered using *Oozie*. It leverages the Hadoop machinery for failover, load balancing, and so on. It is a scalable, reliable, and extensible system. This technology runs more than 2,00,000 jobs every day at *Yahoo*. Detection of completion of tasks by polling and call back is the responsibility of *Oozie*. It provides a unique callback HTTP URL to the task and sends a notification to the URL when the task gets completed. It polls the task for completion in case it does not invoke the callback URL. The main motive behind using *Oozie* is the management of several kinds of jobs that are being processed in the *Hadoop* system. The user specifies several dependencies between jobs in the form of DAG. *Oozie* takes care of this information in a particular order as in the workflow. This way, the user saves time for managing the entire workflow. Not only this, but *Oozie* also mentions the frequency of the execution of a job. Features of *Oozie* are as follows:

- With *Oozie*, the execution of jobs that are scheduled for running periodically is possible.
- After completion of jobs, an e-mail notification can be sent.
- Web service APIs enable the controlling of jobs from anywhere.
- Through client API, launching, controlling, and monitoring a job from the Java application can be done.

Oozie is a service that runs in the cluster. Clients submit workflow definitions for immediate processing. Control-flow nodes and the actions nodes are the two nodes.

The action node in *Oozie* represents workflow tasks such as running a *MapReduce* task, running a Shell script, importing data, and so on. The control-flow node controls workflow execution in between actions. It includes a start node, end node, and an error code. The start node is used for starting a workflow job, the end node designates the end of a job, and the error node points to an error if any. HTTP callback is used by *Oozie* for updating the client with the workflow status at the end of the workflow.

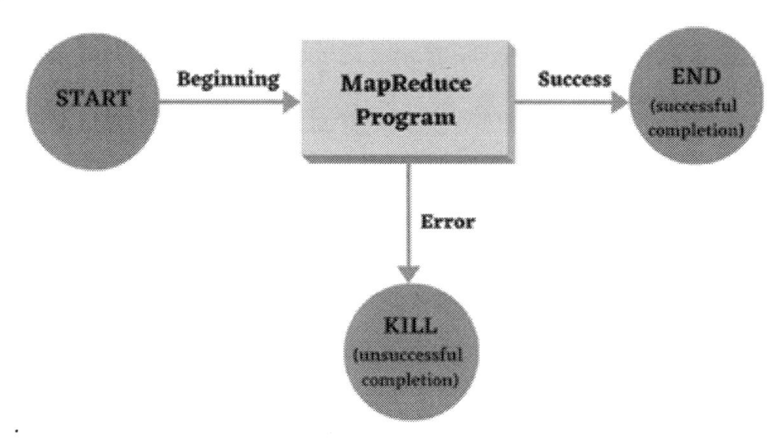

Figure 6.13: *Oozie Service*

There are certain specific attributes being used for defining big data, commonly known as **4Vs**.Provide better customer service, create tailored marketing campaigns based on customer preferences and ultimately amplify profitability. Now businesses can leverage technology to make informed decisions that are actually based on signals generated by actual customers.

Sample big data scripts

BigDataScript can be defined as a cross-system scripting language for working with pipelines of big data that vary in sizes and capabilities in computer systems. To work with heavyweight computation and a big data pipeline, we need several specialized programs. We need to schedule these specialized routines; these need to be called and coordinated with tracking of their progress and logging of results. For this, we need another script or program. This is where BigDataScript would prove extremely beneficial. BigDataScript makes jobs creation that runs seamlessly on any computer system irrespective of its size for big data very easy. It is as easy as creating a shell script.

The benefits of BigDataScript are as follows:

- **Reduced development time**

  Debugging work on big systems with huge data volumes is now less time-consuming. The same jobs can be debugged on a computer using a smaller sample.

- **System independent**

  Cross-system and offers seamless execution. Laptop, server, server farm cluster, or cloud all can run the same program.

- **Easy to learn**

  Reading the code of BigDataScript is easy, as the syntax is intuitive.

- **Automatic checkpointing**

  BigDataScript creates a checkpoint file in case any task fails in execution. From the checkpoint, execution can be resumed.

- **Automatic logging**

  Every time a command or task is executed, the executed commands are automatically logged in.

- **Clean stop with no mess behind**

  All the scheduled tasks can be easily terminated and removed from the cluster by simply hitting Ctrl+C.

- **Task dependencies**

  BigDataScript provides easy management of task dependencies.

- **Avoid re-working**

  Re-do of the tasks already successfully completed can be avoided using BigDataScript, thus saving time.

- **Built-in debugger**

  Debugging forms an integral part of BigDataScript language.

- **Build-in test cases facility**

  BigDataScript has a built-in code testing facility.

Hello world

- Create a simple program and execute it

```
#!/usr/bin/envbds
print "Hello world\n"

$ ./test_01.bds
```

Hello world

- We do it by running a system command (**echo**) using bds' **sys** expression. A **sys** executes the command immediately in the local computer and waits until the command finishes. Everything after **sys** until the end of the line is interpreted as an OS command.

```
#!/usr/bin/envbds  sys echo Hello world
$ ./test_02.bds  Hello world
```

- Now let's run the same in as a "**task**". Tasks schedule the system command for execution (either locally, on a cluster, and so on)

```
#!/usr/bin/envbds
task echo Hello world
```

- Run the script to execute the tasks locally

```
$ ./test_03.bds
Hello world
```

- You also can execute on a cluster; for instance, if you are on a cluster's head node, just run as follows:

```
$ bds -s cluster ./test_03.bds
Hello world
```

Note that to execute on another architecture (cluster), we did not change the **bds** program; we just added a command-line option. Programs can be executed on different computer systems of different sizes without changing the code.

Language

One can learn to code within a few minutes as BigDataScript is a really easy language. You may refer to the following:

- **Comments**: The usual statements are available

```
// Single line comment
# Another single line comment
/*
Multi-line comment
*/
```

- Statements can be terminated either by a semicolon or by a new line

```
    # Two statements
print "Hi\n"; print "Bye\n";
# Two statements, same as before but using lines instead of semicolon
print "Hi\n"
print "Bye\n"
```

- **break**: Breaks from current loop

```
for(inti=0 ; i< 10 ; i++ ) {
          if( i == 5 ) break;      // Finish when we reach 5
          }
```

- **breakpoint**: Inserts a debugging breakpoint, i.e., when the statement is executed, bds switches execution to debug mode (STEP)

```
breakpoint  "Program execution will switch do debug mode here!\n"
```

- **continue**: Continue at the end of the current loop.

```
for( inti=0 ; i< 10 ; i++ ) {
     if( i == 5 ) continue;     // Skip value 5
 }
```

- **debug**: Show a debug message on STDERR only if bds is running in "debug" mode (otherwise, the statement is ignored).

```
debug "Show this message only if we are in debug mode!\n"
```

- **error**: Show an error message and exit the program.

```
if( num<= 0 )warning "Number MUST be positive\n"
```

- **exit**: Exit program, optional expression calculates an exit value.

```
exit 1
```

- **for** C or Java like for statement.

```
for(inti=0 ; i< 10 ; i++ ) print("$i\n")
```

or

```
for(inti=0 ; i< 10 ; i++ ) {   print("$i\n")
}
```

- for Java like for iterator on lists

```
string[ ] mylist
// ... some code to populate the list
for( string s : mylist ) print("$s\n")
```

- **if/else**: It does exactly what you expect.

```
if( i< 10 )  print("Less than ten\n")

or
if( i< 10 ) {
print("Less than ten\n")
} else if( i<= 20 ) {
print("Between ten and twenty\n")
} else {
print("More than twenty\n")
}
```

- **include:** Include source code from another file.

```
include "mymodule"
// ... use functions from 'mymodule.bds'
```

- **kill:** Kill a task.

```
killtaskId
```

- **print / println:** Print to sdtout.
  print "Show this message without a new line at the end." println "This one gets a new line at the end."
- **Return:** Return from a function. Optional expression is a return value.
```
// Define a function i
nttwice(int n) {
return( 2 * n )
}
```
- **Switch:** Switch statements are similar to multiple if/else if statements.
```
in := 'x'
out := 1

switch( in ) {
case 'a':
out *= 3
break
case 'z'+'x':   # Note that the 'case' expressions are evaluated
at run time (you can even call functions here)
out *= 5    # Note that this falls through to "case 'b'"
case 'b':          out *= 7          break
 default:         # You can define 'default' anywhere (no need to
do it after 'case')
out *= 100
}
```
- **While:** Typical while iterator.
```
while( i< 10 ) i++
```
- **TypevarName:** Declare variable "var" as type "type".
```
inti      # 'i' is an 64 bit int variable
real r     # 'r' is a double-precision floating-point number
string s   # 's' is a string
```
- **typevarName = expr:** Declare variable "var" as type "type", evaluate expression and assign result to initialize 'var'.
```
inti = 42
real r = 3.1415927
string s = "Hello!"
```
- **varName := expr:** Declare variable "var", use type inference, evaluate expression "expr' and assign result to initialize "var".
```
i := 42
r := 3.1415927
s := "Hello!"
```
  var = expr Evaluate expression "expr" and assign result to "var"
```
i = j + 1 s = "Hello " + world
```
- **(var1, var2, ..., varN) = expr**
  Evaluate expression "expr" (which must return a list) and assign

results to "var1', "var2", and so on. If the list size is less than the number of variables, variables are assigned default values (e.g., "0" for int). If the list has more values, they are ignored.

```
(name, value) = line.split('\t')
```

- Ternary operator **expr ?exprTrue : exprFalse**: Evaluate "expr", if true evaluate and return "exprTrue", otherwise evalaute and return "exprFalse"

```
sign = ( i>= 0 ? 1 : -1 )
```

Data types

BigDataScript has only a few basic and simple data types. It is statically typed with an intention to avoid any runtime error.

Type	Meaning
String	A string (same a Java's string).
Int	A 64-bit integer number (same a Java's long).
Real	A 64 bit IEEE 754 number (same as Java's double).
Bool	A Boolean value can be "true" or "false" (same as Java's Boolean).
Arrays, list, stacks	These are all the same, just a different way to call a list of elements.
Maps	Maps are hashes (also known as dictionaries that have string keys.

Table 6.4: *Data types*

Strings

Following are a few methods defined for strings:

Return type	Method/operator	Meaning
string	s = s1 + s2	Concatenate strings.
string	s += s2	Append to string.
bool	string.endsWith(string str)	True if a string ends with str.
bool	string.isEmpty()	True if the string is empty.
int	string.indexOf(string str)	Index of the first occurrence of str in string.
int	string.lastIndexOf(string str)	Index of the last occurrence of str in string.

int	string.length()	String's length.
string	string.replace(string str1,stringstr2)	A new string replacing "str1" with "str2".
bool	string.parseBool()	Parse a bool.
int	string.parseInt()	Parse an int number.
Return type	**Method/operator**	**Meaning**
real	string.parseReal()	Parse a real number.
string[]	string.split(string regex)	Split using a regular expression.
bool	string.startsWith(string str)	True if string starts with str.
string	string.substr(int start)	Substring from start to end of the string.
string	string.substr(intstart,int end)	Substring from start to end.
string	string.toLower()	Return a lower case version of the string.
string	string.toUpper()	Return an upper case version of the string.
string	string.trim()	Trim spaces at the beginning and at the end.

Table 6.5: *List of strings*

Strings as files names

There are several ways in which strings can be used. For example, the script can represent a file name in the script. So "file" related method can be used on string as follows:

```
string f = "in.txt" if( f.canRead() ) {     print (" Can read file $f\n" ) }
```

The following are more file-related methods:

Return type	Method	Meaning
String	string.baseName()	File's base name
String	string.baseName(string ext)	File's base name, remove extension "ext"
String	string.download()	Download data from URL (string). Returns local filename (empty string if failed)

Bool	string.download(string file)	Download data from URL to "file". Returns true if succeeded
Bool	string.canRead()	True if file has read permission
Bool	string.canWrite()	True if file has write permission
Bool	string.canExec()	True if file has execution permission
Void	string.chdir()	Change current directory
Bool	string.delete()	Delete file
string[]	string.dir()	List files in a directory ("ls")
string[]	string.dir(string regex)	List files matching a "glob" (regular expression for files)
String	string.dirName()	File's directory name
string[]	string.dirPath()	List files using canonical paths
string[]	string.dirPath(string regex)	List files, matching a "glob" (regular expression for files), using canonical paths
String	string.extName()	File's extension
Bool	string.exists()	True if file exists
Bool	string.isDir()	True if it is a directory
Bool	string.isFile()	True if it is a file
Bool	string.mkdir()	Create dir ("mkdir-p")
String	string.path()	Canonical path to file
String	string.pathName()	Canonical dir to file
String	string.read()	Read the whole file into a string
string[]	string.readLines()	Read the whole file and split the lines
String	string.removeExt()	Remove file extension
String	string.removeExt(string ext)	Remove file extension only if it matches the provided one
Bool	string.rm()	Delete a file
Bool	string.rm()	Delete a file
Bool	string.rmExit()	Remove a file when execution finishes (thread execution)
Int	string.size()	File size in bytes
String	string.swapExt(string newExt)	Swap file extension

String	string.swapExt(string oldExt,stringnewExt)	Swap file extension only if extension matches the provided "oldExt"
String	string.upload()	Upload data to URL (string). Returns true if succeeded
Bool	string.upload(string file)	Upload data from "file" to URL. Returns true if succeeded
String	string.write(string file)	Write string to "file"

Table 6.6: *Strings as filename*

Strings as task IDs

Tasks can also be used to refer to strings. On the creation of a task, task ID is returned by a task expression, which is a string. In the following example, the wait statement will wait until the "**echo Hello**" execution is finished:

```
tid := task echo Hello
wait tid
```

The following are more task-related methods:

Return type	Method	Meaning
bool	string.isDone()	True if the task finished
bool	string.isDoneOk()	True if the task finished without errors
string	string.stdout()	A string with all the STDOUT generated from this task
string	string.stderr()	A string with all the STDERR generated from this task
int	string.exitCode()	Exit code

Table 6.7: *Strings as task IDs*

Arrays, list, and stacks

A list of strings can be created simply by declaring the following:

```
string[] arrayEmpty
string[] array = ["one", "two", "three"]
```

Similarly, a list on "ints" is just as follows:

```
int[] listIntEmpty
int[] primes = [2, 3, 5, 7, 11, 13, 17, 19, 23, 29]
```

Return type	Method	Meaning
String	`string.baseName()`	File's base name
	`+=`	Append element(s) at the end of the list
Element added	`add(X)`	Add X to the end of the list
Element added	`add(int idx,X)`	Add X to position idx in the list
Same list	`delete()`	Delete all files in the list (assumes list elements are file names). Same as list.rm()
int	`count(X)`	Count number of occurrences of X in the list
bool	`has(X)`	Does the list contain X?
First element	`head()`	Get first element
int	`indexOf(X)`	Position of element X in the list
bool	`isEmpty()`	"true" if the list is empty
string	`join()`	A string joining all elements of the list (separator " ")
string	`join(string sep)`	A string joining all elements of the list (separator "sep")
Last element	`pop()`	Get the last element and remove it from the list
Element pushed	`push()`	Add at the end of the list
Element to remove	`remove(X)`	Remove element X from the list
Element to remove	`removeIdx(intidx)`	Remove element at position idx from the list
New reversed list	`reverse()`	Create a new list and reverse it
Same list	`rm()`	Delete all files (assumes list elements are file names)
Same list	`rmOnExit()`	Delete all files when the current thread finishes execution (assumes list elements are file names)
int	`size()`	Return the number of elements in the list

New sorted list	sort()	Create a new list sorting the elements of this list
List	tail()	Create a new list with all but the first element

Table 6.8: Arrays, List, and Stacks

Iterating on an array/list by the following:

```
$ cat z.bds
string[] array = ["one", "two", "three"]
for( string val : array ) { print("Value: $val\n") }
$ bds /z.bds
Value: one
Value: two
Value: three
```

Maps

Maps-hashes with strings as the key can be created by the following:

```
string{} mstr # This maps string keys to string values
mstr{"Hello"} = "Bye"
mstr{"Bonjour"} = "Au revoir"
mstr{"Hola"} = "Adios
```

or a map of real numbers

```
real{} mre   # This maps string keys to real values
mre{"one"}   = 1.0
mre{"two"}   = 2.0
mre{"e"}     = 2.7182818
mre{"three"} = 3.0
mre{"pi"}    = 3.1415927
```

Returns	Method	Meaning
bool	hasKey(string key)	True if the key is in the map
bool	hasValue(value)	True if "value" is in the map
list	keys()	A sorted list of all keys in the map
bool	remove(key)	Remove key from this map
int	size()	Number of elements in this map
list	values()	A sorted list of all values in the map

Table 6.9: Methods

Conclusion

Big data is like an asset, which is valuable, whereas *Hadoop* is like a program that brings out the value from that asset. This is the main difference between big data and *Hadoop*. *Hadoop* is more of an open-source framework, designed by *Apache* foundation, that is capable of processing large amounts of heterogeneous data sets in a distributed fashion across clusters of commodity computers and hardware using a simplified programming model. Due to linear scale, a *Hadoop Cluster* can contain tens, hundreds, or even thousands of servers. *Hadoop* is a cost-effective solution, and it can work with commodity hardware and does not require expensive high-end hardware. Yes, Hadoop is highly flexible and can process both structured as well as unstructured data.

After Hadoop and big data discussions, let us proceed to the processing of the information from this massive data with the help of conventional methods, that is related to the management of big data refers to the storage of huge amount of information, analyzing the same using analytics techniques. MapReduce is a software framework and programming model used for processing huge amounts of data. Map tasks deal with splitting and mapping of data, whereas reduce tasks shuffle and reduce the data.

Points to remember

- Big data is a term that defines unsorted and raw information, whereas *Hadoop* is designed to manage that unsorted data by handling complicated and sophisticated big data.
- *Hadoop* provides a reliable shared storage and analysis system. Hadoop provides reliable shared storage (HDFS) and analysis system (MapReduce), highly scalable, and unlike the relational databases, Hadoop scales linearly.
- *Hadoop* is capable of running MapReduce programs written in various languages: Java, Ruby, Python, and C++.

CHAPTER 7
NoSQL and MapReduce—Too Huge to Avoid

As you have already studied in previous chapters *"Big Data"* refers to the huge amount of data that is extensive in size and is highly complicated, and it is very difficult, or, we can say impossible, to process the information from this massive data with the help of conventional methods. To put it in other words, we can also say that management of big data refers to the storage of a huge amount of information, analyzing the same using analytics techniques. The data in big data is higher in all "v" terms volume, velocity, and variety. By now, we have a clear picture of big data and its processing. Now we will discuss how to handle and access information stored in the form of big data.

Structure

In this chapter, we will cover the following topics:

- What is NoSQL?
- Uses and types of NoSQL database
- MapReduce and its structure
- Examples of NoSQL using MapReduce

Objective

After reading this chapter, you will be able to comfortably work with the NoSQL (non-relational structure) and MapReduce for handling huge databases, which are non-structured and cannot be arranged in relations. NoSQL is today's demand, and this chapter will help you in learning these tech skills, which in turn improve your career prospects. As per the market research, these skills are essential for developers, data scientists, business analysts, or anyone working in related fields with data handling and data sciences. Comparison of relational databases and NoSQL databases is more scalable to provide superior performance. Also, the flexibility of using data easily with their data models would become a speedy development compared with the relational model, especially in the cloud computing environment.

What is NoSQL?

A NoSQL, also referred to as a non SQL or a non-relational structure, offers a mechanism for storage and retrieval of data from the source database. We can also understand the term as when the data is structured or is in different formats other than the tabular formats and relational databases, the language that can be applied to retrieve the information can be termed as NoSQL data management system.

Because NoSQL is open-source and has a distributed architecture with MongoDB, we can also call it the next-generation database. A NoSQL database uses simple designs, simpler horizontal cluster scaling for machines and has fine control over availability. The data structures that are being used by NoSQL DB are considerably different from those which are being used by default in relational approached databases. This makes the operations faster in NoSQL.

Features of NoSQL database

The following are the Features of the NoSQL database:

- The suitability of a given NoSQL database depends on the issue that is to be addressed.
- The data structures used by NoSQL DB are more flexible than relational databases. NoSQL is the futuristic approach to handle and manage the data, which has very few manual interventions.
- Less human efforts make it more reliable and easy to use as once the replication is done, the system will automatically take care of the failovers.
- Non-relational structure can easily handle the massive amount of data which is the most crucial factor about NoSQL, and its performance is also far better

in comparison to other DMS as it can add a good number of machines to the clusters, and we can implement it on commodity hardware as well.

- Non-relational DMS does not require any fixed schema. It can avoid joins and is easy to scale all together.

Uses of NoSQL

Non-relational structure is used for big data and real-time web applications, and the uses are increasing over time with companies such as *Twitter*, *Facebook*, and *Google* that collect terabytes of user data every single day. The conventional RDBMS uses SQL syntax for storing and retrieving data for further insights. A NoSQL database system makes use of a wide range of database technologies that can store structured, semi-structured, unstructured, and polymorphic data.

So, one can increase the capacity of the clusters and need not design the tables/ relations and also, there is no requirement of data pushing. To favor availability, speed, and partition tolerance there are many NoSQL stores that compromise on consistency.

Non-relational structure database simply stands for *"Not Only SQL"* or *"Not SQL."* *Carl Strozz* introduced the NoSQL concept in 1998.

Advantages of NoSQL

The following are the advantages of NoSQL:

1. **High scalability:** Non-relational structure databases use sharding for horizontal scaling. Making the partitions of data that is creating separate database server instances to spread the load and placing it on multiple machines in a way that the order of the data is preserved is called **sharding**.

   Vertical scaling is referred to as adding more resources to the existing machine, whereas horizontal scaling means adding more machines to handle the data. Implementation of vertical scaling is not that easy as compared to horizontal scaling. The horizontal scaling databases are *MongoDB*, *Cassandra*, and so on. Because of the scalability features, only NoSQL can handle the huge amount of data, as we know that as much as the data grows, NoSQL scales itself automatically to handle it efficiently.

2. **High availability:** Non-relational structure databases have the auto replication feature, which makes them highly available. Hence, if in case any failure occurs, the data replicates by itself to its previous consistent state.

Disadvantages of NoSQL

The following are the disadvantages of NoSQL:

1. **Narrow focus:** Non-relational structure database is mainly designed for storage; that is why it has a very narrow focus; also, it provides very little functionality. Here, we can say that relational databases are a better option for transaction management compared with NoSQL.
2. **Open-source:** As we have told earlier that the NoSQL is an open-source database; therefore, it does not have any reliable standard yet.
3. **Management challenge:** Data management with NoSQL is more complex in comparison to a relational DB. The goal is to make management of the massive amount of data, big data, in as simplest way as possible, which is not easy.
4. **GUI is not available:** Graphic user interface tools that we use to access the databases are not available flexibly in the market for NoSQL.
5. **Backup:** Some of the NoSQL Databases has no approach for consistent data backups, like MongoDB; this is a weak point for NoSQL.
6. **Large document size:** MongoDB and CouchDB are a few examples of NoSQL database systems that are used to store data in JSON format. This leads to enlarged document sizes such as big data, network bandwidth, speed. Also, this is using the descriptive key names; hence, it increases the document size.

Types of NoSQL database

Architecture patterns: one of the most logical ways to categorize the data stored in the database is architecture pattern. NoSQL is a type of database that performs multiple operations on big data and also stores data in a specific format that can be used further. It is flexible and widely used for providing a wide range of services.

The data stored in the NoSQL database use the following four data architecture patterns. All these categories have unique attributes with a few limitations. Not any single of these databases can be called a better product to solve all kinds of problems. We can, however, select one database depending upon the requirement:

1. **Key-value pair based**.

   When data is stored in the form of key/value pairs, we call it key-value pair based architecture. This has been designed to handle a massive amount of data with a heavy load. It stores the data in a hash table form, where all the keys are unique, that gives the value in a JSON, **binary large objects**

(**BLOB**) and string format. For example, a key-value pair may contain a key like "*Website*" associated with a value like "*www.kiyaki.biz*".

Key	Value
Name	Kiyaki
Age	45
Occupation	Business
Website	www.kiyaki,biz
Phone	9209029

Table 7.1: *Example of Key-value pair*

Advantages:

- It has the ability to handle massive amounts of data with heavy loads.
- With the key-value, data retrieval is easy.

Limitations:

- Given the complexity of queries using multiple key-value pairs, the performance may suffer a delay.
- While handling many-to-many relationships, data collisions may occur. DynamoDB and Berkeley DB are examples.

2. **Column-oriented database**.

   This category of database work on columns and is used by Google for BigTable Paperwork. In this, every column is treated separately. The values of single column databases are stored in a contiguous fashion.

<table>
<tr><th colspan="3">Column family</th></tr>
<tr><td rowspan="7">Row key</td><td colspan="2">Column name</td></tr>
<tr><td>Key</td><td>Key</td></tr>
<tr><td>Value</td><td>Value</td></tr>
<tr><td colspan="2">Column name</td></tr>
<tr><td>Key</td><td>Key</td></tr>
<tr><td>Value</td><td>Value</td></tr>
</table>

Column-oriented databases deliver higher performance when applied to aggregation queries such as SUM, AVG, COUNT, MIN, and so on., as the data is already available in the columns. Such databases are mainly used to manage data warehouses, CRM, Library card catalogs, HBase, Cassandra, Hypertable, and so on.

Here, the data is stored in individual cells, further grouped into columns, rather than storing the data into relational tuples. It stores a huge amount of data into columns together. It diverges the format and titles of the columns from one row to another. In this architecture, every column is treated as a separate entity, and still, the individual columns may store other columns like the traditional databases.

Advantages:

- The data is available always to be used.
- We can perform the queries such as SUM, AVERAGE, and COUNT easily in columns. The examples include HBase, Bigtable by Google, Cassandra, and so on.

3. **Graph-based architectural database**

This is the type of database that stores entities along with relations among those entities. The entities are stored as nodes and the relationship as edges. An edge gives a relationship between nodes. Every node and edge has a unique identifier.

As compared with a relational database where tables are loosely connected, a graph database is multi-relational in nature.

Graphs are the basic structures to depict the connection of two or more objects present in data. The objects/entities called as nodes are joined together by relationships called **Edges** having a unique identifier. This pattern is very commonly used in social networks where there are a large number of entities, and each entity has one or many characteristics which are connected by edges.

Advantages:

- This is fastest traversal due to its connections in between nodes through edges.
- We can also handle the spatial data easily.

Limitations:

- Wrong connections may lead to infinite loops.
- Its examples are Neo4J and FlockDB (used by Twitter), and so on.

4. **Document-oriented**

The document-oriented NoSQL database stores and retrieves data in the form of a key-value pair, but here the value part is not stored in the column but as a document. This document is stored in JSON or XML formats. The value can be understood by the document-oriented database and can be queried.

The document database architecture is used to extract the data and accumulate it in key-value pair format, where we call the values as documents or complex data structures. Here the documents can be in the form of text, arrays, strings, JSON, XML, nested documents and such. As most of the data is in the form of JSON, unstructured form, it is very effective in processing the data.

Advantages:

- This is a type of format which is very useful.
- Very apt for semi-structured data.
- Storage retrieval is easy.
- Documents management is easy.

Limitations:

- Challenge is to handle multiple documents.
- Operation of aggregation may not work with utmost accuracy.

Its examples are MongoDB, Amazon SimpleDB, CouchDB, and so on.

The CAP theorem? CAP theorem, also called Brewer's theorem, states what is impossible for a distributed data store to offer two at a time out of all three.

- **Consistency:** The data should remain consistent even after the execution of an operation. This means once data is written, any future read request should contain the data updated. For example, if someone has purchased goods, the order status will get updated, and this must be visible to all the clients.
- **Availability:** The data is the key to information, so database availability is the top priority; it should always be available and responsive with no downtime or delays.
- **Partition tolerance:** Sometimes the server is partitioned into multi-groups, with no communication to each other. If this is the situation, or in case a part of the database is unavailable for the time frame, then other parts should not be affected; that is called **partition tolerance**.
- **Eventual consistency:** Replication of data on multiple machines for higher availability and scalability is referred to as *"eventual consistency"*. Thus, the change that is being made to any of these datasets on the machine will get updated/ propagated to its replicas. Instantaneous data replication may not be possible as some copies take due course of time. It may take some time to update data copies mutually, but they become consistent eventually. Hence, we name it as eventual consistency.

- **ACID versus BASE:** NoSQL use BASE in comparison with the generic relational model, which uses ACID.

Features of NoSQL

Some features of NoSQL are explained as follows:

1. **Non-relational:** A database that does not use the tabular schema of rows and columns like traditional database systems is called a **non-relational database**. Instead, these databases use an optimized storage model type for the specific requirements of the type of data being stored.
   - Non-relational structure databases do not follow the relational model approach.
   - They never work in tabular format or fixed-column records.
   - Non-relational structure prefers to work with BLOBs or self-contained aggregates.
   - No need for object-relational mapping and data normalization.
   - This is a simple structure that has no complexity of features like query languages and query planners.
   - Non-relational database is less referential integrity joins, ACID oriented.
   - It uses the BASE format for the retrieval of data.
2. **Schema-free:** A schema-free database is a database where data can be stored without any previously defined structure, and one can simply add records.
   - Non-relational structure databases are schema-free or may have a relaxed schema.
   - Definition of the schema is not required for storing the data.
   - Heterogeneous data structures are offered in the same domain.
3. **Simple API:**
   - Non-relational structure offers an easy to use interface for storing and querying the data.
   - The APIs allows low-level data selection and manipulation methods.
   - Mainly uses a non-standardized query language.
   - A web-enabled database is running as an internet-facing service.
4. **Distributed**
   - A collection of NoSQL databases used to be executed in a distributed manner.

- This has the auto-scaling and failover capabilities offerings.
- Only providing eventual consistency and no synchronous replication between distributed nodes.
- Shared nothing architecture, which enables less coordination and higher distribution.

When should NoSQL be used?

1. For a huge amount of data that needs to be stored and retrieved timely.
2. When the relationship is not that important but the data itself.
3. When the data is changing over time and is unstructured.
4. Constraints and Joins are not required to support the database.
5. When the data is growing continuously, then there is a need to scale it regularly to handle the data efficiently.

Difference between SQL and NoSQL

When there is a question to choose a database, choices are only a relational (SQL) or non-relational (NoSQL) data structure. Although both the databases are viably good options, we need to opt for the one which is most suitable as per our needs, the size of the information to be stored, and certain key differences between the two.

- **The type:** As we know that the SQL databases are called **relational databases (RDBMS)**, whereas NoSQL databases are referred to as non-relational or distributed databases.
- **Language:** SQL databases define and manipulates data in a structured format. An extremely powerful language, the most versatile and widely-used option. A safe choice is available, which makes it usable for great complex queries. But it can be restrictive, as SQL requires use of a predefined schema that determines the structure of data working. The constraint is that all the data must follow the same structure. On the other hand, NoSQL database uses dynamic schema and work on unstructured data. Here, the data is stored in different ways, which means it can be either document-oriented, column-oriented, graph-based, or organized as a key-value store. This means this is highly flexible, and with it, the documents can be created unstructured.
- **The scalability:** Generally, SQL databases are vertically scalable, which means the user can increase the load on a single server with the help of larger RAM, CPU, or SSD. On the other hand, NoSQL databases are horizontally scalable, which means the user can handle more traffic with sharding of data,

or even the user can add more servers in the database. Thus, the NoSQL database has become an ultimate and preferred choice for large data or continuously changing datasets.

- **The structure:** SQL databases are structured in tabular format, whereas NoSQL databases are unstructured and use key-value pairs, document-based, graph databases or wide-column stores for information storing.
- **Property followed:** SQL databases follow **atomicity, consistency, isolation, and durability** (**ACID**) properties, whereas the NoSQL database follows the CAP theorem (consistency, availability, and partition tolerance).
- **Support**: Huge support is available from the vendors for SQL database from their vendors, who can help you with an extremely large scale deployment. The NoSQL database still relies on community support and is limited to outside experts for setting up and deploying your large scale NoSQL deployments.

PostgreSQL, MySQL, Oracle, and *Microsoft SQL Server* are examples of SQL databases. *Redis, RavenDB Cassandra, MongoDB, BigTable, HBase, Neo4j,* and *CouchDB* are a few NoSQL database examples.

SQL	NoSQL
These are relational databases.	It refers to non-relational databases.
These use structured query language and have a predefined schema.	NoSQL databases have a dynamic schema for unstructured data.
SQL databases are vertically scaled.	NoSQL databases are horizontally scaled.
SQL databases are table-based.	NoSQL databases are document, key-value, Graph or Wide-column stores.
SQL databases are better for multi-row transactions.	NoSQL databases are better for unstructured data like documents or JSON.

Table 7.2: *SQL versus NoSQL*

The NoSQL databases for big data were specifically developed by the top internet companies such as Google, Yahoo, Amazon, and so on as the existing relational databases were not able to cope with the increasing data processing requirements.

The NoSQL databases have a dynamic schema, better suited for big data. Flexibility is an important requirement here. The large amounts of analytical data can only be stored in NoSQL database for some larger and more powerful if required. All of this makes NoSQL databases the preferred choice for big data applications.

Programming MapReduce jobs

In today's data-driven market, the algorithms and applications are collecting data 24/7 about people, processes, systems, and organizations, resulting in huge volumes of data. MapReduce programming model addresses the challenge of processing this massive amount of data with speed and efficiency and without sacrificing meaningful insights. Initially, this approach was being used by Google for analyzing its search results. MapReduce gained massive popularity because of its splitting ability and capacity to process terabytes of data parallelly, which aims to achieve faster results.

What is MapReduce?

MapReduce is a programming model or pattern within the Hadoop framework that is used to access big data stored in the **Hadoop file system (HDFS)**. It forms a core component, which is integral to the functioning of the Hadoop framework.

MapReduce facilitates concurrent processing by splitting the petabytes of data into smaller chunks and processing them in parallel on Hadoop commodity servers. After that, it aggregates all the data from multiple servers to return a consolidated output back to the application.

For instance, a Hadoop cluster with 20,000 inexpensive commodity servers and 256 MB block of data in each can process around 5 TB of data at the same time. This results in a drastic reduction of the processing time as compared to sequential processing of such a large data set.

To expedite processing, through MapReduce rather than sending data to where the application or logic resides, the logic is executed on the server where the data already resides. Access to the data and its storage is disk-based—the input is generally stored as files containing structured, semi-structured, or unstructured data, and the output is stored in files as well.

Earlier, MapReduce was the only method through which data stored in the HDFS could be retrieved, but that is no longer the case now. There are other query-based systems such as *Hive* and *Pig* that are used to retrieve data from the HDFS using SQL-like statements in today's world. However, owing to the unique advantages of MapReduce, these usually run along with jobs that are written using the MapReduce model.

How MapReduce works?

MapReduce performs two prime functions: map and reduce, and these are sequenced one after the other.

- The **Map** function takes input from the disk as pairs, processes them, and produces another set of intermediate pairs as output.
- The **Reduce** function also takes inputs as pairs and produces pairs as output.

Keys and values type would differ based on the use case. All of the inputs and the outputs are stored in the HDFS. The map is a mandatory step to filter and sort the initial data, and the reduce function is optional.

```
-> Map() -> list()
-> Reduce() -> list(>)
```

Mappers and reducers run the map and reduce functions, respectively, in Hadoop servers. It does not matter if these are the same or different servers.

Map

The first step is to split the input data into smaller blocks. Each block is then assigned to a mapper for processing.

For better understanding, consider the following example—if a file has 100 records to be processed, 100 mappers could run to process one record each. Or maybe 50 mappers could run together to process two records each. It is the Hadoop framework that decides how many mappers to use, based on the size of the data to be processed and the memory block available on each mapper server.

Reduce

Once the mappers complete their processing, the framework shuffles and sort the results before passing them on to the reducers, a reducer cannot start if a mapper is still in progress. All the map output values with the same key are assigned to a single reducer, which then aggregates the values for that key.

Combine and partition

Between map and reduce, there are two intermediate steps.

The combine is an optional process. The combiner is a reducer that runs individually on each mapping server. Its function is to reduce the data on each mapper further to a simplified form before passing it on. Thus, simplifying the shuffling and sorting as there is less data to work with. The combiner class is usually set to the reducer class itself because of the cumulative and associative functions in the reduce function. But as and when required, the combiner can be a separate class as well.

Partition refers to the process that translates the pairs resulting from mappers to another set of pairs to feed into the reducer. It takes a decision on how the data has to be presented to the reducer, and it also assigns it to a particular reducer.

The default partitioner identifies the hash value for the key resulting from the mapper and assigns a partition basis for this hash value. On completion of the partitioning, data from each partition is sent to a specific reducer.

Implementation

MapReduce framework can be used to write applications to process huge amounts of data, in parallel, on large clusters of commodity hardware in a reliable and efficient manner.

MapReduce refers to the processing technique and is a program model for distributed computing that is based on Java. Two important tasks are map and reduce, which form the MapReduce algorithm. Map's function is to take a set of data and convert it into another set of data, where individual elements are broken down into tuples (key/value pairs). Reduce task is the second task that takes the output from a map as an input and combines those data tuples into a smaller set of tuples.

Easy scaling data processing over multiple computing nodes is the major advantage of MapReduce. Under this model, the data processing primitives are referred to as mappers and reducers. Decomposition of a data processing application into mappers and reducers is at times nontrivial. But once an application is written in the MapReduce form, scaling the application to run over hundreds or even tens of thousands of machines in a cluster is smooth and is merely a configuration change. This sheer simple scalability has attracted many programmers to use the MapReduce model.

The algorithm

MapReduce paradigm is generally based on sending the computer to where the data resides. It is executed in three stages, namely map stage, shuffle stage, and reduce stage.

Map stage: The main job of the mapper is to process the input data, which is usually in the form of a file or directory and is stored in the **Hadoop file system (HDFS)**. The input file is then passed on to the mapper function line by line. The mapper then processes the data and creates several small chunks of data.

Reduce stage: It refers to the combination of the shuffle stage and the reduce stage. Job of the reducer is to process the data that comes from the mapper. It then produces a new set of output, which gets stored in the HDFS. Hadoop, during the MapReduce job, sends the map and reduce tasks to the appropriate servers in the cluster.

All the details of data-passing, such as issuing tasks, verifying task completion, and copying data around the cluster between the nodes, are managed by the framework. Computing takes place on nodes with reduced network traffic. Once the given tasks are completed, the cluster collects and reduces the data to form an appropriate result and then sends it back to the Hadoop server.

Inputs and outputs

The MapReduce framework views the input to the job as a set of pairs and then produces a set of pairs as the output of the job, conceivably of different types.

The key and the value classes should be in a serialized manner by the framework; and hence, the need to implement the writable interface. The key classes, in addition, have to implement the writable–comparable interface to facilitate easy sorting by the framework.

```
Input and Output types of a MapReduce job - (Input) → map → → reduce
→ (Output).
Input Output
Map list ()
Reduce list ()
```

Terminologies:

- **PayLoad**: Applications make use of the **Map** and the **Reduce** functions and form the core of the job.
- **Mapper**: The input key/value pairs are mapped by mappers to a set of intermediate key/value pairs.
- **NameNode**: It is a node that manages the **Hadoop distributed file system (HDFS)**.
- **DataNode**: It is a node where data is presented in advance before any processing takes place.
- **MasterNode**: It is a node where JobTracker runs and which accepts job requests from clients.
- **SlaveNode**: Node where map and reduce program runs.
- **JobTracker**: It schedules jobs and tracks the assigned jobs to the Task tracker.
- **TaskTracker**: It tracks the task and reports status to JobTracker.
- **Job**: A job is an execution of a mapper and reducer across a dataset.
- **Task**: An execution of a mapper or a reducer on a slice of data.

- **Task attempt**: A particular instance of an attempt to execute a task on a SlaveNode.

MapReduce

In earlier times, when MapReduce framework was not there, parallel and distributed processing used to happen in a conventional way. For instance, if a weather log contains the daily average temperature for the years 2010–2015 and one wants to calculate the day having the highest temperature in each year.

Going by the traditional way, one would split the data into smaller parts or blocks and store them in different machines. Then, one would find the highest temperature in each part stored in the corresponding machine.

One would then at last combine the results received from each of the machines to have the final output.

Let us have a look at the challenges associated with this traditional approach as follows:

1 **Critical path**: If, any of the machines delay the job, the whole work gets delayed.

   The amount of time taken to finish the job without delaying the next task or the actual completion date.

2. **Reliaility**: The management of the failover of any of the machines that are working with a part of data is a huge challenge.
3. **Equal split issue**: Dividing the data into smaller chunks so that each machine gets an even part of data to work with is a problem. To put it in other words, how can the data be equally divided so that no individual machine is overloaded or underutilized.
4. **Single split fail**: If any of the machines fail to provide the output, it would not be possible to calculate the result. So, a mechanism that would ensure the fault tolerance capability of the system should be in place.
5. **Result aggregation**: There should be a mechanism to aggregate the result generated by each of the machines to produce the final output.

These challenges need to be addressed individually while performing parallel processing of huge data sets when using traditional approaches.

MapReduce framework helps in overcoming such challenges and allows one to perform such parallel computations without bothering about the issues, such as reliability, fault tolerance, and so on. MapReduce gives the flexibility to write code logic without caring about the design issues of the system.

Let us understand how a MapReduce works by taking an example where we have a text file called example.txt whose contents are as follows:

Dear, Bear, River, Car, Car, River, Deer, Car, and Bear.

Now, suppose we have to perform a word count on the sample.txt using MapReduce. So, we will be finding the unique words and the number of occurrences of those unique words.

MapReduce: (a word count example of MapReduce)

- First, we divide the input into three splits, as shown in the example. This will distribute the work among all the map nodes.
- Then, we tokenize the words in each of the mappers and give a hardcoded value (1) to each of the tokens or words. The rationale behind giving a hardcoded value equal to 1 is that every word, in itself, will occur once.
- Now, a list of key-value pairs will be created where the key is nothing but the individual words and value is one. So, for the first line (Dear, Bear, and River), we have three key-value pairs—Dear, 1; Bear, 1; and River, 1. The mapping process remains the same on all the nodes.
- After the mapper phase, a partition process takes place where sorting and shuffling happen so that all the tuples with the same key are sent to the corresponding reducer.
- So, after the sorting and shuffling phase, each reducer will have a unique key and a list of values corresponding to that very key. For example, Bear, [1,1]; Car, [1,1,1]…, and so on.
- Now, each reducer counts the values which are present in that list of values. As shown in the preceding example, reducer gets a list of values which is [1,1] for the key Bear. Then, it counts the number of ones in the very list and gives the final output as—Bear, 2.
- Finally, all the output key/value pairs are then collected and written in the output file.

Advantages of MapReduce

1. **Parallel processing:** The job, in MapReduce, gets divided among multiple nodes, and each node works with a part of the job side at the same time. Thus, we can say that MapReduce is based on the divide and conquer paradigm that helps in data processing using different machines. Because data processing happens simultaneously by multiple machines, the time taken to process the data gets reduced by a tremendous amount.

2. **Data locality:** In MapReduce framework, instead of moving data to the processing unit, the processing unit is moved to the data. In the traditional way, data used to be brought up to the processing unit and processed. But, with the whooping growth in data, bringing the data to the processing unit brought along the following challenges:
   - It is costly and reduces the performance.
   - As the data is processed by a single unit, processing takes time and becomes a bottleneck.
   - The master node may fail with the overburden.

   So data locality allows us to have the following advantages:
   - It is cost-effective.
   - The processing time reduces considerably.
   - As every node gets a part of the data to process, and therefore, the chances of a node getting overburdened are bleak.

A MapReduce Example [8]

Consider an e-commerce system that receives a million requests every day to process payments. There may be several exceptions thrown during these requests, such as *"payment declined by a payment gateway," "out of inventory,"* and *"invalid address."* A developer wants to analyze past four days' logs to understand which exception is thrown how many times.

Example use case

The objective is to isolate use cases that are most prone to errors and take appropriate action. For example, if the same payment gateway is frequently throwing an exception, is it because of unreliable service or a badly written interface? If the *"out of inventory"* exception is thrown often, does it mean the inventory calculation service has to be improved, or does the inventory stocks need to be increased for certain products?

The developer can ask relevant questions and determine the right course of action. To perform this analysis on logs that are bulky, with millions of records, MapReduce is an apt programming model. Multiple mappers can process these logs simultaneously: one mapper could process a day's log or a subset of it based on the log size and the memory block available for processing in the mapper server.

Map

For simplification, let us assume that the Hadoop framework runs just four mappers. Mapper 1, Mapper 2, Mapper 3, and Mapper 4.

The value input to the mapper is one record of the log file. The key could be a text string such as *"file name + line number."* The mapper, then processes each record of the log file to produce key-value pairs. Here, we will just use a filler for the value as "1." The output from the mappers looks like the following:

```
Mapper 1 -> , , , ,
Mapper 2 -> , , ,
Mapper 3 -> , , , ,
Mapper 4 -> , , ,
```

Assuming that there is a combiner running on each mapper—Combiner 1 … Combiner 4—that calculates the count of each exception (which is the same function as the reducer), the input to Combiner 1 will be as follows:

```
, , , ,
Combine
The output of Combiner 1 will be:
, ,
```

The output from the other combiners will be:

```
Combiner 2:
Combiner 3:
Combiner 4:
```

Partition

After this, the partitioner allocates the data from the combiners to the reducers. The data is also sorted for the reducer.

The input to the reducers will be as follows:

```
Reducer 1: {3,2,3,1}
Reducer 2: > {1,2,1,1}
Reducer 3: > {1,1,2}
```

If there were no combiners involved, the input to the reducers will be as follows:

```
Reducer 1: <Exception A> {1,1,1,1,1,1,1,1,1}
Reducer 2: > {1,1,1,1,1}
Reducer 3: > {1,1,1,1}
```

Here, the example is a simple one, but when there are terabytes of data involved, the combiner process' improvement to the bandwidth is significant.

Reduce

Now, each reducer just calculates the total count of the exceptions as follows:

```
Reducer 1: >
Reducer 2:, 5>
Reducer 3:
```

The data shows that Exception A is thrown more often than others and requires more attention. When there are more than a few weeks' or months' of data to be processed together, the potential of the MapReduce program can be truly exploited.

How to implement MapReduce

MapReduce programs are not just restricted to Java. They can also be written in C, C++, Python, Ruby, Perl, and so on. Following is what the main function of a typical MapReduce job looks like:

```
public static void main(String[] args) throws Exception
{
JobConf conf = new JobConf(ExceptionCount.class);
conf.setJobName("exceptioncount");

conf.setOutputKeyClass(Text.class);
conf.setOutputValueClass(IntWritable.class);

conf.setMapperClass(Map.class);
conf.setReducerClass(Reduce.class);
conf.setCombinerClass(Reduce.class);

conf.setInputFormat(TextInputFormat.class);
conf.setOutputFormat(TextOutputFormat.class);
```

```
FileInputFormat.setInputPaths(conf, new Path(args[0]));
FileOutputFormat.setOutputPath(conf, new Path(args[1]));

JobClient.runJob(conf);
}
```

The parameters—MapReduce class name, map, reduce, and combiner classes, input and output types, input and output file paths—are all defined in the main function. The **Mapper** class extends MapReduceBase and implements the Mapper interface. The **Reducer** class extends MapReduceBase and implements the reducer interface.

Example scenario

Following is the data regarding the electrical consumption of an organization. It contains the monthly electrical consumption and the annual average for various years:

	Jan	Feb	Mar	Apr	May	Jun	Jul	Aug	Sep	Oct	Nov	Dec	Avg
1976	22	22	2	43	24	25	26	26	26	26	25	26	25
1977	26	27	28	28	28	30	31	31	31	30	30	30	29
1978	31	32	32	32	33	34	35	36	36	34	34	34	34
1979	39	38	39	39	39	41	42	43	40	39	38	38	40
1980	38	39	39	39	39	41	41	41	0	40	39	39	45

If the preceding data is given as input, we have to write applications to process it and produce results such as finding the year of maximum usage, year of minimum usage, and so on. This is a walkover for the programmers with a finite number of records. They will simply write the logic to produce the required output and pass the data to the application written.

But, think of the data representing the electrical consumption of all the largescale industries of a particular state since its formation.

When we write applications to process such bulk data:

- They will take a lot of time to execute.
- There will be heavy network traffic when we move data from the source to the network server and so on.

To solve these problems, we have the MapReduce framework.

Input data

The above data is saved as **sample.txt** and given as input. The input file looks as shown as follows:

```
1979  23  23   2  43  24  25  26  26  26  26  25  26  25
1980  26  27  28  28  28  30  31  31  31  30  30  30  29
1981  31  32  32  32  33  34  35  36  36  34  34  34  34
1984  39  38  39  39  39  41  42  43  40  39  38  38  40
1985  38  39  39  39  39  41  41  41  00  40  39  39  45
```

Example Program [9]

Given following is the program to the sample data using MapReduce framework:

```
package Hadoop;
import java.util.*;


import java.io.IOException;

import java.io.IOException;


import org.apache.hadoop.fs.Path;

import org.apache.hadoop.conf.*;

import org.apache.hadoop.io.*;

import org.apache.hadoop.mapred.*;

import org.apache.hadoop.util.*;


public class ProcessUnits {

//Mapper class

public static class E_EMapper extends MapReduceBase implements

Mapper

Text, /*Input value Type*/

Text, /*Output key Type*/

IntWritable> /*Output value Type*/

{

//Map function

public void map(LongWritable key, Text value,

OutputCollector output,
```

```
Reporter reporter) throws IOException {
String line = value.toString();
String lasttoken = null;
StringTokenizer s = new StringTokenizer+(line,"\t");
String year = s.nextToken();

while(s.hasMoreTokens()) {
lasttoken = s.nextToken();
}
int avgprice = Integer.parseInt(lasttoken);
output.collect(new Text(year), new IntWritable(avgprice));
}
}

//Reducer class
public static class E_EReduce extends MapReduceBase implements Reducer<
Text, IntWritable, Text, IntWritable > {

//Reduce function
public void reduce( Text key, Iterator values,
OutputCollector output, Reporter reporter) throws IOException {
int maxavg = 35;
int val = Integer.MIN_VALUE;

while (values.hasNext()) {
if((val = values.next().get())>maxavg) {
output.collect(key, new IntWritable(val));
}
}
}
}
```

```
//Main function
public static void main(String args[])throws Exception {
JobConf conf = new JobConf(ProcessUnits.class);

conf.setJobName("max_eletricityunits");
conf.setOutputKeyClass(Text.class);
conf.setOutputValueClass(IntWritable.class);
conf.setMapperClass(E_EMapper.class);
conf.setCombinerClass(E_EReduce.class);
conf.setReducerClass(E_EReduce.class);
conf.setInputFormat(TextInputFormat.class);
conf.setOutputFormat(TextOutputFormat.class);

FileInputFormat.setInputPaths(conf, new Path(args[0]));
FileOutputFormat.setOutputPath(conf, new Path(args[1]));

JobClient.runJob(conf);
}
}
```

Save the preceding program as **ProcessUnits.java**. The compilation and execution of the program are explained as follows:

Explanation of MapReduce program

The entire MapReduce program can be fundamentally divided into three parts:

- Mapper phase code
- Reducer phase code
- Driver code

We will understand the code for each of these three parts sequentially.

Mapper code:

```
public static class Map extends
Mapper<LongWritable,Text,Text,IntWritable>
{
```

```
public void map(LongWritable key, Text value, Context context) throws
IOException,InterruptedException
{
String line = value.toString();
StringTokenizer tokenizer = new StringTokenizer(line);
while (tokenizer.hasMoreTokens())
{
value.set(tokenizer.nextToken());
context.write(value, new IntWritable(1));
}
```

- We have created a class **Map** that extends the class **Mapper** which is already defined in the MapReduce **Framework.Input** Text File—MapReduce Tutorial—Edureka
- We define the data types of input and output key/value pair after the class declaration using angle brackets.
- Both the input and output of the mapper is a key/value pair.
- **Input**:
    - o The key is nothing but the offset of each line in the text file: **LongWritable**
    - o The value is each individual line (as shown in the figure at the right): **Text**
- **Output**:
    - o The key is the tokenized words: **Text**
    - o We have the hardcoded value in our case, which is 1: **IntWritable**
    - o Example—Dear 1, Bear 1, and so on.
- We have written a Java code where we have tokenized each word and assigned them a hardcoded value equal to 1.

Reducer code:

```
public static class Reduce extends Reducer<Text, IntWritable, Text,
IntWritable>
{
public void reduce(Text key, Iterable<IntWritable> values,Context
context)
throws IOException,InterruptedException
```

```
{
int sum=0;
for(IntWritable x: values)
{
sum+=x.get();
}
context.write(key, new IntWritable(sum));
}
}
```

- We have created a class **Reduce,** which extends class **Reducer** like that of mapper.
- We define the data types of input and output key/value pair after the class declaration using angle brackets as done for mapper.
- Both the input and the output of the reducer is key-value pair.
- **Input**:
  - o The key is nothing but those unique words which have been generated after the sorting and shuffling phase: **Text**
  - o The value is a list of integers corresponding to each key: **IntWritable**
  - o Example—Bear, [1, 1], and so on.
- **Output**:
  - o The key is all the unique words present in the input text file: **Text**
  - o The value is the number of occurrences of each of the unique words: **IntWritable**
  - o Example—Bear, 2; Car, 3, and so on.
- We have aggregated the values present in each of the lists corresponding to each key and produced the final answer.
- In general, a single reducer is created for each of the unique words, but you can specify the number of reducer in **mapred-site.xml**.

Driver code:

```
Configuration conf= new Configuration();
Job = new Job(conf,"My Word Count Program");
job.setJarByClass(WordCount.class);
job.setMapperClass(Map.class);
```

```
job.setReducerClass(Reduce.class);
job.setOutputKeyClass(Text.class);
job.setOutputValueClass(IntWritable.class);
job.setInputFormatClass(TextInputFormat.class);
job.setOutputFormatClass(TextOutputFormat.class);
Path outputPath = new Path(args[1]);
//Configuring the input/output path from the filesystem into the job
FileInputFormat.addInputPath(job, new Path(args[0]));
FileOutputFormat.setOutputPath(job, new Path(args[1]));
```

- In the driver class, we set the configuration of our MapReduce job to run in Hadoop.
- We specify the name of the job, the data type of input/output of the mapper and reducer.
- We also specify the names of the mapper and reducer classes.
- The path of the input and output folder is also specified.
- The method **setInputFormatClass ()** is used for specifying how a mapper will read the input data or what will be the unit of work. Here, we have chosen **TextInputFormat** so that a single line is read by the mapper at a time from the input text file.
- The **main ()** method is the entry point for the driver. In this method, we instantiate a new configuration object for the job.

Source code:

```
package co.edureka.mapreduce;
import java.io.IOException;
import java.util.StringTokenizer;
import org.apache.hadoop.io.IntWritable;
import org.apache.hadoop.io.LongWritable;
import org.apache.hadoop.io.Text;
import org.apache.hadoop.mapreduce.Mapper;
import org.apache.hadoop.mapreduce.Reducer;
import org.apache.hadoop.conf.Configuration;
import org.apache.hadoop.mapreduce.Job;
import org.apache.hadoop.mapreduce.lib.input.TextInputFormat;
```

```
import org.apache.hadoop.mapreduce.lib.output.TextOutputFormat;
import org.apache.hadoop.mapreduce.lib.input.FileInputFormat;
import org.apache.hadoop.mapreduce.lib.output.FileOutputFormat;
import org.apache.hadoop.fs.Path;

public class WordCount{
public static class Map extends
Mapper&lt;LongWritable,Text,Text,IntWritable&gt; {
public void map(LongWritable key, Text value,Context context) throws
IOException,InterruptedException{
String line = value.toString();
StringTokenizer tokenizer = new StringTokenizer(line);
while (tokenizer.hasMoreTokens()) {
value.set(tokenizer.nextToken());
context.write(value, new IntWritable(1));
}
}
}
public static class Reduce extends
Reducer&lt;Text,IntWritable,Text,IntWritable&gt; {
public void reduce(Text key, Iterable&lt;IntWritable&gt;
values,Context context) throws IOException,InterruptedException {
int sum=0;
for(IntWritable x: values)
{
sum+=x.get();
}
context.write(key, new IntWritable(sum));
}
}
public static void main(String[] args) throws Exception {
Configuration conf= new Configuration();
Job = new Job(conf,"My Word Count Program");
```

```
job.setJarByClass(WordCount.class);
job.setMapperClass(Map.class);
job.setReducerClass(Reduce.class);
job.setOutputKeyClass(Text.class);
job.setOutputValueClass(IntWritable.class);
job.setInputFormatClass(TextInputFormat.class);
job.setOutputFormatClass(TextOutputFormat.class);
Path outputPath = new Path(args[1]);
//Configuring the input/output path from the filesystem into the job
FileInputFormat.addInputPath(job, new Path(args[0]));
FileOutputFormat.setOutputPath(job, new Path(args[1]));
//deleting the output path automatically from hdfs so that we don't
have to delete it explicitly
outputPath.getFileSystem(conf).delete(outputPath);
//exiting the job only if the flag value becomes false
System.exit(job.waitForCompletion(true) ? 0 : 1);
}
}
```

Run the MapReduce code:

```
hadoop jar hadoop-mapreduce-example.jar WordCount /sample/input /
sample/output
```

The MapReduce programming paradigm can be used with any complex problem that can be solved through parallelization.

A social media site could use it to determine how many new sign-ups it received over the past month from different countries to gauge its increasing popularity among different geographies. A trading firm could perform its batch reconciliations faster and also determine which scenarios often cause trades to break. Search engines could determine page views, and marketers could perform sentiment analysis using MapReduce.

How MapReduce organizes work? [13]

There are two types of tasks:

- Map tasks (splits and mapping)
- Reduce tasks (shuffling and reducing)

  The complete execution process (execution of map and reduce tasks, both) is controlled by two types of entities: jobtracker and multiple task trackers:

- **Jobtracker**: acts like a master (responsible for complete execution of submitted job).
- **Multiple task trackers**: acts like slaves, each of them performing the job.

  For every job submitted for execution in the system, there is one Jobtracker that resides on the Namenode, and there are multiple task trackers which reside on Datanode.

- A job is divided into multiple tasks, which are then run onto multiple data nodes in a cluster.
- It is the responsibility of the job tracker to coordinate the activity by scheduling tasks to run on different data nodes.
- Execution of individual tasks is then to look after by task tracker, which resides on every data node executing part of the job.
- Task tracker's responsibility is to send the progress report to the job tracker.
- In addition, the task tracker periodically sends "heartbeat" signal to the Job tracker so as to notify him of the current state of the system.
- Thus, job tracker keeps track of the overall progress of each job. In the event of task failure, the job tracker can reschedule it on a different task tracker.

Important Commands [9]

All Hadoop commands are invoked by the **`$HADOOP_HOME/bin/hadoop`** command. They are running the Hadoop script without any arguments prints the description for all commands.

`Usage:` **hadoop [--config confdir] COMMAND**

The following table lists the options available and their description:

Sr.No. Option and Description

1 **namenode -format**

Formats the DFS filesystem.

2 **Secondarynamenode**

Runs the DFS secondary namenode.

3 **Namenode**

Runs the DFS namenode.

4 **Datanode**

Runs a DFS datanode.

5 **Dfsadmin**

Runs a DFS admin client.

6 **Mradmin**

Runs a Map-Reduce admin client.

7 **Fsck**

Runs a DFS filesystem checking utility.

8 **Fs**

Runs a generic filesystem user client.

9 **Balancer**

Runs a cluster balancing utility.

10 **Oiv**

Applies the offline fsimage viewer to an fsimage.

11 **Fetchdt**

Fetches a delegation token from the NameNode.

12 **Jobtracker**

Runs the MapReduce job tracker node.

13 **Pipes**

Runs a pipes job.

14 **Tasktracker**

Runs a MapReduce task tracker node.

15 **Historyserver**

Runs job history servers as a standalone daemon.

16 **Job**

Manipulates the MapReduce jobs.

17 **Queue**

Gets information regarding JobQueues.

18 **Version**

Prints the version.

19 **jar**

Runs a jar file.

20 **distcp**

Copies files or directories recursively.

21 **distcp2**

DistCp version 2.

22 **archive -archiveName NAME -p ***

Creates a hadoop archive.

23 **Classpath**

Prints the class path needed to get the Hadoop jar and the required libraries.

24 **Daemonlog**

Get/set the log level for each daemon

How to interact with MapReduce Jobs?

Usage: **hadoop job [GENERIC_OPTIONS]**

The following are the generic options available in a Hadoop job:

Sr.No. GENERIC_OPTION and Description

1 **-submit**

Submits the job.

2 **-status**

Prints the map and reduce completion percentage and all job counters.

3 **-counter**

Prints the counter value.

4 **-kill**

Kills the job.

5 **-events <#-of-events>**

Prints the events' details received by jobtracker for the given range.

6 **-history [all] - history < jobOutputDir>**

Prints job details, failed and killed tip details. More details about the job, such as successful tasks and task attempts made for each task, can be viewed by specifying the [all] option.

7 **-list[all]**

Displays all jobs. -list displays only jobs which are yet to complete.

8 **-kill-task**

Kills the task. Killed tasks are NOT counted against failed attempts.

9 **-fail-task**

Fails the task. Failed tasks are counted against failed attempts.

10 **-set-priority**

Changes the priority of the job. Allowed priority values are VERY_HIGH, HIGH, NORMAL, LOW, VERY_LOW.

Conclusion

In this chapter, we have learned that NoSQL database is a non-relational data management system, which does not require a fixed schema. It avoids joins and is easy to scale used for distributed data stores with humongous data storage needs, big data and real-time web apps. Mostly applied by most of the internet giants such as Google, Facebook, Amazon, and so on who deal with huge volumes of data. NoSQL databases never follow the relational model. It is either schema-free or has relaxed schemas. Four types of NoSQL database are (1) key-value pair based, (2) column-oriented graph, (3) graphs based, and (4) document-oriented. NoSQL can handle structured, semi-structured, and unstructured data with equal effect. To understand the importance of logging and how through logging application can be maintained in production.

The non-relational structure is an approach to database design that can be used for a wide variety of data models, including key-value, document, columnar and graph formats. NoSQL, which stands for *"not only SQL,"* is an alternative to traditional relational databases in which data is placed in tables and data schema is carefully designed before the database is built. NoSQL databases are especially useful for working with large sets of distributed data.

Questions on how to script NoSQL DB configuration? When should we use a NoSQL database instead of a relational database?

List the applications of big data that is being resolved using NoSQL?

Key terms: NoSQL, non-relational database, unstructured data, big data.

Points to remember

- Traditional B-Tree and T-Tree indexing is commonly used in traditional databases.
- Improvements and enhancements can be offered by combining the characteristics of multiple indexing structures to come up with the Tree.
- Further work can and should be done to enhance the consistency of NoSQL DBMSs. The integration of both systems, NoSQL and relational databases, is an area to further explore.

Chapter 8
Application of Big Data—Real Use Cases

Many industries have benefitted from big data as it has aided numerous industries in storing and processing the massive amount of information as per the requirement. It has undoubtedly been a game-changer for many industries. Helping businesses make informed decisions is the primary goal of big data applications. It does it by analyzing large volumes of data that includes everything such as the web server logs, data collected from Internet click stream, the social media content which is growing in a fraction of seconds, and those activity reports which we generate multiple times to keep track of our work and analyzing or auditing data, the text received from customer emails, the mobile phone/landline call details and the machine data being captured by multiple sensors at one moment. Big data has witnessed huge investments from various organizations of multiple domains. Organizations want to have their large data sets examined to uncover all hidden patterns, correlations, trends of the market, customer preferences, and other relevant business information.

It is a known and evident fact that today's world is generating an enormous amount of data every minute. The experts have predicted that it will result in a great wave of data or better termed as a data tsunami. This scenario will direct us to a necessity to have a tool to handle this data in a systematic manner for many applications in various fields, including government, scientific research, industry, and so on. This will directly aid in a comprehensive study, proper storage, and desired processing format of the relevant data.

Structure

This chapter will cover how applications of big data have helped industries in the following sectors:

- Healthcare
- Finance
- Retail
- Travel
- Media

Objective

Big data has been playing a very important role as a big game-changer for almost all the industries over the last few years. The primary goal of big data applications is to help companies make more informative business decisions by analyzing large volumes of data. It could include web server logs, internet clickstream data, social media content and activity reports, text from customer emails, mobile phone call details, and machine data captured by multiple sensors. The aim of the current chapter is to understand and highlight the importance of big data in various industries, namely healthcare, finance, retail, travel, and so on.

Big data applications in healthcare

The manner in which we manage, examine, analyze, and leverage data in any industry today has been completely changed through big data. Healthcare is one of the most promising areas where big data applications can and has contributed significantly. Substantial reduction in the cost of treatment, well in time prediction of outbreaks of deadly epidemics, ways to march towards healthy living in general, and improvement in lifestyle are some of the areas where big data applications can play an important role. With the rapid increase in the population around the world, the average human lifespan has also seen growth, and this has challenged the conventional treatment delivery channels. Like other businesses, the healthcare sector is also capable of collecting enormous data and deploying the best strategies that can lead to the generation of valuable information. Through this chapter, we will help you understand the need for big data applications in the healthcare sector: why and how can big data help the healthcare industry? What are the possible obstacles to the smooth adoption of big data in healthcare? We will then throw some light on the already existing big data examples in healthcare and discuss how we benefit from them.

What is big data in healthcare?

Numerous positive and lifesaving outcomes have been offered by the application of big data to the healthcare industry. Big data, as you are aware, refers to the huge quantities of data and information that get generated through the digital sphere and can be consolidated and examined through specific technologies. When big data is applied to the healthcare sector, it uses health-specific data of a population or of an individual to predict potential epidemics, combat diseases effectively and reduce costs, and so on.

Treatment models prevalent today have undergone impressive changes, and many of these changes have been backed up by big data. Healthcare professionals, to contribute effectively, need to understand as much as they can and as early as they can about an individual's health to pick up warning signs well in time of any serious illness that may arise. Treatment of many diseases, if detected at an early stage, gets easier and does not burn a hole in the pocket. With the provision of healthcare data analytics, prevention (which is any day better than the cure) of diseases is now possible. Big data has also enabled health insurance providers to offer tailored insurance packages basis a comprehensive picture of the patient's health. This is industry's attempt to tackle the information silo of a patient's health records that traditionally were collected in bits and bytes and archived in various hospitals and clinics, which result in duplication of efforts and, of course, increase in costs as well.

Well known fact that gathering data for medical use has been a costly and time-consuming affair. Today's always evolving technologies have made this huge data collection task not only easy but has also facilitated its conversion into a critical information source that can be deployed to offer better and improved health care. Providing data-driven findings that can predict and resolve a health complication in its early stage, before it gets too late, is one of the prime purposes of healthcare data analytics. Finding the best and faster treatment methods and approaches is another. Keeping a better track of the inventory, empowering patients with tools to monitor their health on a timely basis, and adopting a better lifestyle are among various other offerings of big data in healthcare.

Why do we need big data analytics in healthcare?

Due to the ever-rising costs for health services in many nations like the United States, a huge need for big data has been realized in healthcare lately. To quote from *McKinsey* report, "*After more than 20 years of steady increases, healthcare expenses now represent 17.6 percent of GDP—nearly $600 billion more than the expected benchmark for a nation of the United States's size and wealth.*"

To put it in simple words for better understanding, costs involved in healthcare services are much higher than they ideally should be, and they also have been on a steep rise for over the past 20 years now. Undoubtedly, we are in dire need of some smart, cost-effective, data-driven strategy in this area. Many health insurance providers are now reworking their approach from fee-for-service offerings, which focus on rewarding patients for using expensive and at times not required treatments for quick results, to designing plans that prioritize patient health outcomes.

Financial incentives matter, and incentives that focus on prioritizing patient's health over treating large amounts of patients are a good thing. But why does this matter? Let us discuss. In the previous scheme, healthcare providers have rewarded no direct incentive for sharing patient's health information with the health professional's community, which made it tough to fully utilize the power of analytics. With the evolution in approach, now more of the doctors are getting paid basis patient outcomes; they also have a financial incentive for sharing data that can be utilized in improving the lives of patients while reducing costs for health insurance companies.

Finally, doctor's decisions are now becoming more and more evidence-based, which means that they now largely rely on large sets of research and clinical data for providing treatment as opposed to earlier methods of relying solely on their schooling. Like in other industries, data gathering in the healthcare sector is also getting bigger, and its management has given rise to the demand for data professionals and analytics than ever witnessed before. The rise of SaaS BI tools is, to some extent, answering that need.

Obstacles to widespread adoption of big data in healthcare

Medical data has widespread across many sources that are governed and controlled by various states, administrative departments and hospitals, and so on. This is one of the main and biggest impediments to the adoption of big data applications in healthcare. Integration of these data from these data sources would mean designing and developing a new infrastructure where all data providers can collaborate with each other to provide better healthcare services.

Implementation of new online reporting software and business intelligence strategies cannot be missed and are equally important. It is widely recognized that healthcare needs to catch up with other industries that have already moved to future-oriented methods such as predictive analytics, machine learning, and graph analytics from the traditional standard regression-based methods.

However, there are a few great examples where health care does not lag behind, such as EHRs, especially in the USA. So, even if these services are not something that you are looking at and you are a potential patient, so you should care about new analytics applications in healthcare. It is good to take a look around and see how other industries cope with it. They can be a source of inspiration for you to adapt and adopt some good approaches.

Twelve big data applications in healthcare

Twelve applications on big data in healthcare are explained as follows:

- **Improved staffing through patient predictions**: How many people do I put on staff at any given time period? This is the classic issue that any shift manager deals with; if you put more than required workers, you are at the risk of having unnecessary labor costs adding up. If the number of workers is too few, this can lead to compromised customer service outcomes, which can prove fatal for patients.

  Big data has helped a few hospitals in Paris to solve this problem. Four hospitals, part of the Assistance Publique-Hôpitaux de Paris have been deploying data from various sources to draw insights on daily and hourly predictions of the number of expected patients at each hospital; this was also featured in a Forbes article.

  In total, 10 years' worth of hospital admissions records is one of the key data sets, which data scientists analyzed using "*time series analysis*" techniques. This data crunching allowed the researchers to identify relevant patterns of admission rates. Then, using machine learning, they could predict the future admission trends through the most accurate algorithms.

  To sum up the product of this approach, Forbes states: "*The result is a web browser-based interface designed to be used by doctors, nurses and hospital administration staff—untrained in data science—to forecast visit and admission rates for the next 15 days. Extra staff can be drafted in when high numbers of visitors are expected, leading to reduced waiting times for patients and better quality of care.*"

- **Electronic health records (EHRs)**: Every patient now has access to his or her own health records in a digital format. The records include demographics, medical history, lab test results, past surgery procedures, medicine prescriptions, and so on. This is the most widespread and powerful application of big data in healthcare. Health data records can be shared through secure information systems and readily available for both public and private sector providers. Every record is available in an editable file, which means that doctors can make changes over time without any paperwork and chances of data replication.

Electronic health records offer a great tracking mechanism. It can also trigger warnings and reminders to a patient if there are any prescheduled lab tests or track medicine prescriptions to see if a patient has been following doctors' recommendations.

Many nations still struggle to fully implement EHRs, although it is a great idea. The United States of America has made a noteworthy leap with the majority of its hospitals adopting EHRs, but the EU still lags behind. With the ambitious directive drafted by European Commission in place, a centralized European health record system should soon become a reality. EU could follow the model of *Kaiser Permanente,* which is leading the way in the USA HealthConnect system followed by *Kaiser Permanente,* shares data across all their facilities and makes use of EHRs way easier. A McKinsey report on big data in healthcare states, "*The integrated system has improved outcomes in cardiovascular disease and achieved an estimated $1 billion in savings from reduced office visits and lab tests.*"

- **Real-time alerting**: Real-time alerting is another example of big data analytics in healthcare. **Clinical decision support (CDS)** software in hospitals analyzes medical data right on the spot, assisting health practitioners with advice for them to make effective prescriptive decisions. As doctors want patients to stay away from the hospitals and avoid costly in-house treatments, big data analytics, already a business intelligence trending buzzword, has the required potential to become part of a new cost-effective strategy with better outcomes. Wearable's will collect patients' health data periodically and send this data to the cloud. This information accessible to the database of the state health of the general public will allow health professionals to compare this data in a socio-economic context and make amendments to the existing delivery strategies accordingly. Through the usage of sophisticated and intelligent tools, institutions and health care managers will be able to monitor this huge data stream and react timely if the results are deviating from the desired form. For instance, if a patient's blood pressure varies alarmingly from the normal stable range, the doctor would receive an instant notification through the system in real-time. Through this, necessary action can be taken to reach out to the patient and administer measures to control the blood pressure. Asthmapolisis is another example of big data applications in medicine. GPS-enabled trackers on inhalers help health professionals identify asthma trends both on an individual level and the population at large. This data used in conjunction with data from the CDC can help the development of better treatments for people suffering from asthma.

- **Patient engagement enhancement**: Many consumers, or we can say the potential patients—already have an inclination towards smart devices that track and record every step they take, monitor their heart rates, sleeping habits, and so on, on a daily basis. All this vital information can be coupled with other trackable data to identify approaching health risks well in advance. Chronic insomnia and an increased heart rate can point towards a risk of heart disease in the future, for instance. Patients, in this case, are directly involved in the regular monitoring of their own health, and decent incentives from health insurance providers can motivate them to follow a healthy lifestyle (e.g., giving money back to people using smartwatches). New wearables that are under development will track specific health trends and relay them to the cloud, where experts can monitor them on a regular basis. This will reduce unnecessary visits to the doctor; patients suffering from asthma or blood pressure could benefit from it, making them a little more independent.
- **Prevention of opioid abuse in the USA**: As of this year, overdoses from misused opioids have lead to more accidental deaths in the USA than road accidents, the most common cause of accidental death earlier. We will now discuss how big data in healthcare is tackling this serious problem in the USA.

  As per *Bernard Marr*, an analytics expert, this situation has gotten so dire and out of control that USA had declared opioid abuse to be a "*national health crisis*," and President Obama had earmarked $1.1 billion dollars for brainstorming and developing solutions to get rid of the issue while he was in office. An application of big data analytics in healthcare can help with a solution to deal with this issue. Blue Cross Blue Shield data scientists have started working with analytics experts from Fuzzy Logix to deal with the problem. Leveraging years of insurance and pharmacy data, Fuzzy Logix analysts have been able to establish 742 risk factors that predict with an impressively high degree of accuracy whether someone is at risk for opioid abuse. Brandon Cosley, data scientist at Blue Cross Blue Shield data states in the Forbes piece: "*It's not like one thing—'he went to the doctor too much'—is predictive ... it's like 'well you hit a threshold of going to the doctor and you have certain types of conditions and you go to more than one doctor and live in a certain zip code...' Those things add up.*"

  This project definitely offers a lot of hope towards tackling the menace which is destroying the lives of many people and costing the system a lot of money. Though reaching out to "*high risk*" people and preventing them from developing a drug issue is a delicate undertaking.

- **Informed strategic planning through health data**: Big data in healthcare allows strategic planning through access to better insights into people's motivations. Factors discouraging people from taking up treatment can be identified through analysis of check-up results among individuals of different demographic groups.

  The University of Florida prepared heat maps targeted at various concerns like population growth and chronic diseases by using *Google Maps* and free public health data. Academicians then compared this data with the medical services available in the most heated areas. The insights from the heat maps allowed them to review their delivery strategy and add more healthcare units to the most problematic areas.

- **Cure for cancer**: Cancer Moonshot program is yet another interesting example of the use of big data in medicine. President Obama came up with this program before the end of his second term that had the goal of accomplishing 10 years' worth of progress towards curing cancer in half that time. Using large amounts of data of treatment plans and recovery rates of patients suffering from cancer, medical researchers can find trends and treatments that have the highest success rate in the real world. For instance, tumor samples in biobanks linked up with patient treatment record scans be examined by researchers. Through this data, researchers can see things like how certain mutations and cancer proteins interact with different treatments and find trends that will lead to better patient outcomes. This data can also direct researchers to unexpected benefits, for example, finding that Desipramine, which is an anti-depressant, can help cure certain types of lung cancer.

  To make such insights more available, the health database of patients from various institutions such as hospitals, universities, and nonprofits has to be linked up. Then researchers will have access to patient biopsy reports from other institutions irrespective of their location. Another potential use of Big data in healthcare would be genetically sequencing cancer tissue samples from clinical trial patients and making this data available to the wider cancer database.

  But it is not an easy task. There are a lot of obstacles in the way, including:

- **Incompatible data systems**: This is perhaps the biggest and the main technical challenge, as making these data sets able to interface with each other is not easy.

- **Patient confidentiality issues**: The existence of no universal law governing patients' health information is an issue in itself. Laws that govern what patient information can be released with or without consent differ state by state, and all of these would have to be navigated.

Institutions that have invested a lot of time and money into developing their own cancer datasets may not be willing to share with others, even though it could lead to a quicker cure.

An article by Fast Company states, there are precedents to navigating these types of problems: "*...the U.S.* ***National Institutes of Health (NIH)*** *has hooked up with a half-dozen hospitals and universities to form the Undiagnosed Disease Network, which pools data on super-rare conditions (like those with just a half-dozen sufferers), for which every patient record is a treasure to researchers.*"

- **Predictive analytics**: Predictive analytics in healthcare is one of the biggest business intelligence trends two years in a row, with potential applications reaching far beyond business and much further in the future. Optum Labs, a USA research collaborative, has worked towards collecting EHRs of over 30 million patients to create a database for predictive analytics tools to improve the quality and delivery of healthcare. With the goal to help doctors make data-driven decisions within seconds and improve patients' treatment, healthcare business intelligence is particularly useful in the case of patients that have complex medical histories and suffer from multiple health conditions. New tools would also enable the prediction of, for example, individuals with a high risk of diabetes, and thereby being advised to make use of additional screenings or track weight.
- **Reducing fraud and enhancing security**: Basis some studies healthcare industry is more likely to experience data breaches than any other industry. The reason is quite obvious and simple: personal data is extremely valuable; and therefore, invites eyes from black markets because of the high profits. And any breach would have unimaginable consequences. With that in mind, many organizations have started using analytics to help prevent security threats. Identification of changes in network traffic or any other behavior that reflects a cyber-attack can be picked up using big data applications. Big data is believed to have inherent security issues, and many think that using it will make organizations more vulnerable than they already are. But advances in technology and security such as encryption technology, firewalls, anti-virus software, and so on answer that need for more security, and the benefits brought largely overtake the risks. Likewise, it can help prevent fraud and inaccurate claims in a systemic, repeatable way. Big data analytics in healthcare can help streamline the processing of insurance claims, enabling patients to get better returns on their claims and caregivers to be paid swiftly. For instance, the centers for medicare and medicaid services said they saved over $210.7 million in frauds in just a year.

- **Telemedicine**: Telemedicine has been present for over 40 years now in the market but could bloom to its full potential only today, with the arrival of online video conferences, smartphones, wireless devices, and wearables. Telemedicine refers to the term delivery of clinical services using technology remotely. It is now being widely adopted for primary consultations and initial diagnosis, remote patient monitoring, and medical education by health professionals. Some more uses include telesurgery—doctors can now perform operations using robots and high-speed real-time data delivery remotely, without physically being in the same location with a patient. Clinicians use telemedicine and provide customized treatment plans and prevent hospitalization or re-admissions. As discussed previously, such use of healthcare data analytics can be linked to the use of predictive analytics. It allows clinicians to predict acute medical events at an early stage and prevent deterioration of patient's conditions. Telemedicine helps to reduce costs and improve the quality of service by keeping patients away from hospitals. It also helps patients avoid long waiting lines, and doctors save on time by not having to go through unnecessary consultations and paperwork. Patients' states can be monitored anywhere and anytime; thus, improving the availability of care.
- **Big data and medical imaging integration**: Medical imaging is important, and each year in the USA, close to 600 million imaging procedures are performed; this clearly depicts the vital role medical imaging plays in the healthcare industry. As radiologists and hospitals need to reckon these images time and again for years, their storage is really important. Analysis and storage of these images manually are both expensive and time-consuming. Carestream, the medical imaging provider, explains how big data analytics for healthcare can change the way images are read. Algorithms developed through analysis of hundreds and thousands of images could identify specific pixels patterns and convert them into a number to help the professional with the diagnosis. It is also possible that radiologists will no longer need to look at the images but instead analyze the outcomes of the algorithms that will inevitably study and remember more images than they could in a lifetime. This would undoubtedly impact the role of radiologists, their education, and their required skill set.
- **No more unnecessary ER visits**: It is important and necessary to save time, money, and energy using big data analytics for healthcare. It was reported that over the course of 3 years, one woman who suffered from mental illness and substance abuse went to a variety of local hospitals on an almost daily basis more than 900 times in Oakland, California. The lack of shared medical records between local emergency rooms (ER) made it hard for this woman to get good care. This also increased the cost

to taxpayers and hospitals. Tracy Schrider, the care management program coordinator at *Alta Bates SummitMedical Center* in Oakland, stated in a *Kaiser Health News* article:

"Everybody meant well. But she was being referred to three different substance abuse clinics and two different mental health clinics, and she had two case management workers both working on housing. It was not only bad for the patient, it was also a waste of precious resources for both hospitals."

To avoid any such situations in the future, Alameda county hospitals came forward to together create a program called PreManage ED, which shares patient records between emergency departments. This system lets emergency room staff know things such as:

- Has the patient they are treating got certain tests already done at any other hospital, and what are the results of those tests are.
- If the patient they are treating already has a case manager at another hospital, this would save them from unnecessary assignments.
- If any advice has already been given to the patient, so that a coherent message to the patient can be maintained by providers.

Earlier, hospitals without PreManage ED would repeat tests over and over, and even if they could see that a test had already been done at another hospital, they would go old school way and request or send long fax just to get the information they needed.

How to use big data in healthcare

Through these 12 examples of big data applications in healthcare, three main trends can be observed: the patient's experience could improve dramatically, including quality of treatment and satisfaction, the overall health of the population would also improve over time, and the general costs would reduce. Let us now have a look at an example of how to use data analytics in healthcare, in a hospital, for instance.

The healthcare dashboard helps with the overview needed by a hospital director or a facility manager. Gathering all the required information at one central point, all the data on every department of the hospital, the attendance, its nature, the costs incurred, and so on, you have the big picture of your facility, which will be of great help to run it smoothly.

One can review here the most vital metrics concerning various aspects: the number of patients that were walked in your facility, for how long, did they stay and where, and how much it costs to treat them, and their average waiting time in emergency rooms. Such overview assists the top management in the identification of potential bottlenecks, spot trends and patterns over time, and in general, assess the situation. This is important to make better-informed decisions that will improve the overall operations performance and aim at treating patients better and having the right staffing resources.

List of 12 big data examples in healthcare

The healthcare industry is changing at a face pace, and like any other, an application of big data is starting to transform it, and there is still a lot of work to be done. The sector is adopting new technologies that will push it into the future, help it to make better-informed decisions and improve overall operations, and so on. To sum it up following is a shortlist of the examples we have discussed. With healthcare data analytics in place, one can:

- Predict the daily incoming patients and tailor staffing accordingly.
- Make use of electronic health records (EHRs).
- Leverage real-time alerting for instant care.
- Preventing opioid abuse in many countries.
- Build patient engagement in their own health.
- Make better-informed decisions using health data.
- Cure cancer using a more research-intensive approach.
- Make use of predictive analytics.
- Work towards reducing fraud and enhancing data security.
- Easily practice telemedicine.
- Use big data and medical imaging integration for broader diagnosis.
- Save on time and money by preventing unnecessary ER visits.

The aforementioned examples of big data in healthcare prove that the development of medical applications of data should be the apple in the eye of data science, as they have the potential to save money and, most importantly, people's lives. Today it allows early identification of illness of an individual and socio-economic group and takes preventive actions right on time because, as we all know, prevention is better than cure.

Applications of big data in finance

In the realm of information technology and quantitative methods, big data is a popular new catchphrase that refers to the collection and analysis of huge amounts of information. Every day advances in computing power paired with the falling prices make big data projects increasingly more technically feasible and economical. With the advent of cloud computing, the cost of big data analysis is now within reach of many smaller firms, which now do not need to make significant capital investments in their own computing infrastructure.

In finance, big data refers to the petabytes of structured and unstructured data that can be used to predict customer behaviors and design strategies for banks and financial institutions.

In response to the growth of big data, a new career category, data science, has sprung up. Within finance, specifically within the financial services industry, Big data is being utilized in an increasing number of applications, such as:

- Employee surveillance and monitoring.
- Predictive models, such as those that may be used by insurance underwriters to set premiums and loan officers to make lending decisions.
- Developing algorithms for forecasting the direction of financial markets.
- Pricing of illiquid assets such as real estate.

Every single transaction that happens online and penny that gets transmitted digitally creates hundreds of data points. These massive amounts of data can be incredibly useful when properly processed, scrubbed, and analyzed. Big data can help financial services providers make smarter, faster decisions that are backed more by data than intuition.

It is important to know which data is valuable to track and to figure out the best ways to measure it. A clear understanding of the metrics and key performance is indicator necessary for discerning important insights is the foundation of the smartest financial dashboards. The process of finding the right uses for big data begins with understanding where does data come from and how you can best measure it.

It is important that the sources of data are known in advance, and it is also essential to have the knowledge to identify the right ways to track the sources as these both are vital in the creation of powerful financial analytics. There are a variety of sources and channels from where data is received and can prove useful for different types of analysis and metrics.

- **Expenses and revenues**: Irrespective of the services that you offer, every organization has overheads and revenues that provide vital data such as payrolls, income from transactions, operational costs, and fixed costs, for example, leases, utility costs, and debt payments.
    - Increased customer satisfaction and increased revenue- There are now many companies, for example, Slidetrade, that have applied big data

solutions to develop analytics platforms that predict clients' payment pattern. By having insight into the client's behavior, a company can shorten payment delays and generate more cash while improving customer satisfaction.

- **Transactions**: Information on business transactions alone is not a reliable measure of a business' success. Data on transactions can showcase the cost of every deal along with the margins. A series of investments that cost more than they earn is not made better with bigger numbers.
- **Regular financial data**: For companies that are into financial services such as banks, lenders, and investment funds, a deep understanding of growth over time (with measures like cumulative annual growth rate) is important for updating investment and lending strategies, as well as building new ones.
- **Data of shareholders**: It includes information about shareholders' benefits, dividends, and earnings. Information about dividends paid as a percentage of profits, earnings per share, and even the value of shares provides useful data for making major financial decisions.
- **Data on debt**: For financial services providers, data on debt can represent both an asset and a liability. Lenders must keep track of outstanding debts, paid ones, and interest rates. It is also an important consideration when making investments, expanding, setting future strategies and lending levels, and understanding the impact of transactions and loan decisions.
- **Real-time insights on the stock market**: Through machine learning, trade and investments have witnessed a change. Instead of simply analyzing stock prices, big data can now take into account political and social trends that may affect the stock market. Machine learning monitors trends in real-time, allowing analysts to compile and evaluate the appropriate data and make smart decisions.
- **Timely detection of fraud and its prevention**: Machine learning, fueled by big data, is greatly responsible for fraud detection and prevention. The security risks once posed by credit cards have been mitigated with analytics that interprets buying patterns. Now, when secure and valuable credit card information is stolen, banks can instantly freeze the card and transaction and notify the customer of security threats.

  The most precious visualizations for companies that provide financial services deliver a clear understanding of historic data and offer potential trends and insights. Some relevant big data use cases in financial service providers focus on the performance of long-term assets such as investments, loans, and other financial products. As such, the right big data analytics tools feature a combination of short and long-term data visualizations that provide a more comprehensive view of a financial services company's performance.

- **Calculation of profit and loss—profit and loss (P&L)** detail aid in building your understanding of profits and costs on a historic basis. This permits tracking of real-time changes and measuring the impact of strategy changes and new policies. P&L visualizations also help to identify where profit margins can be widened and which areas of the business are more profitable and valuable relative to others.
- **Data on loan volumes and information on outstanding loans**: Insights on the number of outstanding loans can help providers to form a better understanding of policy efficacy and that customers are more likely to pay on time. Interpreting the number of loans can show consumer preferences and possible areas for heightened profitability. Comparing it with the outstanding and delinquent loans can assist in highlighting the effectiveness of underwriting processes and loan extensions.
- **Knowing performance of investment portfolio**: The majority of the financial services providers, keep their funds as a combination of cash on hand and diversified investments. Keeping track of investment portfolios' performances can help the companies allocate resources to optimize profits while concurrently advancing better liquidity and financial stability over the long term. It can also identify and highlight under-performing assets and lead to better reinvestment strategies.
- **Accurate risk analysis**: Unbiased machine learning is now helping in big financial decisions like investments and loans. Calculated moves and decisions based on predictive analytics take into account everything from the economy, customer segmentation, and business capital and identify potential risks like bad investments or payers.
- **The relative income per customer type**: Financial services providers, banks, lenders, and others cater to a variety of customers and needs. Gaining insights and understanding each revenue stream's profitability helps companies make better decisions about which customers should be pursued more aggressively and where should more resources be allocated. In addition to this, it can also highlight trends among customer types for services such as loans and mortgages.
- **Improved path to purchase**: Legacy tools no longer offer the solutions needed for large, disparate data and often have limited flexibility in the number of servers they can deploy. Cloud-based data management tools have helped companies like *MoneySuperMarket* get data from several web services into data warehouses for consumption by various departments, such as finance, marketing, business intelligence, market intelligence, and

reporting. Cloud strategies like these improve the path to purchase for customers, enable daily metrics and performance forecasts and ad hoc data analysis.

- **Streamlined workflow and reliable system processing:** Ever-rising data volumes in banking are leading to the modernizing of core banking data and application systems through uniform integration platforms. Matched with a streamlined workflow and a reliable system for processing, companies like Landesbank Berlin have applied application integration to process 2 TB of data daily, implement 1,000 interfaces, and use just one process for all information logistics and interfacing.
- **Analyze financial performance and control growth**: With thousands of assignments per year and dozens of business units, analyzing financial performance and controlling growth between company employees can be complex. Processes of data integration have enabled many companies like Syndex to automate daily reporting, assist IT departments gain productivity, and allow business users to access and analyze critical insights easily.

Big data solutions for finance industries

Data is now becoming a second currency for finance organizations, and they need the right tools to monetize it. As large firms continue to shift towards full adoption of big data solutions, new technology offerings will provide cost-effective solutions that give both small and large companies access to innovation and a sharp competitive edge.

The end-to-end cloud-based platform of Talend's, accelerates financial data insights with data preparation, enterprise data integration, quality management, and governance.

Big data applications in retail

In an industry where brands face the challenge of e-commerce giants such as *Amazon*, dynamic pricing, and the growing thrift shopping trend, retailers need all the help they can get to stay competitive. Big data has become so prevalent and accessible that more retail brands than ever are relying on data-driven insights to optimize pricing, streamline operations, and improve customer experience.

The first step to using big data to stay competitive? Understanding how big data is working in the retail industry and gleaning insights from how other brands have already put it into practice.

To stay competitive, retailers make better buying decisions, must offer relevant discounts, convince customers to hop on new trends, and remember their customers' birthdays—all while making the business run behind the scenes. How do they keep up? Big data in retail is essential to target and retain customers, streamline operations, optimize the supply chain, improve business decisions, and ultimately save money.

Before the cloud was readily available, companies were limited to tracking what a person bought and when. With the more sophisticated technology, companies can capture a wealth of data about their customers, such as their age, geographical location, gender, favorite restaurants, other stores they shop at, what books or news they read—the list goes on and on. Retailers have now turned to cloud-based big data solutions to aggregate and manage that data.

Big data benefits for retail

Big data analysis can predict emerging trends, target the right customer at the right time, decrease marketing costs, and increase the quality of customer service.

The following list is the common benefits of using big data in retail:

1. **Maintaining a 360-degree view of each customer**: Create the kind of personal engagement that customers have come to expect by knowing each individual at scale.
2. **Optimize pricing**: Get the most value out of upcoming trends and know when and how much to decrease off-trend product prices.
3. **Streamline back-office operations**: Imaging maintaining perfect stock levels throughout the year and gathering data from registered products in real-time.
4. **Enhanced customer service**: Unlock the customer service data hiding in recorded calls, in-store security footage, and social media comment.
    - **360-degree view of the customer**: The *"360-degree view"* term gets thrown around a lot, but what does that mean? It all boils down to a comprehensive picture of a customer that is as accurate as possible. Retailers need to know a customer's likes and dislikes, their likelihood of using coupons, their gender, their location, their social media presence, and so on.
    - Blending just a few of these data points can lead to sophisticated marketing strategies. For instance, fashion retailers generally hire expensive celebrity brand ambassadors. But by paying attention to customer gender, likes, and social media presence, fashion brands can find more affordable and effective micro-influencers to represent their brands on *Instagram*.

- **Optimization of prices**: Big data gives businesses an advantage when products are being priced. Monitoring relevant search words on a constant basis can enable companies to forecast trends before they happen. Retailers can prepare new products and can anticipate an effective dynamic pricing strategy.

  Pricing can leverage the 360-degree view of the customer as well. This is because pricing is largely based on a customer's geographical location and purchasing habits. Companies can run beta tests for segments of their customer population to see which pricing fits best. Understanding what a customer expects can inform the retailer of ways they can stand out against their competition.

- **Streamlined back-office operations**: Anyone who has worked in retail has experienced that sinking feeling when their stock is depleted. For the rest of their shift, that manager will be dealing with angry customers. Ideally, companies would eliminate this situation entirely. Although that may not always be possible, big data can help companies manage the supply chain and product distribution.

  Product logs and server data can give retailers clues as to how their operations are running upstream. The products themselves can expose bugs, too. Customers that register their wearables, for example, can show the product performance over time.

- **Enhanced quality of service**: Think about the last time you called a toll-free number. Usually, there is a warning that your call will be *"recorded for quality purposes."* Big data analysis can bring top issues from those recorded calls to light and then measure the success of company-led quality changes over time.

  Some retail companies scrutinize in-store video footage and motion sensors to improve customer experience. Retailers measure how often customers gravitate towards an area in the store and strategically place items they want to sell first. This is not a new concept—grocery stores deliberately design their layout, causing you to come out with more food than intended.

  There are insights waiting to be uncovered in customer reviews and comments as well. Analyzing these reviews can allow retailers to notify customers that particular garments may run small or large. Analysis of sentiments can also be used to identify whether customers are talking positively or negatively about certain products and companies at large. As it is now very clear that the retail industry is accelerating rapidly, and with it, the need for businesses to find the best retail use cases for big data is also on the rise. New data sources, ranging from log files and transaction information to sensor data and social media metrics, offer new opportunities to retail organizations in achieving unmatched value and competitive advantage in an ever-expanding industry space. If we talk from a business standpoint, retailers will have to empower people across their organization to make quicker decisions with accuracy and with confidence. The only way to achieve this is to leverage big data in making the best plans and decisions, understanding customers more deeply, uncovering hidden trends that unwrap new opportunities, and more.

- **Analysis of customer behavior**: Deeper, data-based customer insights are highly crucial in addressing challenges of the kinds of improving customer conversion rates, increasing revenue through personalized campaigns, predicting and avoiding customer churn, and lowering the cost of customer acquisition. Today's consumers interact with companies through multiple interaction channels such as social media, mobile, e-commerce sites, stores, and more. This increases the complexity and variety of data types you have to aggregate and analyze quite dramatically.
- When all of this data is consolidated, examined, and analyzed together, it can lead to insights you would have never had of before, for instance, who are the high-value customers, what is their motivation to buy more, what is their behavior, and how and when is it best to approach them? Fully armed with these insights, one can improve customer acquisition significantly and drive customer loyalty.

  Data engineering is indeed the key for unlocking insights from customer behavior data both in structured and unstructured formats, as one can combine, integrate, and analyze all of the data in one go to generate the valuable insights required to drive customer acquisition and loyalty.
- **Personalized in-store experience through big data**: Earlier, merchandising was regarded as an art form, but it had no true way of measuring the impact of merchandising decisions specifically. And as online sales gained momentum, a new trend emerged where shoppers liked to first perform their own physical research on products in-store and then purchase online at a later time.

  With the advent of people-tracking technology, new ways to analyze store behavior and measure the impact of merchandising efforts came into existence. A data engineering platform now helps retailers make sense of their data to optimize merchandising tactics, customize the in-store experience with loyalty apps and drive timely offers to attract consumers to complete purchases, with the end goal being to accelerate sales across all channels.

Data engineering can offer a major competitive advantage to retailers through their in-store customer data. Insights can lead to cross-selling, increased promotional effectiveness, and much more. These valuable insights can be collated from:

- Mobile applications
- Websites
- Supply chain systems
- Point-of-sale systems
- In-store sensors
- Cameras, and so on.

Omni-channel retailers, through data engineering platforms, can:

- Test and measure the results of different marketing and merchandizing tactics on sales and customer behavior.
- Identifying the needs and interests of the customers through their browsing and purchasing history and then providing personalized in-store services to them.
- Monitoring in-store behavior of the customer and releasing timely offers for the customers to attract more in-store purchases or maybe online purchases later, thereby keeping the purchase within the fold of the retailer.
- Using predictive analytics and targeted promotions to increase conversion rates. Retail companies should target customer promotions effectively to see an increase in customer acquisition and a dip in costs. An accurate 360-degree view of customers and prospects is required to achieve this.
- Gauge and measure the impact of various promotional tactics on customer behavior and conversion.
- Personalize promotions for customers leveraging their purchase and browsing history to identify their needs and preferences.

Until now, customer information was limited to demographic data that was collected mainly during sales transactions. But today, customers interaction is way more than the transaction, and these interactions majorly happen over social media and through other various channels. Given these trends, it would not be incorrect to say that retailers should utilize this data that customers generate via interactions to gain deeper insights into valuable customer information such as understanding their preferences and so on.

Correlation of customer purchase histories and profile information along with behavior on social media sites is now possible through data engineering. These correlations can at times lead to unexpected valuable insights—for instance, let us say many of a retailer's high-value customers *"liked"* watching the food channel on television and shopped often at whole foods. The retailer can then make use of these insights to target their advertisements by placing ads and special promotions on cooking-related TV shows, Facebook pages, and in organic grocery stores. As a result, the retailer will encounter much higher conversion rates and a considerable.

- **Analysis of customer journey:** We all know that today's customers are way more empowered and connected than ever before. Using various channels such as mobile, social media, and e-commerce, customers have access to just about any kind of information within seconds. This helps them know what they should buy, from where they should buy, and at what price they should buy. Based on the information available to them, customers make buying decisions and purchase whenever and wherever it is convenient for them.

  Nowadays, customers also expect more. For instance, they would want companies to provide consistent information and seamless experiences across channels based on their history, preferences, and interests. More than ever before, the quality of the customer experience drives sales and customer retention today. Basis these trends, marketers should continuously adapt how they understand and connect with customers. This would demand data-driven insights that can help one understand each customer's journey across various channels.

  With the help of big data engineering technologies, one can bring together all of the structured and unstructured data into *Hadoop* and analyze all of it as a single data set, regardless of the data type. The analytical results can lead to totally new patterns and insights whose existence was never known before—and would not have even been conceivable with traditional analytics. It can help one get answers to complicated retail questions as follows:

  What is really happening in the customer journey across every step?

  - Who are the real high-value customers, and how do they behave?
  - How and when is it best to reach the high-value customers?

- **Operational and supply chain analysis**: Faster product life cycles and ever-complex operations make retailers use big data analytics to understand supply chains and product distribution to cut down on costs. Retailers now know well the intense pressure to optimize asset utilization, performance and quality, budgets, and service quality. It is now essential for gaining a competitive edge and driving better business performance.

  For increasing operational efficiency, the key to utilize data engineering platforms is to use them to unlock valuable insights buried under the log, sensor, and machine data. These insights contain information about trends, patterns, and outliers that can improve decisions, drive better operations performance and save millions of dollars.

Examples of assets that generate valuable data insights include servers, plant machinery, cell towers, customer-owned appliances, energy grid infrastructure, and even product logs. Collecting, preparing, and analyzing this fragmented (and often unstructured) data is not an easy or small task. The data volumes generally double every few months, and the data itself is quite complicated and complex—often in thousands of different semi-structured and unstructured formats.

Data engineering permits one to quickly combine structured data such as CRM, ERP, mainframe, geolocation, and public data with unstructured data. Then, after utilizing the right analytical tools, one can use this data to detect outliers, run time series and root cause analyses, and parse, transform and visualize data.

Big data applications in travel

Big data, in a big way, is transforming the way businesses conduct operations. Data is now being gathered in many ways through analysis of consumer buying behavior, online searches, and through various other channels, and companies make use of this data to improve their profit margins and provide an overall better experience to customers. While big data is being used by many industries around the globe, the travel industry is known to have gained a tremendous amount from its use. Many larger companies are already using big data creatively, but you may not understand the true value it can provide to your business. With a closer look at how big data is transforming the travel industry, one can better determine how your own business can benefit from its use.

- **Revenue management**: The majority of the companies in the travel and tourism industry face the challenge of selling the right product, at the right time, to the right customer without compromising on the right price and through the right channel. All this requires internal as well as external data. Internal data includes details such as past customer expectations, occupancy rates, room revenue, and current bookings. External data generally comprises information about local events, weather, flights, and school holidays. Both the internal and external data help to get more accurate data. It also assists in predicting future demand and anticipating it in advance. As a result of this, hotels are then better able to manage prices and room rates, increasing them at times of high demand to maximize the revenue that is generated. It should be noted that more data is better only when the revenue management system helps to improve the price-demand estimates. This system helps in controlling a particular business mix and pricing strategy. It also helps with the enhancement of the optimization process. Here, big data usage basically gives an edge over the competitors and helps the marketer to make a niche for themselves. Revenue management helps in incorporating the analytics and determining which competitive properties are actually relevant to the customer's that are willing to pay. Through it, competitor rate information can also be known, and thus, this also helps a business in planning the next move.

- **Reputation management**: Running a hotel is not a cakewalk. Cleaning, room service, bar, restaurant, and most importantly, the customer service management asks for a lot of money, time, and courtesy. Here is how *Taj* treats its customers.

  Hotels like *Taj* facilitate their service to the customers very well. These services hold immense value and are of great use as they help the hotels build and manage their reputation. Having the record of its customer data and information helps to drive to its core service, that is, hospitality, for which it is known for. If the website and services are shown would not have been appealing, a person would never have taken a decision to stay there. Apart from that, order-taking is also one of the kinds of experience.

  Big data has helped the functioning to get smooth, starting from billing and payment to the use the mode of payment everything has become flexible. The augmented service are the services for which one is ready to spend so much money. For instance, Hotel Taj is known for its hospitality. The humble, polite, and courteous staff is the reason what differentiates it from the other operational hotels. Employees are given separate training, and a tough process is followed by them to get themselves enrolled in the hotel management courses.

  In the internet age, customers can leave reviews on a wide range of different platforms, including social media sites, search engines, and dedicated review websites, sharing their opinions and experiences. The customer's tendency is to trust reviews more than the website.

  It is assumed that businesses bend the truth in their marketing. But other patrons generally do not have much reason to lie in a positive review. If they think a hotel is good, it most likely is a good hotel. Moreover, customers are increasingly checking these reviews and comparing different hotels before they make a booking.

So, when all this data get combined with the feedback that is acquired internally, it can be used to spot the most significant strengths and weaknesses. With data, it can be known that whether customers are impressed or disappointed. Once this information has been gathered, hotels can use it to inform their training efforts to make improvements and ensure future reviews are positive.

- **Strategic marketing:** By combining big data with an integrated marketing management strategy, marketing organizations can make a substantial impact on these key areas. Big data helps in delivering facts and figures. This, when converted into stats, helps to find insights into not just who your customers are, but where they are, what they want, how they want to be contacted, and when.

  In the travel industry, it might be difficult to get the right marketing done because potential customers are varied in who they are, where they come from, and what they are looking for. But, big data helps tourism companies to adopt a more strategic approach in their marketing efforts, targeting the right people in the right way.

  More specifically, it can help businesses to identify the trends that exist among the customers, where the similarities are, and what the best marketing opportunities are. It can also help businesses to understand where those people are and when marketing is most relevant to them. This can enable marketing messages to be sent based on time, location, and other data. This allows targeted promotional content to be delivered.

- **Customer experience**: Customer experience is a factor that decides whether the customer will be a loyal customer, need-based customer, or wandering customer. A loyal customer is the one who makes up a minority of the customer base but generates a large portion of sales. The main aim is to make the customer loyal.

  Hotels and other businesses in the travel and tourism industry have a vast array of interactions with their customers, and each of these interactions can provide valuable data, which can be used to improve the overall customer experience. This data can include everything from social media conversations and online reviews to service usage data.

  Effectively used, this information can reveal which services customers use most, which they do not use at all, and which they are most likely to request or talk about. Through this data, companies can make more informed, data-driven decisions about the services they currently provide, the services they no longer need to provide, the services they want to introduce, and the new technology they choose to invest in.

- **Market research**: The travel and tourism industry uses big data to compile and analyze information about its main competitors. To gain a clearer understanding of what other hotels or businesses are offering customers, data can be acquired from a variety of sources. There is no shortage of places where customers go to share their opinions on hotels and travel companies, especially online.

  All this data can be used to pinpoint the strengths, weaknesses, and overall reputation of rival companies. This can be extremely valuable, as it helps business leaders to spot potential gaps in the market or opportunities to deliver in ways that rivals are failing to. This can, in turn, lead to greater demand and higher revenue.

  Big data has benefited people in the travel industry immensely, allowing them to make more evidence-driven decisions. It includes the ability to anticipate future demand more accurately, optimize pricing strategies, target marketing more precisely, and improve customer experience.

- **Targeted marketing**: The guests come from varied backgrounds and can be categorized into n number of categories. It can be according to their spending habits, purchasing power parities, expectations. If we take two extremes like family on holiday to business travelers, the budget, focus, and the purpose of staying in a hotel will be totally different. Now, this is where big data comes into the picture. By understanding the requirements, customer experience, and doing market research, the guest experience can be enhanced. All this will also help to create a win-win situation and a loyal customer.

  With the development of booking search engines, modern tourists are now less dependent on travel agencies and are increasingly using the digital world for viewing reviews, online comparison tools, and real photos uploaded by other travelers. What is that the tourism industry can do to not lose control of the market? The answer is adapting to big data.

  By analyzing the massive amount of information that travelers leave around the internet about their likings, habits, and preferences, the sector can provide personalized services and adapt efficiently to the demand. Many companies in this sector have already started taking advantage of it. The IMF business school reviewed five case studies focused on big data in the tourism industry.

- **Smart bracelets**: Smart bracelets use radio-frequency system that allows one to open a hotel's room as if it were a key, one can also store credit/debit cards details to make quicker purchases, it can also be used in theme parks to help control quick pass, or to save photos that have been taken. In addition to the above, they have hidden sensors containing details about the users that park employees can scan; it allows them to surprise visitors by knowing their names or wish them if they happen to celebrate their anniversary or birthday during the trip.

- **Geolocated offers**: There is a difference in the offers that a visitor from Location A and one from Location B would receive, and there would be variance in offers received by a loyal client compared to a new one. Big data has helped tourism companies in a big way; travel agencies can send their client's personalized offers and benefits based on their geographical location, traffic, weather, browsing history, reservations history, trip expenses, and so on.
- **Airports**: Travelers provide data in their passage through airports. This data can be used by airlines to plan their services and resources effectively. It can be followed by another technology known as "*seeking*," which would allow them to know anonymously how passengers move through airports if they are swift through duty-free stores at the airport, and if they rent a car or take a taxi.
- **Personalized welcome experience at the hotel**: Many hotels hold staff meetings prior to the arrival of new guests to establish who they are like through the public information found in their social network profiles or in the client's file if the person is a regular. In this manner, the staff gets to welcome their guests in a personalized way, greeting them by name or leaving their favorite chocolates in the room.
- **Direct charge of mini-bar fees**: Now, there are hotels where you do not have to pay for your mini-bar consumption at the time of checkout, but instead, charges are added directly to the card used to pay for the stay. Mini-bar nowadays has a built-in scanner of the available items and uses its sensors to charge the consumed goods.

As per *Carlos Martínez*, president of IMF business school, modern tourists want personalized experiences. They do not appreciate seeing the same every time they book their stay, for example, the kind of pillow they are used to or the type of bed they prefer. Through the use of big data, business owners can maintain a much more personalized relationship with their clients, increasing the possibility of their return.

This does not help just in revenue management, reputation management, strategic marketing, customer experience, market research, and targeting marketing but also helps in understanding their marketing content effectively. It helps to gain a competitive advantage and many other benefits to a business in the long run.

A massive amount of data that is captured through phones can provide travel businesses with valuable insight about their current locations as they travel around the world. Many travel companies in the world leverage this real-time data to offer travel assistance and recommendations. For instance, if a travel app identifies that your smartphone is in close vicinity of a popular theme park, or a restaurant, it may send you special offers or deals that can offer special discounts on a visit to these places. Some also make use of travel tips or links to local services that may prove helpful.

Many travel businesses use big data analysis to improve operations in numerous ways and make them more efficient. Data analysis may reveal, for instance, that one specific aspect of marketing is effective and better than the other, and the company can accordingly alter its marketing efforts to generate a greater return on investment. Another way a company can benefit from big data is that it can learn if customers are opting the competition more heavily because of special promotions or because of better quality. These are only a few ways big data can reveal valuable insights, and its proper analysis can help travel businesses to improve operations for enhanced success and improved profitability in the future.

There is a wide range of businesses a travel industry can include, for example, rental car companies, cruise liners, hotels, tour operators, airlines, and more. These businesses must find means to improve the overall customer experience and to satisfy the needs of customers, and big data can assist in the process. With the help of Big data analytics, companies in the travel industry can learn more about the preferences of their target audience or even about individuals in some cases. This allows them to tailor special promotions, design personalized experiences, deals, and more. For example, a resort can find out that its customer base largely comprises of younger adults, basis which it may plan hosting a popular national hip hop star's concert in its auditorium to attract more visitors. Improving the customer experience through personalization also allows travel businesses to generate repeat business through their loyal clients and to draw more word-of-mouth referrals.

Big data analysis allows travel businesses to find out why their customers are choosing them over their competitors or vice versa, with great ease. It is important to stand out in a crowded marketplace, and businesses that understand why customers are choosing their business over the competition can design marketing campaigns and products accordingly. It can be used to improve branding, make marketing more cost-effective, and even design new products or promotions that appeal specifically to consumers based on why they are choosing to work with a specific company.

Big data applications in media

Media creators and distributors now embrace big data analytics in creating a connection with their customers with the rise of the use of smartphones and associated entertainment devices. It will also aid in unlocking hidden insights on customer behavior and facilitate achieving the ultimate goal—delivering personalized content. It has been reported that *Facebook* collects and processes 500 TB of data on a daily basis. *Google* is believed to process 3.5 billion requests on a daily basis. The e-commerce giant *Amazon* is reported to receive close to 152 million customer purchase data on a daily basis.

Thus, it is quite evident that data volumes are skyrocketing on a daily basis. Big data is too big to ignore. If harnessed, it can be used as a massive force for boosting your business. Big data holds the key to future business profitability for many forward-thinking media companies. Close to every media associated business with large volumes of data can leverage big data to its benefit.

Big data in the media and entertainment industry will be of immense benefit for the following:

- **Video publishers**: Video creators who publish content including video, audio, text, and images.
- **Media owners**: Businesses that own the copyright to sell content that can be sold through retail or mass content distribution mediums.
- **Gaming companies**: Online or offline video game makers that can log gamer reactions for fine-tuning gaming experience.
- **TV channels**: Television channels that broadcast owned or purchased video content to a mass population.

Now, we will explore ways how big data is helping the entertainment and media industry make sense of the massive flood of data that gushes in from multiple sources.

- **Prediction of audience interests:** Media content was earlier served only in limited forms. Today, they are replaced by a variety of media services such as pay per view, on-demand, live streaming, and much more. Content delivery across these forms helps broadcasters collect a vast amount of user data, which can give in-depth insights into the understanding of behavior and preferences.

  According to the statistics compiled by *YouTube*, it has been found that YouTube's lion share of viewers is audience falling in the age group of 18–34 years. *YouTube* has also unearthed several other interesting statistics about its users, like what kind of videos viewers watch the most, what devices are used for video streaming, how long each video was watched, and much more.

Traditional entertainment methods gave TV viewers the option to just change the channel or switch the television set off. However, with the advent of customer-centric media services in the form of pay-per-view, subscription-based viewing, and live streaming, the face of entertainment has undergone a transformation.

A large volume of user data is tracked while utilizing content from any media or entertainment platform. This includes user preference that we know plays a major role in providing an in-depth understanding of the genres of content and what kind of user would prefer a particular genre.

YouTube reports that a majority of its viewers are within the age range of 18–34 years. It has even streamlined statistics to determine the type of videos a particular user would watch, how much time was spent watching videos, and whether it has any recurrent patterns.

- **Insights into customer churn**: Customer churn is a serious menace that media companies find almost impossible to tackle. As per reports, at least 30% of customers post their reviews through social media. Until big data arrived, it was next to impossible to combine and make sense of all the user data from multiple sources, including social media.

  It is now possible to understand why customers subscribe and unsubscribe. It is also possible to determine what kind of programs they like and dislike with crystal clear clarity. All this has been made possible by big data. Deeper valuable insights into responses towards pricing and subscription models can also be gained with the help of big data. Using big data analytics, content pricing, media content, and even delivery modes can be tailor-made to reduce customer churn.

  It is only through big data analytics that *YouTube* knows so much in detail about its users. Big data throws deep insights into YouTube's audience behavior and helps it to syndicate content that is closely aligned to their viewer preferences.

  Earlier, it was difficult for entertainment companies to analyze why some customers subscribe and unsubscribe from their channels or platforms. If they now unfollow or follow a particular show or celebrity, the data collected from their usage patterns or reviews on social media can be processed with clarity using big data analytics.

In addition to the above, how customers react to pricing and subscription models can also be now determined using big data. This can, in turn, help generate better pricing models and delivery modes of content.

- **Optimized scheduling of media streams**: The rapid growth of digital media distribution platforms has literally torn down the barrier that existed between end-users and distributors. Reaching the end-users directly without any intermediary is feasible than ever before.

  Social networks have now set the stage for creating individual connections with viewers, unlike in the past where mass distribution of media was practiced. Connecting with the relevant audiences straight through scheduled live videos can maximize revenues for media companies.

  Through big data, it is easy to identify the content that the audience would relate well with the audiences on a regular basis. Business models such as on-demand and scheduled viewing can also be attained through big data-enabled customer behavior analytics.

  Big data gave more power to the customer by easing the complexities of on-demand and scheduled viewing. Advanced analytics can be used to derive accurate predictions about users' actions from multiple sources. This knowledge can be beneficial in identifying the right type of content for a particular user.

- **Content monetization**: Big data analytics has helped media companies explore and create new revenue sources. It also has armed media owners' new avenues to capitalize on the media interests of customers. Let us go through the success story of *The Weather Channel*.

  The weather channel (TWC) is a privately owned weather business co-owned by IBM. TWC uses big data to observe and understand customer behavior in specific weather conditions.

  Using big data, TWC has fabricated a *WeatherFX* marketplace where sellers can advertise their products that have higher chances of selling in a given weather scenario. Presently, TWC is estimated to earn at least half of its advertising revenue with the help of big data analytics.

  Thanks to mobile profusion and bandwidth expansion, now it is possible to reach out to a larger chunk of the digitally connected audience for content monetization. Big data facilitates zeroing in on the right content that such an audience will prefer.

- **Effective ad targeting**: The revenue models of media and advertising are largely dependent on programmatic advertising. All these years, programmatic advertising has been done in a random manner, with the hope that customers will like what is shown to them.

Big data takes the guesswork out of programmatic advertising. It helps advertisers and businesses pinpoint the exact preferences of customers. It also gives a better understanding of what type of content viewers watch at what time and duration.

This granular visibility of customer preferences helps improve the efficiency of ad targeting resulting in higher conversion rates or TRP as the case may be.

Furthermore, in the case of live streaming, Big data also helps advertisers to modify their broadcasts in real-time to deliver a far enriched, engaged, and personalized media experience.

Advertising using ads on search engines and social media can be done more accurately with the help of big data. Since it has made it possible to understand the exact preferences of viewers, it is easier for entertainment industries to suggest a specific type of content to different users. High efficiency in ad targeting leads to an increase in conversion rates.

Therefore, the applications of big data in the media and entertainment are here to stay. As the entire industry is customer-driven, catering to customer preferences will be essential in its longevity. Big data plays a major role in this process. If you are keen on riding the big data Wave, register for Acadgild's big data course.

The media and entertainment industry, including publishers, broadcasters, news organizations, cable companies, and gaming companies, are designing new models for creating, marketing, and distributing their content. Since today's consumer is searching and accessing content online irrespective of the location, time, or device, there is heightened pressure to execute new digital production and multi-channel advertising and distribution strategies that rely on a detailed understanding of consumers' media consumption preferences and behaviors. And, as consumer interests shift from analog to digital media, there are substantial opportunities to monetize content and to identify new products and services.

With the ever-growing number of digital consumers, media and entertainment companies are in a unique position to use their big data assets for more profitable and effective customer engagement. We will discuss here a few examples of how media and entertainment companies can benefit from big data applications.

With the rise in digitization, media and entertainment companies are handling enormous amounts of data like never before. It has been estimated that *Facebook* alone gathers and processes more than 500 TB of data. While the largest search engine in the world, *Google* handles 3.5 billion requests every day, wherein over 1,000 computers are used to tackle a single user query! *Netflix*, the most popular online media service, provides almost 500 events (like video viewing and troubleshooting) that consume 1.3 PB/day and 8 million events that consume 24 GB/second during peak time. All of these organizations have leveraged big data applications in media and entertainment in a massive way.

Big data applications can chalk out the lane to the fast success of businesses in the entertainment and media industry. It can help negate the biggest risk factor in the industry-changing customer behavior. Big data helps reduce customer churn, creates alternate revenue channels, and also boosts customer acquisition and retention through data intelligence. This way, it can help have a steady pulse on the shifting customer preferences.

In the end, it creates a new ecosystem where customer experience is put as the centerpiece. After all, the entire entertainment and media industry thrives on the end-user experience that it creates.

Given all of its applications, no wonder there is so much hype around big data. The importance of big data lies in how an organization is using the collected data and not in how much data an organization has been able to collect. Various big data solutions are now available that make the analysis of big data easy and efficient. These big data solutions are used to draw benefits and immense value from the massive amounts of data in almost every industry vertical.

Having gone through five industry verticals, including how big data plays a role in these industries, the following are a few key takeaways:

- There is substantial real spending on big data.
- To capitalize on big data opportunities, you need to.
- Familiarize yourself with and understand industry-specific challenges.
- Know and understand the data characteristics of each industry.
- Understand where spending is occurring.
- Match market needs with your own capabilities and solutions.
- The sole key for utilizing big data effectively and efficiently is expertise in the vertical industry.

Most organizations generally have many goals for adopting big data projects. While the primary goal for many organizations is the enhancement of customer experience, other goals revolve around better-targeted marketing, cost reduction, and fine-tuning the existing processes for improved efficiency. In view of recent data breaches, enhanced security has been incorporated as an important goal by various data projects.

Conclusion

In this chapter, we have studied the importance of big data across industries. We understood that in the finance industry, whenever we require analysis and reporting, we can do it better with the help of big data. Similarly, in other industries such as healthcare, retail, travel, and so on—big data plays an important role not when we need to assess the data but for other reporting and supporting purposes.

In the next chapter, we will learn machine learning and see how to create the models and train the machine to get better results.

Questions

1. How is big data useful to make informative decisions in any industry?
2. Create a use case for the finance industry and prepare an analysis report using big data
3. Describe the top 10 challenges in the healthcare industry and how we can overcome these challenges with the help of big data?
4. How can we manage expenses and revenues with the help of big data?
5. Take a use case of any industry we discussed in this chapter and give the challenges and their resolution with the help of big data.

You would like to enhance your knowledge with these readings:

- *Big data and Hadoop* by *Mayank Bhushan* from BPB Publications [**https://in.bpbonline.com/products/big-data-and-hadoop**]
- *Hands-On data visualization* by *Pablo* from BPB Publications [**https://in.bpbonline.com/products/hands-on-data-virtualization-with-polybase**]

Chapter 9

Introducing Machine Learning - Making Machine to Run the Show

Introduction

We have seen machine learning as a mainstream articulation for whatever length of time that scarcely any years; the reason behind this might be the high proportion of data created by applications, the development of estimation power in the past scarcely any years, and the headway of better algorithm. Man-made insight plans to rehash a human brain, the way wherein a human psyche thinks, works, and limits. Truth be told, we cannot set up an authentic AI till now, yet we are close to set-up it; one of the examples of AI is Sophia, the most evolved AI model present today. The central target here is to extend the accomplishment pace of computation instead of growing precision. It works like a PC program that achieves adroit work.

Structure

This chapter will highlight the following topics:

- Introduction to machine learning
- Foundations of supervised learning
- Advanced supervised learning
- Classification and regression algorithm

- Random forest and decision tree
- Unsupervised learning

Objectives

Machine learning is a new programming paradigm, a new way of communicating to a computer / system. Machine learning is a branch of AI that pursues the development of techniques that allow machines to learn automatically and improve through the experience without being explicitly programmed for it. The goal is to develop software that is fed by, and learns from, specific data sets. There is an initial training phase in which the software is fed with examples, direct experience, or instructions. It is a targeted phase in which it is very important to have relevant data sets to meet the objectives.

Need for machine learning

By far, most of us are uninformed that we are starting now at the interface with machine learning every single day. Each time we *Google* something, check out a tune, or even snap an image, machine learning is ending up being a bit of the engine behind it, ceaselessly taking in and improving every participation. It is also behind world-changing advances such as recognizing illness, making new drugs, and self-driving vehicles.

There are a couple of stages drawn in with AI, which are a desire, game plan, proposition, gathering, and dynamic. Right, when all these five work together, we call it mechanized thinking. After the first undertaking, you comprehend that you have put a great deal of intensity into it. After the second undertaking, you comprehend you are closer to the target any way you need to construct your hurl point. What is happening here is, in a general sense, after each hurls, we are getting the hang of something and improving the last item. We are altered to pick up from our experience.

This construes the tasks where AI is concerned and offers an essential level operational definition instead of describing the field in mental terms. This follows *Alan Turing's* recommendation in his paper *"Preparing Machinery and Intelligence"*, in which the request *"Can machines accept?"* is superseded with the request *"Can machines do what we (as instinct components) can do?"*

Inside the field of data examination, AI is used to devise complex models and computations that credit themselves to desire; in business use, this is known as farsighted assessment. These orderly models license authorities, data analysts, fashioners, and inspectors to "*produce trustworthy, repeatable decisions and results*" and uncover "*covered bits of information*" through picking up from recorded associations and examples in the data set (input).

Simulated intelligence is used wherever from mechanizing unremarkable assignments to offering sharp encounters, adventures in each part endeavor to benefit by it. You may be starting to use a contraption that utilizes it. For example, wearable health trackers like *Fit-bit*, or a shrewd home partner like *Google Home*.

Let us talk about some uses of machine learning. Regardless, there are impressively more occurrences of ML being utilized.

- **Prediction**: Machine learning can similarly be used in the estimate structures. Considering the credit model, to enlist the probability of an inadequacy, the structure should describe the open data in social events.
- **Image affirmation**: Machine learning can be used for face acknowledgment in an image as well. There is an alternate class for each person in a database of a couple of individuals.
- **Speech recognition**: It is the understanding of verbally communicated words into the substance. It is used in voice look, and that is just a hint of something larger. Voice UIs consolidate voice dialing, call guiding, and mechanical assembly control. It can in like manner be used an essential data section and the arranging of sorted out files.
- **Medical examination**: ML is set up to see cancer-causing tissues.
- **The financial industry and trading**: Associations use ML in deception assessments and credit checks.

To get comfortable with the gauges managing a miracle, machines need to encounter a learning strategy, endeavoring different standards, and picking up from how well they perform. Thus, why it is known as machine learning.

- To present the key thoughts of AI.
- To discover around a couple of the most noteworthy AI algorithm's and structure an intuition into how they work and when and where they are significant.
- To get an appreciation of what are the fundamental advances and how they can be applied to an AI adventure through a certifiable from beginning to end model.

Main components of machine learning

There are three basic sections you need to set up your AI systems:

- **Data**: Data can be accumulated both genuinely and normally. For example, customers' own one-of-a-kind nuances like age and sexual direction, all of their snaps, and purchase history are significant data for an online store. Do you audit "*ReCaptcha*" which forces you to "*Select all the street signs*"? That is an instance of some free troublesome work! Data is not by and large pictures; it could be tables of data with various components (features), content, sensor accounts, sound models, and so on, depending upon the present issue.
- **Features**: Features are as often as possible, moreover called **elements** or **parameters**. These are essentially the components for a machine to look at—the properties of the "*object*" being alluded to, e.g., customers' age, stock worth, district of the venture properties, number of words in a sentence, petal length, size of the telephones. Picking critical features is noteworthy, yet it takes practice and thought to comprehend what features to use as they are not, for the most part as clear as in this frivolous model.
- **Algorithm**: Man-made intelligence relies upon extensively helpful computations. For example, one kind of count is the game plan. The course of action licenses you to put data into different social occasions. Strikingly, a comparative request count used to see composed by hand numbers could in like manner be used to bunch messages into spam and not-spam without changing a line of code! How is this possible? Regardless of the way that the algorithm is proportionate, it is dealt with different data, so it considers different game plan justification. Regardless, this is not proposed to gather that one count can be used to deal with a wide scope of issues! The choice of the computation is critical in choosing the idea of the last AI model. Acquiring anyway much data as could be normal is a critical starting stage in starting with AI structures.

A quick history of machine learning

It was during the 1940s when the chief truly worked PC system, **electronic numerical integrator and computer** (**ENIAC**), was created. Around then, "*PC*" was being used as a name for a human with raised numerical algorithm capacities; thus, ENIAC was known as a numerical enlisting machine! Taking everything into account, you may state it has nothing to do with learning?! WRONG, from the most punctual beginning stage, the idea was to gather a machine prepared to duplicate human thinking and learning.

During the 1950s, we see the primary PC game program pronouncing to have the alternative to beat the checkers best on earth. This program helped checkers players a lot in improving their capacities! By then, we see a long time of stagnation of the neural framework field due to its difficulties in dealing with explicit issues. Around 200 years afterward, these key musings were fundamental in machine learning. Notwithstanding what the issue is, it is information can be plotted onto an outline as data centers. Computer-based intelligence, by then, endeavors to find the logical models and associations concealed inside the main information. We start now, are using contraptions that utilization them.

- **Prediction**: Machine learning can, in like manner, be used in gauge systems. Contemplating the credit model, to calculate the probability of an issue, the system should arrange the open data in social events.
- **Image affirmation**: Machine learning can be used for face distinguishing proof in an image moreover. There is an alternate order for each person in a database of a couple of individuals.
- **Speech recognition**: It is the understanding of verbally communicated words into the substance. It is used in voice look, and that is just a hint of something larger. Voice UIs fuse voice dialing, call directing, and device control. It can, in like manner, be used as a clear data area and the arranging of composed reports.
- **Medical break down**: ML is set up to see dangerous tissues.

Sorts of machine learning

Computer-based intelligence can be gathered into three sorts of counts as follows:

- Supervised learning
- Unsupervised learning
- Reinforcement learning

Human versus machine

Ever thought about how a machine is one of a kind comparable to individuals? For what reason cannot a machine learn without any other individual? Let us answer these requests in this portion. Our history and our composing give us that for most of humankind's history, machines were seen as gadgets to help people with achieving more than they were fit for in solitude. From direct stone instruments to the advancements of the *Iron Age* and *Bronze Age*, development augmented human capacity for perseverance, competitive favored position, and solace.

Machines followed solicitations of individuals and performed assignments, whereas individuals are prepared for performing endeavors without any other person. Individuals can do this since they gain from past comprehension and choose a decision according to the experiences, while the machine does not pick up from past comprehension. Along these lines, machines are not fit for choosing decisions without any other individual.

Along these lines, a machine cannot learn without any other individual and requires learning dynamic. In ML, we solidify dynamic limits in machines so they can imitate humans directly. The creating relationship of *"machines"* in the field infers a change in profile for the present modernized publicist. Regardless of that, there is up 'til now a central requirement for human creative mind and sense, which implies there is not a looming danger of mechanized sponsors getting obsolete. Coincidentally, while advancing toward the introduction of new developments, it is earnest not to disregard legitimate parts and the human level to ensure feasible execution and agent satisfaction. Those associations that have moved snappy to improve the entire customer adventure by using the latest inventive advances while similarly recollecting the human level will be those that achieve the race for mechanized predominance.

Human versus machine—the relationship after some time

An essential point in the ever-changing association between humans and machines was in 1997 when chess expert *Gary Kasparov* was beaten at chess by IBM's Deep Blue machine. It was starting at since people began to consider how possible it is that the capacities of PCs would develop with the ultimate objective that they would render individuals outdated eventually. This made craze, with people contemplating whether, really, they ought to just acquiescence.

Regardless, believe it or not, since the time program has gotten progressively open, chess experts started to utilize this development to improve their chess execution and become on a standard with the PCs fit for beating them. Kasparov, in truth, said that the PC's show enabled him to be progressively key by methods for the expansive use of PCs to practice, while up till now leaving a noteworthy space for a human touch:

"The PC could expand the consequences of each move we considered, raising potential outcomes and countermoves we may some way or another have missed. With that managed for us, we could concentrate on indispensable organizing instead of contributing such a lot of vitality in checks. Human ingenuity was altogether progressively focal under these conditions."

Supervised learning

Supervised learning is the AI task of learning a limit that maps a commitment to a yield subject to show data yield pairs.

1. It assembles a limit from checked getting ready data containing a great deal of planning examples.
2. In oversaw learning, each example is a couple including a data object (regularly a vector) and perfect yield regard (in like manner called the authoritative sign). A coordinated learning estimation analyzes the readiness data and produces a concluded work, which can be used for mapping new examples. A perfect circumstance will consider the computation to precisely choose the class marks for covered examples. This requires the taking in estimation to summarize from the arrangement data to covered conditions in a "*reasonable*" way (see inductive tendency).

For example, accept you have to anticipate whether someone will have a coronary disappointment inside a year. You have a ton of data on past patients, including age, weight, stature, beat, and so on. You know whether the past patients had coronary scenes inside a period of their estimations. Along these lines, the issue is joining all the present data into an example that can envision whether a recharged individual will have a coronary scene inside a year.

In supervised learning, examples are readied using the stamped dataset, where the example gets some answers concerning each kind of data. At the point when the arrangement system is done, the example is given based on a shot test data (a subset of the planning set), and a short time later, it predicts the yield.

Examples of supervised learning

The following are some examples of supervised learning:

- **Visual recognition**: An AI that is making sense of how to recognize individuals by walking on a street is set up with 2 million short chronicles of street scenes from self-driving vehicles. A part of the chronicles contains no walkers at all, whereas others have up to 25. A combination of learning algorithms is set up on the data, with each moving toward the correct answers. Each count develops a grouping of examples to perceive individuals by walking in fast-moving scenes. The computations are then attempted against another plan of data to survey precision and exactness.
- **Sorting**: A robot is making sense of how to sort refuse using visual ID. It sits the whole day picking recyclable things from the junk as it passes on a

vehicle line. It places things, for instance, glass, plastic, and metal, into 12 compartments. Everything is named with a distinctive evidence number on a sticker. At the point when every day, human masters take a gander at the holders and enlighten the robot which things were improperly masterminded. The robot uses this analysis to improve.

- **Decision support**: An AI is making sense of how to assess contributing peril. It is dealt with a huge number of trades that certified examiners made and mentioned to evaluate a risk/reward extent for each trade reliant on association rudiments, cost, and various variables, for instance, volume. The surveyed possibility/reward extent is when appeared differently in relation to the chronicled outcomes of the trade at a grouping of time breaks, for instance, a day or a year.

Steps in supervised learning

Although there are various statistics and machine learning toolbox counts for coordinated learning, most use a comparative major work process for getting a pointer example. (Point by point direction on the methods for outfit learning is in framework for ensemble learning.) The methods for coordinated learning are as follows:

- Prepare data,
- choose an algorithm, and
- fit an example.

Choose a validation method:

- Examine fit and update until satisfied.
- Use fitted examples for predictions.

We should see now how you can develop oversaw learning example of this example which helps the customer to choose the drive time. The key thing you require to make is a planning set. This arrangement set will contain the full-scale drive time and looking at factors such as atmosphere, time, and so on. Taking into account this readiness set, your machine may see there is a quick association between the proportion of deluge and the time you will take to get back. Thus, it finds that the more it rains, the more you will make a beeline to come back to your home. It might moreover watch the relationship between the time you return home and the time you will be making the rounds. The closer you are to 6 p.m., the more it takes for you to get back. Your machine may find a bit of the relationship with your stamped data.

Two types of supervised learning

There are two types of supervised learning:

- **Classification**: Machine is set up to arrange something into some class.
  - Orchestrating whether a patient has contamination or not
  - Orchestrating whether an e-mail is spam or not
- **Regression**: Machine is set up to foresee some value like worth, weight, or height.
  - Foreseeing house/property cost
  - Foreseeing money related trade cost

Classification: Course of action expects to total the yield inside a class. In case the estimation endeavors to check commitment to two indisputable classes, it is called a twofold request. Picking between various classes is insinuated as a multi-class request.

Example: Determining whether someone will be a defaulter of the development.

Characteristics: The classification tree performs very well for all intents and purposes.

Weaknesses: Unconstrained, particular trees are slanted to overfitting.

For example, when filtering messages *"spam"* or *"not spam"*, when looking at trade data, *"bogus"*, or *"endorsed"*. In short, classification either predicts straight clobber checks or gatherings data (assemble an example) considering the planning set and the characteristics (class names) in organizing properties and usages it in portraying new data. There are different game plan examples. Request examples fuse key backslide, decision tree, sporadic timberland, incline helped tree, multilayer perception, one-versus rest, and *Naive Bayes*.

For example, which of coming up next is/are plan problem(s)?

- Predicting the sex of a person by his/her handwriting style.
- Predicting house cost subject to locale.
- Predicting whether tempest will be customary one year from now.
- Predict the amount of copies a music assortment will be sold one month from now.

Solution: Predicting the sexual direction of an individual, Predicting whether rainstorm will be conventional one year from now. The other two are backsliding.

The following are a few sorts of classification algorithms:

1. **Naive Bayes classifiers: Naive Bayesian (NBN)** example is definitely not hard to build and accommodating for gigantic datasets. This methodology is made out of direct non-cyclic graphs with one parent and a couple of adolescents. It expects self-sufficiency among adolescent centers segregated from their parent.

2. **Decision trees:** Decision trees bunch events by masterminding them reliant on the component regard. In this system, each mode is the component of a case. It should be described, and each branch addresses a value that the center can acknowledge. It is a (for the most part) used technique for gathering. In this procedure, the gathering is a tree which is known as a **decision tree**. It makes you measure certified characteristics (cost of purchasing a vehicle, number of calls, total month-to-month bargains, and so on).

3. **Support vector machine: Support vector machine (SVM)** is a sort of learning count made in 1990. This technique relies upon results from the verifiable learning theory introduced by *Vap Nik*. SVM machines are moreover solidly connected with parcel limits which is a central thought for most by far of the learning assignments. The bit structure and SVM are used in a combination of fields. It consolidates sight and sound information recuperation, bioinformatics, and plan affirmation.

Implementation of supervised learning

Let us see where we can implement supervised learning:

1. **BioInformatics**: This is one of the most striking employments of supervised learning because most of us use it in our regular day-to-day existence. BioInformatics is the limit of biological information of us individuals, for instance, fingerprints, iris surface, ear ligament, and so forth. Cellphones of today are prepared for learning our normal information and are then prepared to affirm us raising the security of the structure. Mobile phones, for instance, *iPhones*, *Google Pixel*, are prepared for facial affirmation, whereas *OnePlus*, *Samsung* is fit for in-show finger affirmation.

2. **Speech recognition**: This is the kind of use where you educate the algorithm about your voice, and it will have the choice to recall you. The most outstanding veritable applications are remote aides, for instance, *Google Assistant* and *Siri*, which will wake up to the catchphrase with your voice, so to speak.

3. **Spam detection**: This application is used where the shocking or PC-based messages and e-mails are to be blocked. G-mail has a count that learns the

different watchwords which could be fake, for instance, "You are the champ of something, and so forth and hinders those messages honestly." *OnePlus Messages App* gives the customer the endeavor of making the application acknowledge which watchwords ought to be blocked, and the application will frustrate those messages with the catchphrase.

4. **Object-recognition for vision**: This kind of utilization is used when you need to perceive something. You have a colossal dataset which you use to support your computation, and this can be used to see another event. *Raspberry Pi* counts, which recognize objects are the most eminent example.

Challenges in supervised AI

The following are challenges glanced in oversaw AI:

- Irrelevant data feature present getting ready data could give incorrect results.
- Data arranging and pre-taking care of is continually a test.
- Accuracy suffers when incomprehensible, impossible, and insufficient characteristics have been inputted as getting ready data.
- If the concerned ace is not open, by then, the other technique is "*creature power*." It suggests you need to feel that the right features (input factors) to set up the machine on. It could be erroneous.

Best practices for supervised learning:

- Before doing whatever else, you need to pick what kind of data is to be used as a planning set.
- You need to pick the structure of the academic limit and learning algorithm.
- Gather relating yields either from human masters or from estimations.

Overview

- In supervised learning, you train the machine using data that is well "*checked*."
- You have to set up a machine that urges you to anticipate to what degree it will take you to drive home from your workplace is an instance of oversaw learning.
- Regression and classification are two sorts of managed AI techniques.
- *Supervised learning is a less troublesome method, whereas unsupervised learning is a perplexing methodology.
- The best test is coordinated learning is that irrelevant data incorporate present getting ready data could give off base results.

- The key favored situation of oversaw learning is that it grants you to assemble data or produce a data yield from past experience.
- The drawback of this example is that the decision-breaking point might be overstrained if your readiness set does not have examples that you have to have in a class.
- As the best demonstration of overseeing learning, you first need to pick what kind of data should be used as a readiness set.

Classification and regression algorithm

Classification is a method to sort out information into an ideal and unmistakable number of classes where we can relegate names to each class. Applications of classification are: discourse acknowledgment, penmanship acknowledgment, biometric distinguishing proof, record order, and so forth. We utilize the training dataset to show signs of improvement limit conditions which could be used to decide each target class. When the limit conditions are resolved, the following errand is to anticipate the objective class. The entire procedure is known as **order**.

Target class examples:

- Analysis of the client information to anticipate whether he will purchase PC extras (Target class: Yes or No).
- Classifying natural products from highlights like shading, taste, size, weight (Target classes: Apple, Orange, Cherry, and Banana).
- Gender arrangement from hair length (Target classes: Male or Female).

How about we comprehend the idea of arrangement algorithm with sexual orientation order using hair length (in no way, shape or form am I attempting to generalization by sex, this is just an example). To order sexual orientation (target class) utilizing hair length as highlight parameter, we could prepare an example using any classification algorithms to think of some arrangement of limit conditions that can be used to separate the male and female sexes utilizing hair length as the preparation include. In the sex characterization case, the limit condition could be the correct hair length esteem. Assume the separated limit hair length esteem is 15.0 cm; then we can say that on the off chance that hair length is under 15 cm, at that point, sexual orientation could be male or, more than likely, female.

Basic terminology in classification algorithms:

1. **Classifier**: An algorithm that maps the information to a particular classification.

2. **Classification example**: A characterization example attempts to make some determination from the information esteems given for preparing. It will foresee the class names/classifications for the new information.
3. **Feature**: An element is an individual quantifiable property of a marvel being watched.
4. **Binary classification**: Classification task with two potential results. For example, gender classification (Male/Female)
5. **Multi-class classification**: Classification with multiple classes. In multi-class order, each example is doled out to one and only one objective mark. For example, A creature can be a feline or pooch; however, not both simultaneously.
6. **Multi-mark characterization:** Classification task where each example is mapped to a lot of target names (more than one class). For example, A news story can be about games, an individual, and an area simultaneously.

Instances of classification problems:

- Content categorization (for example, spam sifting).
- Fraud detection.
- Optical character recognition.
- Machine vision (for example, face location).
- Normal language processing (for example, communicated in language understanding).
- Market segmentation (for example, anticipate if the client will react to advancement).
- Bioinformatics (for example, order proteins as indicated by their capacity).

Implementation of classification algorithms:

- E-mail spam order.
- Bank clients advance compensation ability expectation.
- Cancer tumor cells ID.
- Sentiment examination.
- Drugs order.
- Facial key focuses recognition.
- Pedestrians recognition in a car vehicle driving.

An order issue is the point at which the yield variable is a classification, for example, "red" or "blue" or "ailment" and "no illness". An order example endeavors to make some determination from watched esteems. Given at least one sources of info a characterization example will attempt to anticipate the estimation of at least one result.

For instance, when sifting messages, "*spam*" or "*not spam*", when taking a gander at exchange information, "*deceitful*" or "*approved*". In short, classification either predicts straight-out class names or arranges information (develop an example) in light of the preparation set and the qualities (class marks) in characterizing characteristics and utilizations it in ordering new information. There are various classification examples. Classification examples incorporate strategic regression, choice tree, irregular timberland, slope supported tree, multilayer perception, one-versus rest, and *Naive Bayes*.

Classification problem(s):

- Predicting the sexual orientation of an individual by his/her penmanship style.
- Predicting house cost dependent on the zone.
- Predicting whether the storm will be typical one year from now.
- Predict the quantity of duplicates a music collection will be sold one month from now.

Arrangement: Predicting the sexual orientation of an individual predicting whether the storm will be ordinary one year from now. The other two are regression.

Different types of classifications:

1. Classification predictive example
2. Binary classification
3. Multi-class classification
4. Multi-label classification
5. Imbalanced classification

Classification predictive specimen: In AI, order alludes to a prescient displaying issue where a class name is anticipated for a given case of the information.

Instances of classification issues include:

- Given an example, a group in the event that it is spam or not.
- Given a written by hand character, order it as one of the known characters.
- Given ongoing client conduct, order as agitate or not.

1. Binary classification

Binary classification refers to those characterization errands that have two class names:

- E-mail spam discovery (spam or not).
- Churn prediction (stir or not).
- Conversion prediction (purchase or not).

Ordinarily, double classification errands include one class that is the typical state and another class that is the unusual state.

Mainstream algorithms that can be used for binary classification include:

1. k-nearest neighbors
2. Decision trees
3. Support vector machine
4. Naive Bayes

A few algorithms are explicitly intended for paired characterization and do not locally bolster multiple classes; examples incorporate logistic regression and support vector machines.

2. Multi-class classification

Multi-class arrangement alludes to those characterization errands that have in excess of two class marks.

- Face classification
- Plant species classification
- Optical character recognition

In contrast to binary classification, multi-class order does not have the idea of ordinary and strange results. Rather, examples are delegated having a place with one among a scope of known **classes**. The quantity of class names might be exceptionally enormous on certain issues. For instance, an example may anticipate a photograph as having a place with one among thousands or a huge number of countenances in a face acknowledgment framework.

Algorithms that are intended for paired classification can be adjusted for use for multi-class issues. This includes utilizing a technique of fitting numerous parallel order examples for each class versus every single different class (called one-versus-rest) or one example for each pair of classes (called one-versus-one).

- **One-versus-rest**: Fit one binary classification example for each class versus every single different class.
- **One-versus-one**: Fit one binary classification example for each pair of classes.

3. Multi-label classification

Multi-label classification refers to those order undertakings that have at least two class names, where at least one class name might be anticipated for every example. Think about the case of photograph classification, where a given photograph may have different articles in the scene, and an example may anticipate the nearness of numerous known items in the photograph, for example, *"bike," "apple," "individual,"* and so on. Classification algorithms utilized for binary or multi-class classification cannot be used straightforwardly for multi-mark classification. Particular adaptations of standard classification algorithms can be utilized, supposed multi-label versions of the algorithms, including:

- Multi-label decision trees
- Multi-label random forests
- Multi-label gradient boosting

Another methodology is to utilize a different characterization algorithm to foresee the marks for each class. Next, how about we investigate a dataset to build up an instinct for multi-label classification issues.

4. Imbalanced classification

Imbalanced classification alludes to order undertakings where the quantity of examples in each class is inconsistently disseminated. Regularly, imbalanced classification undertakings are binary classification errands where most the examples in the preparation dataset have a place with the ordinary class, and a minority of examples have a place with the unusual class. These issues are demonstrated as binary arrangement undertakings, in spite of the fact that they may require particular strategies. Particular strategies might be used to change the organization of tests in the preparation dataset by under-sampling the greater part class or oversampling the lion's share class.

- Random under-sampling
- SMOTE oversampling

Specific demonstrating algorithms might be utilized that give more consideration to the minority class when fitting the example on the preparation dataset, for example, cost-touchy AI algorithms.

- Cost-sensitive decision trees
- Cost-sensitive support vector machines

At last, elective execution measurements might be required as detailing the classification precision might be deluding.

a. Precision
b. Recall
c. F-measure

In AI and insights, the order is a directed learning approach in which the PC program gains from the information and afterward utilizes this figuring out how to group new perceptions. This information collection may essentially be bi-class (like recognizing whether the individual is male or female or that the mail is spam or non-spam), or it might be multi-class. Some functional instances of classification issues are: discourse acknowledgment, penmanship acknowledgment, biometric distinguishing proof, record arrangement, and so on.

Here we have not many kinds of classification algorithms in AI:

- Linear classifiers
- Nearest neighbor
- Support vector machines
- Decision trees
- Boosted trees
- Random forest
- Neural networks

1. **Naive Bayes classifier (Generative learning example)**: It is an order method dependent on Bayes' theorem with the supposition of autonomy among indicators. At the end of the day, Naive Bayes classifiers expect that the nearness of a specific component in a class is random to the nearness of some other element or that these properties have a free commitment to the likelihood. This group of classifiers is generally simple to manufacture and especially valuable for extremely enormous informational indexes as it is exceptionally versatile. Alongside straightforwardness, Naive Bayes is known to outflank even profoundly complex classification techniques.

   - **Closest neighbor**: The k-closest neighbor algorithms is a regulated order method that utilizes closeness as an intermediary for *"equivalence"*. The algorithms take a lot of marked focuses and use them to figure out how to name different focuses. To mark another point, it takes a gander at the named guides nearest toward that new point (those are its closest neighbors). Closeness is regularly communicated as far as divergence work. When it checks with "k" number of closest neighbors, it appoints a name dependent on whichever mark the large portion of the neighbors has.

2. **Predictive learning example**: It is a factual technique for breaking down an informational index wherein there are at least one free factors that decide a result. The result is estimated with a dichotomous variable (where there are just two potential results). The objective of strategic regression is to locate the best fitting example to depict the connection between the dichotomous quality of intrigue (**subordinate variable = reaction or result variable**) and a lot of autonomous (indicator or informative) factors. This is better than other paired orders like closest neighbor since it likewise clarifies quantitatively the elements that lead to the arrangement.

   - **Decision trees**: A decision tree constructs classification or regression examples as a tree structure. It separates an informational index into littler and littler subsets while simultaneously a related choice tree is gradually evolved. The conclusive outcome is a tree with choice hubs and leaf hubs. A choice hub has at least two branches, and a leaf hub speaks to order or choice. The highest decision hub in a tree, which relates to the best indicator called **root hub**. Choice trees can deal with both unmitigated and numerical information.
   - **Random forest**: Random forests or random decision forests are a group learning technique for classification, regression, and different undertakings, that work by developing a large number of choice trees at preparing time and yielding the class that is the method of the classes (order) or mean forecast (regression) of the individual trees. Random decision forests right for decision trees' propensity for overfitting to their preparation set.
   - **Neural network**: A neural network comprises of units (neurons), masterminded in layers, which convert an information vector into some yield. Every unit takes information, applies a (regularly nonlinear) capacity to it, and afterward gives the yield to the following layer. Mostly, the systems are classified to be feed-forward: a unit takes care of its yield to all the units on the following layer; however, there is no criticism to the past layer. Weightings are applied to the signs going starting with one unit then onto the next, and it is these weightings that are tuned in the preparation stage to adjust a neural system to the specific issue close by.

Regression in machine learning

Linear and logistics regressions are typically the first algorithms individuals learn in quite a while science. Because of their prevalence, a great deal of examiners even winds up imagining that they are the main type of regressions. The ones who are somewhat progressively included imagining that they are the most significant among all types of regression investigation. In all actuality, there are incalculable types of regressions, which can be performed. Each structure has its own significance and a particular condition where they are most appropriate to apply. In this article, we have clarified the most normally used seven kinds of regression in information science in a straightforward way.

In regression, we plot a diagram between the factors which best fit the given data points; utilizing this plot, the AI example can make expectations about the information. In straightforward words, *"Regression shows a line or bend that goes through all the data-points on track indicator diagram so that the vertical separation between the data-points and the regression line is least."* The separation among data points and line tells whether an example has caught a solid relationship or not.

A few instances of regression can be as follows:

- Prediction of downpour utilizing temperature and different components.
- Determining market patterns.
- Prediction of street mishaps because of rash driving.

Terminologies related to the regression analysis:

- **Dependent variable**: The principle factor in regression examination which we need to foresee or comprehend is known as the **reliant variable**. It is additionally called the **target variable**.
- **Independent variable**: The components which influence the reliant factors or which are utilized to anticipate the estimations of the needy factors are called **autonomous variable**, likewise called as an **indicator**.
- **Outliers**: Outlier is a perception that contains either low worth or exceptionally high incentive in contrast with other watched values. An exception may hamper the outcome, so it ought to be maintained a strategic distance from.
- **Multicollinearity**: If the free factors have profoundly corresponded with one another than different factors, at that point, such condition is called **Multicollinearity**. It ought not to be available in the dataset on the grounds that it makes an issue while positioning the most influencing variable.

- **Underfitting and overfitting**: If our algorithms function admirably with the preparation dataset; however, not well with the test dataset, at that point, such issue is called **overfitting**. Furthermore, in the event that our algorithms do not perform well even with preparing the dataset, at that point, such an issue is called **underfitting**.

What are the kinds of regressions?

There are two types of regression:

1. Linear regression
2. Logistic regression

What is regression analysis?

Regression analysis is a type of prescient displaying procedure which researches the connection between a needy (target) and free factor (s) (indicator). This procedure is utilized for estimating, time arrangement demonstrating, and finding the causal impact connection between the factors. Regression analysis is a significant device for demonstrating and examining information.

For what reason do we use regression analysis?

As referenced previously, regression analysis assesses the connection between at least two factors.

Example: Suppose you need to assess the development in deals of an organization dependent on current monetary conditions. You have the ongoing organization information, which demonstrates that the development in deals is around more than multiple times the development in the economy. Utilizing this understanding, we can foresee future deals of the organization dependent on current and past data.

Regression analysis additionally permits us to analyze the impacts of factors estimated on various scales, for example, the impact of value changes and the quantity of limited time exercises. These advantages help economic specialists/ information examiners/information researchers to wipe out and assess the best arrangement of factors to be utilized for building prescient examples.

Regression analysis in machine learning: Regression analysis is a factual strategy to show the connection between needy (target) and autonomous (indicator) factors with at least one free factor. All the more explicitly, regression examination causes us to see how the estimation of the needy variable is changing compared to an autonomous variable when other free factors are held fixed. It predicts constant/

genuine qualities, for example, temperature, age, compensation, cost, and so on.

Example: Suppose there is a promoting organization A, who does different notice each year and get deals on that. The underneath list shows the ad made by the organization over the most recent 5 years and the comparing deals:

Presently, the organization needs to do the ad of $200 in the year 2019 and needs to know the forecast about the deals during the current year. So to take care of such kinds of forecast issues in AI, we need regression investigation.

How many types of regression techniques do we have?

There are different sorts of regression techniques accessible to make expectations. These procedures are, for the most part, determined by three measurements (number of free factors, sort of ward factors, and state of regression line). We will examine them in detail in the accompanying areas. For the innovative ones, you can even concoct new regressions in the event that you want to utilize a mix of the parameters above, which individuals have not used previously. In any case, before you start that, let us comprehend the most ordinarily used regressions:

1. **Linear regression:** It is one of the most broadly known demonstrating procedures. Linear regression is as a rule among the initial not many themes which individuals pick while learning prescient displaying. In this method, the needy variable is consistent, autonomous variable(s) can be constant or discrete, and the nature of the regression line is direct.

   Direct regression sets up a connection between subordinate variable (Y) and at least one autonomous factor (X) utilizing a best fit straight line (otherwise called **regression line**).

   It is spoken to by a condition $Y=a+b*X+e$, where a is a block, b is the incline of the line, and e is the mistake term. This condition can be utilized to foresee the estimation of target variable dependent on given indicator variable(s).

   The contrast between simple linear regression and different linear regression is that various direct regression has (>1) free factors, while basic direct regression has just 1 autonomous variable. Presently, the inquiry is *"How would we acquire best fit line?"*

   How to get best-fit line (value of *a* and *b*)?

   This assignment can be handily practiced by *least square method*. It is the most widely recognized strategy utilized for fitting a regression line. It computes the best-fit line for the watched information by limiting the entirety of the squares of the vertical deviations from every datum point to the line. Since the deviations are first squared, when included, there is no counteracting among positive and negative qualities.

We can assess the example execution utilizing the metric R-square. To know more insights concerning these measurements, you can peruse: example Performance measurements Part 1 and Part 2.

2. **Logistic regression**: Logistic regression is used to find the *Probability of event=Success* and *Event=Failure*. We should use logistic regression when the dependent variable is binary (0/ 1, True/ False, Yes/ No) in nature. Here, the value of Y ranges from 0 to 1 and it can be represented by following equation:

$$odds = p/(1-p) = \text{probability of event occurrence / probability of not event occurrence}$$

$$ln(odds) = ln(p/(1-p))$$

$$logit(p) = ln(p/(1-p)) = b0+b1X1+b2X2+b3X3....+bkXk$$

where p is the probability of the presence of the characteristic of interest. A question that you should ask here is, "*why have we used log in the equation*?".

Since we are working here with a binomial distribution (dependent variable), we need to choose a link function that is best suited for this distribution. And, it is a logit function. In the equation above, the parameters are chosen to maximize the likelihood of observing the sample values rather than minimizing the sum of squared errors (like in ordinary regression).

Note: You can comprehend the above regression strategies in a video design—fundamentals of regression analysis

3. **Polynomial regression**: A regression condition is a polynomial regression condition if the intensity of the free factor is multiple. The condition beneath speaks to a polynomial condition:

$$y = a + b * x^2$$

In this regression procedure, the best fit line is certifiably not a straight line. It is fairly a bend that fits into the information focuses.

4. **Stepwise regression**: This type of regression is utilized when we manage different autonomous factors. In this procedure, the determination of autonomous factors is finished with the assistance of a programmed procedure, which includes no human mediation. This accomplishment is accomplished by watching factual qualities such as R-square, t-details, and AIC metric to perceive critical factors. Stepwise regression fundamentally

fits the regression example by including/dropping co-variants, each in turn dependent on a predefined basis.

The point of this displaying procedure is to expand the forecast power with the least number of indicator factors. It is one of the strategies to deal with the higher dimensionality of informational collection.

5. **Ridge regression**: Ridge regression is a strategy utilized when the information experiences multicollinearity (free factors profoundly correspond). In multicollinearity, despite the fact that the least-squares gauges (OLS) are fair-minded, their fluctuations are huge, which goes amiss the watched an incentive a long way from the genuine worth. By adding a level of inclination to the regression gauges, ridge regression lessens the standard blunders.

   Previously, we saw the condition for direct regression. Keep in mind? It very well may be spoken to as:

   $$y = a + b^{*}x$$

   This equation also has an error term. The complete equation becomes:

   $y=a+b^{*}x+e$ *(error term)*, [error term is the value needed to correct for a prediction error between the observed and predicted value]

   => $y=a+y= a+ b1x1+ b2x2+....+e$, for multiple independent variables.

   In a straight condition, expectation mistakes can be disintegrated into two subparts. The first is because of the one-sided, and the second is because of the difference. Expectation blunder can happen because of any of these two or the two parts. Here, we will examine the mistake caused because of the difference.

   Ridge regression takes care of the multicollinearity issue through shrinkage parameter λ (lambda). Take a gander at the condition beneath.

   In this condition, we have two parts. The initial one is least-square term, and the other one is the lambda of the summation of β^2 (beta-square), where β is the coefficient. This is added to least-square term so as to recoil the parameter to have an extremely low change.

6. **Rope regression**: Like ridge regression, **least absolute shrinkage and selection operator (LASSO)** additionally punishes unquestionably the size of the regression coefficients. What is more, it is equipped for diminishing the inconstancy and improving the precision of direct regression examples. Take a gander at the condition beneath LASSO regression varies from ridge regression such that it utilizes supreme qualities in the punishment work rather than squares. This prompts punishing (or proportionately compelling the aggregate of the total estimations of the evaluations) values which causes

a portion of the parameter appraisals to turn out precisely zero. The bigger the punishment applied, the further the appraisals get contracted towards outright zero. This outcome to variable determination out of given n factors.

6. **ElasticNet regression:** ElasticNet is half and half of LASSO and ridge regression methods. It is prepared with L1 and L2 earlier as a regularizer. A flexible net is valuable when there are various highlights which are associated. The rope is probably going to pick one of these indiscriminately, while the versatile net is probably going to pick both. A functional bit of leeway of exchanging off among LASSO and ridge is that it permits Elastic-Net to acquire a portion of ridge's solidness under revolution.

How to choose the correct regression example?

Life is generally basic when you know just a couple of strategies. One of the preparation establishments we are aware of tells their understudies—if the result is nonstop—to apply straight regression. On the off chance that it is binary—utilize strategic regression! Be that as it may, the higher the quantity of choices accessible available to us, the progressively troublesome it becomes to pick the correct one. A comparative case occurs with regression examples.

Inside various sorts of regression examples, it is critical to pick the most appropriate strategy dependent on kind of free and ward factors, dimensionality in the information, and other fundamental attributes of the information. The following are the key factors that you should practice to choose the correct regression example:

1. Information investigation is an inescapable piece of building a prescient example. It ought to be your initial step before choosing the correct example, like recognizing the relationship and effect of factors.
2. To think about the decency of fit for various examples, we can examine various measurements like factual essentialness of parameters, R-square, Adjusted r-square, AIC, BIC, and blunder term. Another is Mallow's Cp basis. This basically checks for conceivable predisposition in your example by contrasting the example and all conceivable sub-examples (or a cautious choice of them).
3. Cross-approval is the most ideal approach to assess examples utilized for the forecast. Here you isolate your informational index into two gatherings (prepare and approve). A basic mean squared distinction between the watched and anticipated qualities gives you a measure for the forecast exactness.
4. On the off chance that your informational index has numerous perplexing factors, you ought not to pick the programmed example determination technique since you would prefer not to put these in an example simultaneously.

5. It will likewise rely upon your goal. It can happen that a less ground-breaking example is anything but difficult to execute when contrasted with a profoundly factually huge example.
6. Regression regularization methods (LASSO, ridge, and ElasticNet) functions admirably in the event of high dimensionality and multicollinearity among the factors in the informational index.

Decision tree and random forest

Decision tree learning is one of the prescient displaying approaches utilized in insights, information mining, and AI. It utilizes a decision tree (as a prescient example) to go from perceptions about a thing (spoke to in the branches) to decisions about the thing's objective worth (spoke to in the leaves). Tree examples where the objective variable can take a discrete arrangement of qualities are called **classification trees**; in these tree structures, leaves speak to class marks, and branches speak to conjunctions of highlights that lead to those class names. Decision trees where the objective variable can take consistent qualities (regularly genuine numbers) are called **regression trees**.

In decision investigation, a decision tree can be utilized to outwardly and unequivocally speak to decisions and dynamics. In information mining, a decision tree depicts information (yet the subsequent classification tree can be a contribution for dynamic). The decision standards are, for the most part, in the type of on the off chance that else proclamations. The more profound the tree, the more mind-boggling the principles and fitter the example.

Before we jump profound, we should get acquainted with a portion of the wordings:

- **Instances**: Refer to the vector of highlights or qualities that characterize the info space.
- **Attribute**: An amount depicting a case.
- **Concept**: The capacity that maps contribution to yield.
- **Target concept**: The capacity that we are attempting to discover, i.e., the genuine answer.
- **Hypothesis class**: Set of all the potential capacities.
- **Sample**: A lot of information sources combined with a name, which is the right yield (otherwise called the **training set**).
- **Candidate concept**: An idea that we believe is the objective idea.
- **Testing set**: Similar to the preparation set and is utilized to test the up-and-comer idea and decide its exhibition.

Why decision trees?

- Decision trees frequently copy the human-level reasoning, so it is so easy to comprehend the information and make some great understandings.
- Decision trees really make you see the rationale for the information to interpret (not like discovery algorithms such as SVM, NN, and so on)

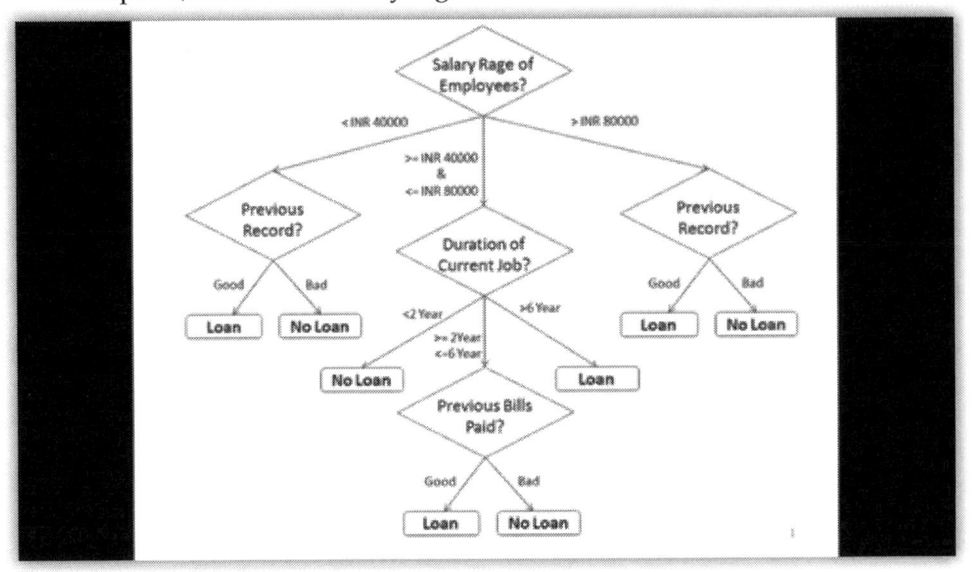

Figure 9.1: *Decision Tree*

For instance: on the off chance that we are classification bank advance application for a client, the decision tree may resemble this. Here, we can see the rationale of how it is settling on the decision.

Decision tree

A decision tree is a tree-like chart with hubs speaking to where we pick a property and pose an inquiry; edges speak to the appropriate responses to the inquiry, and the leaves speak to the real yield or class mark. They are utilized in non-linear dynamics with easy to understand direct decision surface. Decision trees group the examples by arranging them down the tree from the root to some leaf hub, with the leaf hub giving the arrangement to the example. Every hub in the tree goes about as an experiment for some trait, and each edge dropping from that hub compared to one of the potential responses to the experiment. This procedure is recursive in nature and is rehashed for each subtree established at the new hubs.

We should delineate this with the assistance of an example. How about we expect we need to play Badminton on a specific day—state Saturday—in what manner will you conclude whether to play or not. Suppose you go out and check if it is blistering or cold, check the speed of the breeze and moistness, how the climate is, for example, is it radiant, overcast, or blustery. You consider every one of these components to choose if you need to play or not.

In this way, you figure every one of these components throughout the previous ten days and structure a query table like the one beneath.

Day	Weather	Temperature	Humidity	Wind	Play?
1	Sunny	Hot	High	Weak	No
2	Cloudy	Hot	High	Weak	Yes
3	Sunny	Mild	Normal	Strong	Yes
4	Cloudy	Mild	High	Strong	Yes
5	Rainy	Mild	High	Strong	No
6	Rainy	Cool	Normal	Strong	No
7	Rainy	Mild	High	Weak	Yes
8	Sunny	Hot	High	Strong	No
9	Cloudy	Hot	Normal	Weak	Yes
10	Rainy	Mild	High	Strong	No

Table 9.1: *Observations of the last ten days*

Presently, you may utilize this table to conclude whether to play or not. Be that as it may, imagine a scenario in which the climate design on Saturday does not coordinate with any of the lines in the table. This might be an issue. A decision tree would be an incredible method to speak to information like this since it considers all the potential ways that can prompt an ultimate conclusion by following a tree-like structure.

Figure 9.1 delineates an educated decision tree. We can see that every hub speaks to a trait or highlight, and the branch from every hub speaks to the result of that hub. At long last, it is the leaves of the tree where the ultimate decision is made. On the off chance that highlights are nonstop, inside hubs can test the estimation of an element

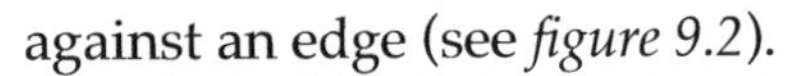
against an edge (see *figure 9.2*).

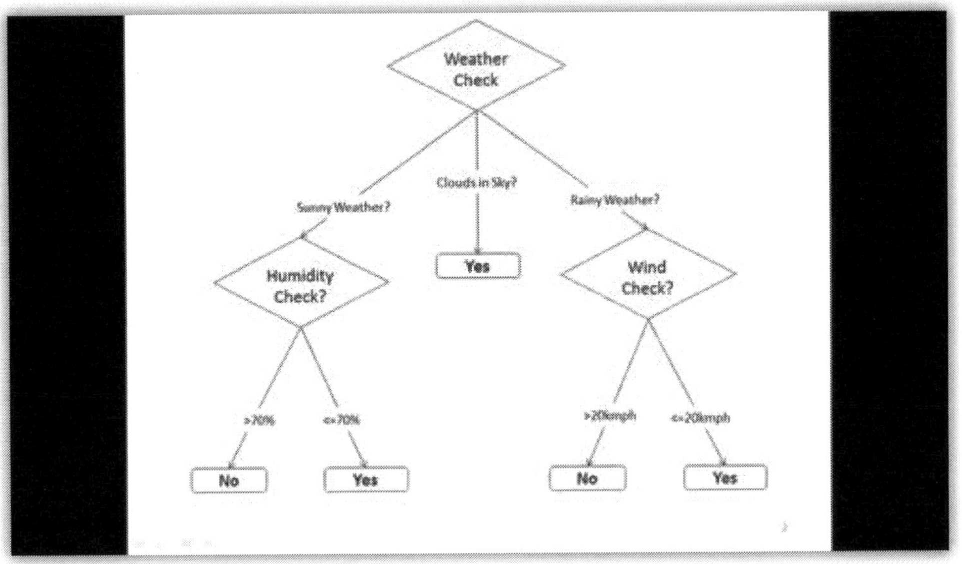

Figure 9.2: *A decision tree for the idea Play Badminton (when qualities are constant)*

A general algorithm for a decision tree can be depicted as follows:

1. Pick the best quality/highlight. The best characteristic is one that best parts or isolates the information.
2. Pose the significant inquiry.
3. Follow the appropriate response way.
4. Go to stage 1 until you show up to the appropriate response.
5. The best split is one that isolates two unique marks into two sets.

The expressiveness of decision trees

Decision trees can speak to any Boolean capacity of the info properties. We should utilize decision trees to play out the capacity of three Boolean doors AND, OR, and XOR.

Boolean function: AND

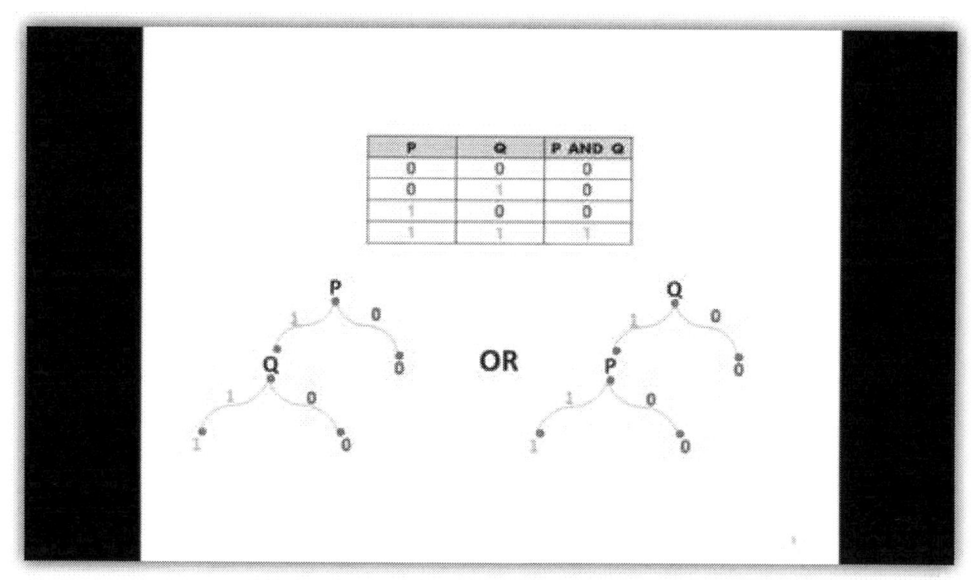

P	Q	P AND Q
0	0	0
0	1	0
1	0	0
1	1	1

Figure 9.3: *Decision tree for an AND activity*

In *figure 9.3*, we can see that there are two competitor ideas for creating the decision tree that plays out the AND activity. Correspondingly, we can likewise deliver a decision tree that plays out the Boolean OR activity.

Boolean function: OR

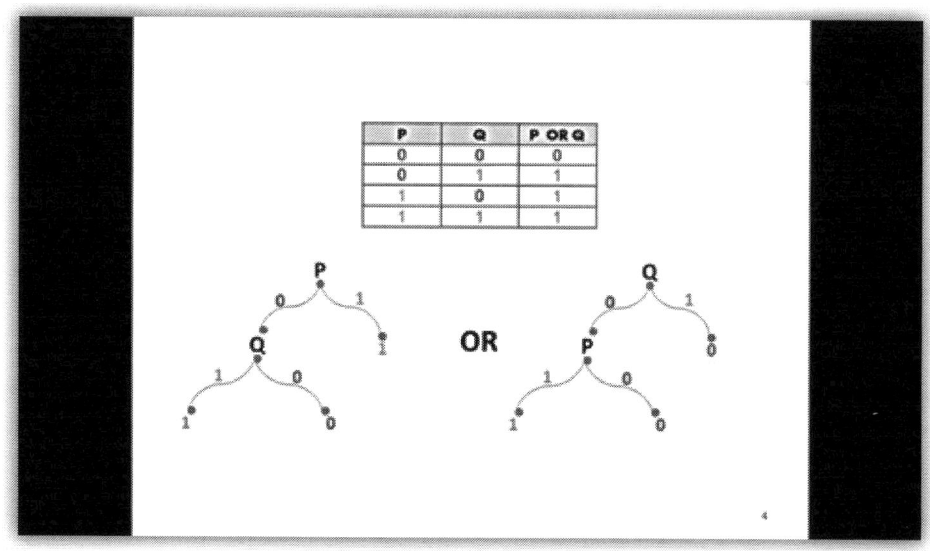

P	Q	P OR Q
0	0	0
0	1	1
1	0	1
1	1	1

Figure 9.4: *Decision tree for an OR activity*

Also, Boolean XOR activity:

Boolean function: XOR

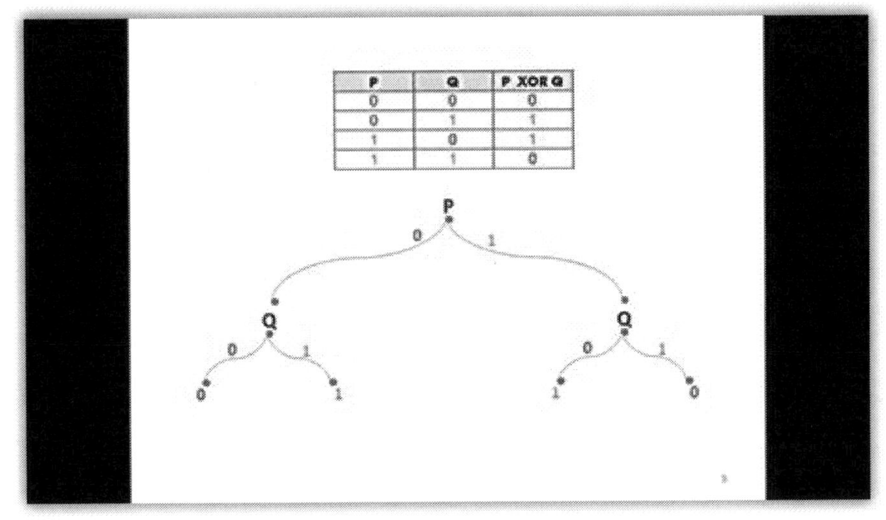

P	Q	P XOR Q
0	0	0
0	1	1
1	0	1
1	1	0

Figure 9.5: Decision tree for an XOR activity

How about we produce a decision tree performing XOR usefulness using three properties:

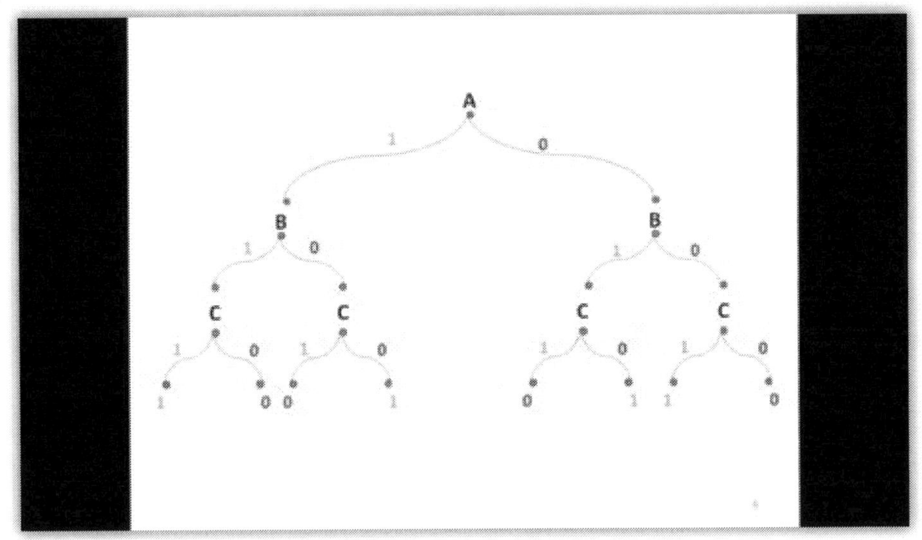

Figure 9.6: Decision tree for an XOR activity including three operands

In the decision tree, appeared in *figure 9.6*, for three characteristics, there are seven hubs in the tree, i.e., for $n = 3$, the *number of hubs* = 2^3-1. Essentially, in the event that we have n properties, there are 2^n hubs (approx.) in the decision tree. In this way, the tree requires an exponential number of hubs in the most pessimistic scenario. We can speak to Boolean activities utilizing decision trees. Be that as it may, what other sort of capacities would we be able to speak to, and in the event that we search over the different conceivable decision trees to locate the correct one, what number of decision trees do we need to stress over. We should respond to this inquiry by discovering the conceivable number of decision trees we can create given *N* various qualities (expecting the properties are Boolean). Since a fact table can be changed into a decision tree, we will shape a reality table of *N* traits as information.

X1	X2	X3	....	XN	OUTPUT
T	T	T	...	T	
T	T	T	...	F	
...	...	...	...	...	
...	...	...	...	...	
...	...	...	...	...	
F	F	F	...	F	

The above truth table has 2^n columns (for example, the quantity of hubs in the decision tree), which speaks to the potential blends of the information characteristics, and since every hub can hold a twofold worth, the quantity of approaches to fill the qualities in the decision tree is ${2^{2^n}}$. Hence, the space of decision trees, i.e., the speculation space of the decision tree, is expressive on the grounds that there are a variety of capacities it can speak to. Be that as it may, it likewise implies one needs to have a cunning method to look through the best tree among them.

Decision tree boundary

Decision trees partition the element space into pivot equal square shapes or hyper-planes. We should show this with the assistance of an example. We should think about a basic AND procedure on two factors (see *figure 9.3.*). Expect *X* and *Y* to be the directions on the *x* and *y* tomahawks, separately, and plot the potential estimations of *X* and *Y* (as observed in the table underneath). *Figure 9.7* speaks to the arrangement of the decision limit as every decision is taken. We can consider that to be every decision is made, the component space gets isolated into littler square shapes, and more information focuses get effectively classified.

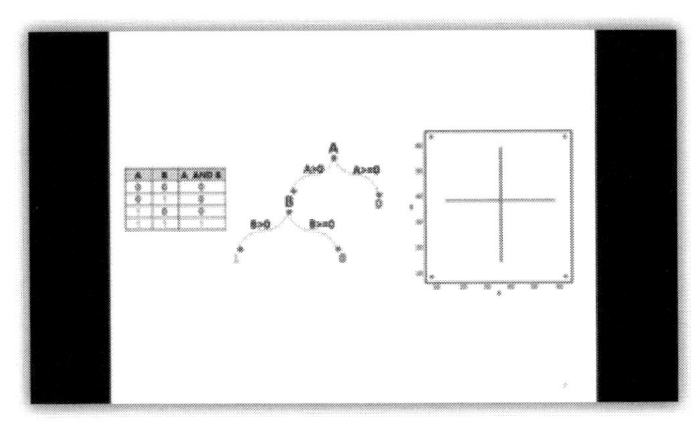

Figure 9.7: Activity indicating the arrangement of the decision tree limit for AND activity

The decision tree learning algorithm—the fundamental algorithm used in decision trees is known as the **ID3** (by *Quinlan*) algorithm. The ID3 algorithm manufactures decision trees using a top-down, avaricious methodology. Quickly, the means to the algorithm are: – Select the best property → A – Assign An as the decision quality (experiment) for the NODE. – For each estimation of A, make another relative of the NODE. – Sort the preparation guides to the fitting relative hub leaf. – If examples are impeccably classified, at that point, STOP else repeat over the new leaf hubs. Presently, the following central issue is the manner by which to pick the best trait. For ID3, we think about the best quality as far as which property has the most data increase, a measure that communicates how well a trait parts that information into bunches dependent on characterization.

1. **Pseudocode**: ID3 is an eager algorithm that develops the tree top-down, at every hub choosing the quality that best groups the nearby preparing examples. This procedure proceeds until the tree superbly arranges the preparation examples or until the sum total of what traits have been utilized. The pseudocode accepts that the characteristics are discrete and that the classification is double. Examples are the preparation example. Target_attribute is the credit whose worth is to be anticipated by the tree. Properties is a rundown of different traits that might be tried by the scholarly decision tree. At long last, it restores a decision tree that effectively arranges the given examples.

   ID3 (examples, Target_attribute, attributes): create a root hub for the tree. – If all examples are certain, arrival the single-hub tree root, with positive names. – If all examples are negative, return the single-hub tree root with negative marks. – If Attributes is unfilled, return the single-hub tree root, with the most well-known names of the Target_attribute in Examples. – Otherwise, start – A ← the quality from Attributes that best* characterizes Examples –

The decision property for pull ← A – For every conceivable worth v_i, of A, – Add another tree limb beneath root, relating to the test A = v_i – Let Examples_vi be the subset of Examples that have esteem v_i for A. – If Examples_vi is vacant –

2. **Calculating data gain**: As expressed before, data gain is a factual property that estimates how well a given characteristic isolates the preparation examples as per their objective classification. In the figure underneath, we can see that a trait with uninformed addition (right) parts the information moderately uniformly and accordingly does not present to us anymore like a decision. Though, a characteristic with high data increase (left) parts the information into bunches with a lopsided number of positives and negatives and accordingly helps in isolating the two from each other.

Issues in decision trees

Abstaining from overfitting

Since the ID3 algorithm keeps parting on qualities until it is possible that it arranges all the information focuses or there are no more ascribes to parts on. Therefore, it is inclined to make decision trees that over-fit by performing truly well on the preparation information to the detriment of precision as for the whole conveyance of information.

There are, as a rule, two ways to deal with keeping away from this in decision trees:

- Allow the tree to develop until it over-fits and afterward prunes it.
- Prevent the tree from becoming excessively profound by halting it before it consummately characterizes the preparation information.

  A decision tree's development is indicated regarding the quantity of layers or profundity it is permitted to have. The information accessible to prepare the decision tree is part of preparing and testing information, and afterward, trees of different sizes are made with the assistance of the preparation information and tried on the test information. Cross-approval can likewise be utilized as a component of this methodology. Pruning the tree, then again, includes testing the first tree against pruned variants of it. Leaf hubs are expelled from the tree as long as the pruned tree performs preferred on the test information over the bigger tree.

Incorporating continuous-valued attributes

Our underlying meaning of ID3 is confined to traits that take on a discrete arrangement of qualities. One approach to make the ID3 algorithm progressively helpful with consistent factors is to turn them, as it were, into discrete factors. Suppose in our case of Play Badminton the temperature is consistent (see the accompanying table); we could test the data increase of specific parcels of the temperature esteems, for example, temperature > 42.5. Commonly, at whatever point the characterization changes from no to yes or yes to no, the normal of the two temperatures is taken as a potential parcel limit.

Day	Weather	Temperature	Humidity	Wind	Play?
1	Sunny	80	High	Weak	No
2	Cloudy	66	High	Weak	Yes
3	Sunny	43	Normal	Strong	Yes
4	Cloudy	82	High	Strong	Yes
5	Rainy	65	High	Strong	No
6	Rainy	42	Normal	Strong	No
7	Rainy	70	High	Weak	Yes
8	Sunny	81	High	Strong	No
9	Cloudy	69	Normal	Weak	Yes
10	Rainy	67	High	Strong	No

Table 9.2: *Observations of the last ten days.*

Since 42 relates to No and 43 compares to Yes, 42.5 turns into an applicant. On the off chance that any of the segments wind up showing the best data increase, at that point, it is utilized as a quality, and temperature is expelled from the arrangement of potential ascribes to part on.

Elective measures for choosing attributes

The data gain equation utilized by the ID3 algorithm treats the entirety of the factors as the equivalent, paying little heed to their dissemination and their significance. This is an issue with regards to nonstop factors or discrete factors with numerous potential qualities since preparing examples might be rare for every conceivable worth, which prompts low entropy and high data gain by the excellence of parting the information into little subsets; however, it brings about a decision tree that probably will not sum up well. One approach to keep away from this is to utilize some other measure to locate the best trait rather than data gain.

Advantages and disadvantages

Following are the benefits of decision trees:

- Easy to utilize and comprehend.
- Can deal with both all out and numerical information.
- Resistant to exceptions, consequently require little information preprocessing.
- New highlights can be effortlessly included.
- Can be utilized to manufacture bigger classifiers by using troupe techniques.

Following are the disadvantages of decision trees:

- Prone to over-fitting.
- Require an estimation concerning how well they are getting along.
- Need to be cautious with parameter tuning.
- Can make one-sided learned trees if a few classes rule.

Forest tree

The random forest classifier: Random forest, similar to its name suggests, comprising an enormous number of individual decision trees that work as a group. Every individual tree in the random forest lets out a class forecast, and the class with the most votes turns into our example's expectation (see *figure 9.9*).

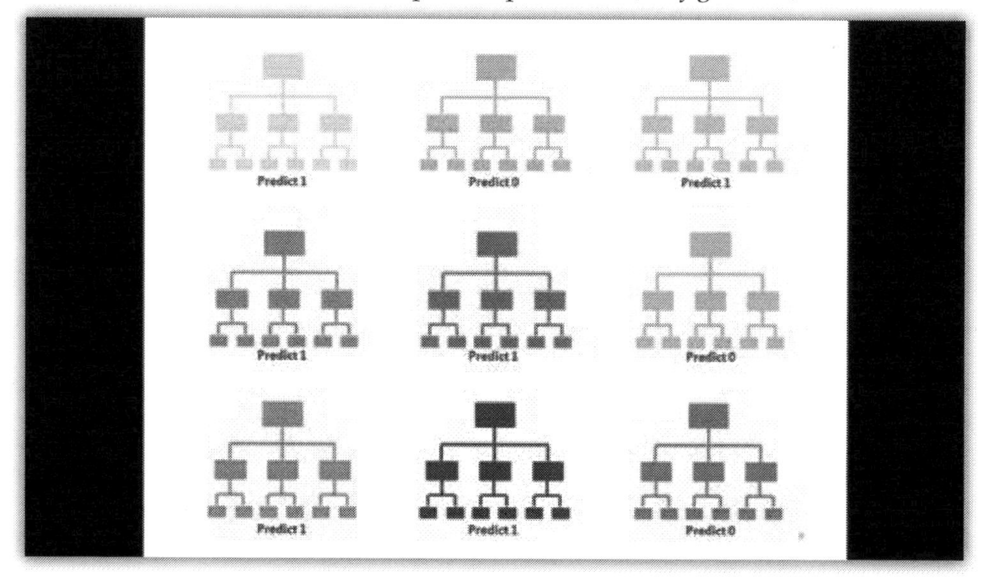

Figure 9.8: *Perception of a Random Forest Example Making a Prediction*

The essential idea driving random forest is easy to understand yet amazing one—the intelligence of groups. In information science talk, the explanation that the random forest example works so well is: countless generally uncorrelated examples (trees) working as an advisory group will outflank any of the individual constituent examples.

The low connection between examples is the key. Much the same as how ventures with low relationships (like stocks and securities) meet up to shape a portfolio that is more noteworthy than the entirety of its parts, uncorrelated examples can deliver outfit forecasts that are more precise than any of the individual expectations. The explanation behind this brilliant impact is that the trees shield each other from their individual blunders (as long as they do not continue, all fail a similar way). Although a few trees might not be right, numerous different trees will be correct, so as a gathering, the trees can move in the right course.

Random forest algorithm: In the first place, a random forest algorithm is a directed classification algorithm. We can see it from its name, which is to make a forest in some way and make it random. There is an immediate connection between the quantity of trees in the forest and the outcomes it can get: the bigger the quantity of trees, the more exact the outcome. In any case, one thing to note is that making the forest is not equivalent to building the decision with data increase or addition list approach. The creator gives four connects to help individuals who are working with decision trees just because to learn it and comprehend well. On the off chance that you input a preparation dataset with targets and highlights into the decision tree, it will figure some arrangement of rules. These guidelines can be utilized to perform forecasts. The creator uses one guide to outline this point: assume you need to foresee whether your little girl will like an energized film, you should gather the past enlivened motion pictures she prefers and accept a few highlights as the info. At that point, through the decision tree algorithm, you can produce the principles. You would then be able to enter the highlights of this film and see whether it will be loved by your little girl. The way toward ascertaining these hubs and shaping the standards is utilizing data increase and Gini record counts.

The contrast between the random forest algorithm and the decision tree algorithm is that in a random forest, the procedure of finding the root hub and parting the element hubs will run arbitrarily.

Why random forest algorithm?

The creator gives four preferences to outline why we utilize random forest algorithm.

- The one referenced over and again by the creator is that it tends to be utilized for both characterization and regression errands.

- Over-fitting is one basic issue that may exacerbate the outcomes, yet for random forest algorithms, if there are sufficient trees in the forest, the classifier will not overfit the example.
- The third preferred position is the classifier of random forest can deal with missing qualities, and the last bit of leeway is that the random forest classifier can be demonstrated for all-out qualities.

Random forest algorithm

In this area, the creator gives us a genuine guide to make the random forest algorithm easy to understand. Assume John needs to go to better places that he may like for his 14 day get-away, and he approaches his companion for exhortation. His companion will ask where he has been to as of now and whether he prefers the spots that he is visited. In view of John's answers, his companion begins to give the proposal. Here, his companion frames the decision tree.

John needs to approach more companions for guidance since he figures just a single companion cannot assist him with settling on an exact decision. So his different companions likewise pose him irregular inquiries, finally, gives an answer. He thinks about the spot with the most votes as his get-away decision. Here, the creator gives an examination of this example.

His one companion posed him a few inquiries and gave the proposal of the best spot dependent on the appropriate responses. This is a run-of-the-mill decision tree algorithm approach. The companion made the standards dependent on the appropriate responses and utilized the guidelines to discover the appropriate response that coordinated the principles.

John's companions additionally haphazardly asked him various inquiries and offered responses, which for John are the decisions in favor of the spot. Toward the end, the spot with the most elevated votes is the one John will choose to go to. This is the common random forest algorithm approach.

How does random forest algorithm function?

There are two phases in random forest algorithm; one is irregular forest creation, the other is to make a forecast from the random forest classifier made in the primary stage. The entire procedure is demonstrated as follows, and it is easy to understand utilizing the figure.

Here the creator initially shows the random forest creation pseudocode:

- Randomly select "K" highlights from absolute "m" highlights where $k << m$.

- Among the "K" highlights, Figure the hub "d" utilizing the best part point.
- Split the hub into little girl hubs utilizing the best split.
- Repeat the a to c ventures until "l" number of hubs has been reached.
- Build forest by rehashing stages a to d for "*n*" number occasions to make "*n*" number of trees.

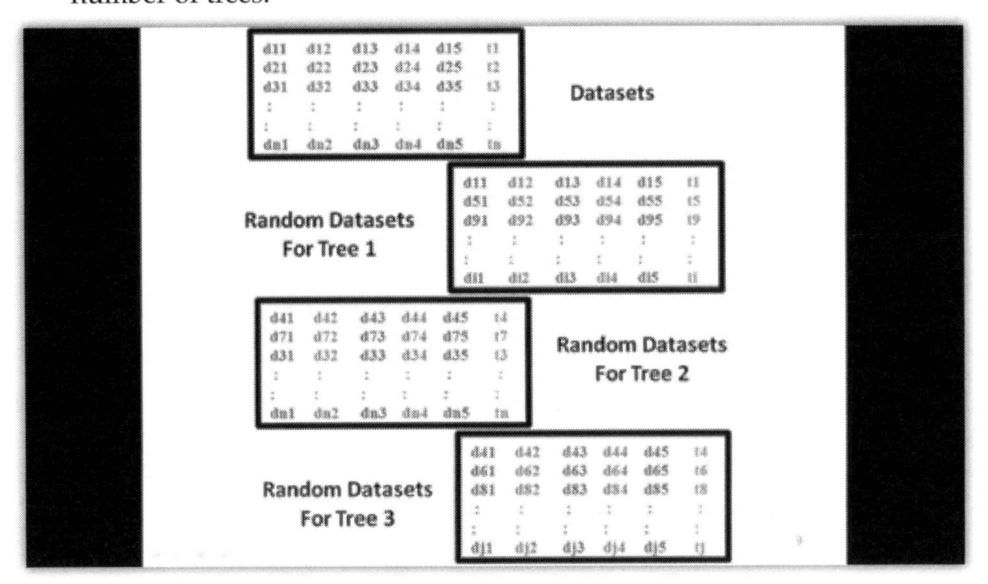

Figure 9.9: Random forest algorithm functions

In the following stage, with the random forest classifier made, we will make the forecast. The irregular forest expectation pseudocode is demonstrated as follows:

- Takes the test highlights and utilizes the principles of each haphazardly made decision tree to foresee the result and stores the anticipated result (target).
- Calculate the decisions in favor of each anticipated objective.
- Consider the high casted a ballot anticipated objective as the last expectation from the irregular forest algorithm.

The procedure is easy to understand; however, it is, in one way or another, productive.

Figure 9.10: Random forest algorithm

In this topic, the explanation of four uses of utilizing random forest algorithm is given: banking, medicine, stock market, and e-trade:

- Banking, random forest algorithm is utilized to discover faithful clients, which implies clients who can take out a lot of credits and pay enthusiasm to the bank appropriately, and extortion clients, which implies clients who have awful records like inability to take care of an advance on schedule or have perilous activities.
- Medication, random forest algorithm can be utilized to both distinguish the right blend of parts in medication and to recognize maladies by breaking down the patient's clinical records.
- Securities exchange, random forest algorithm can be utilized to distinguish a stock's conduct and the normal misfortune or benefit.
- Internet business, random forest algorithm can be utilized for anticipating whether the client will like the suggested items in light of the experience of comparable clients.

Advantages of random forest algorithm

Contrasted and other classification procedures, there are three favorable circumstances as the creator referenced.

- For applications in classification issues, a random forest algorithm will maintain a strategic distance from the overfitting issue.
- For both classification and regression tasks, a similar random forest algorithm can be utilized.
- The random forest algorithm can be utilized for distinguishing the most significant highlights from the preparation dataset, as such, including building.

Disadvantages of the random forest:

- Not effectively interpretable.
- Random forest over-fit with loud classification or regression.
- It can be utilized for both decision and random trees, some of the time indistinct.

Examination between decision tree and random tree

When using a decision tree example on a given preparing dataset, the exactness continues improving with an ever-increasing number of parts. You can, without much of a stretch, overfit the information and does not have the foggiest idea when you have gone too far except if you are utilizing cross approval (on preparing informational index). The upside of a basic decision tree is example is anything but difficult to decipher; you recognize what variable and what estimation of that variable is utilized to part the information and foresee the result.

A random forest resembles a black box and fills in as referenced in the above answer. It is a forest you can construct and control. You can indicate the quantity of trees you need in your forest(n_estimators), and furthermore, you can determine max number of highlights to be utilized in each tree. Be that as it may, you cannot control the randomity, you cannot control which highlight is a piece of which tree in the forest, you cannot control which information point is a piece of which tree. Exactness continues expanding as you increment the quantity of trees yet gets consistent at a certain point. Not at all like the decision tree; it will not make an exceptionally one-sided example and decreases the difference.

When to use to decision tree:

1. At the point when you need your example to be basic and logical.
2. At the point when you need non-parametric example.

3. At the point when you would prefer not to stress over the component decision or regularization or stress over multicollinearity.
4,. You can overfit the tree and assemble an example in the event that you make certain of approval or test informational collection will be a subset of preparing informational index or nearly covering rather than sudden.

When to use random forest:

1. At the point when you do not trouble much about deciphering the example yet need better exactness.
2. Random forest will diminish change some portion of blunder as opposed to inclination part, so on a given preparing informational collection decision tree might be more precise than a random forest. Be that as it may, on a surprising approval informational index, random forest consistently wins as far as precision.

Unsupervised learning

In basic words, solo learning is the workmanship or procedure of having the PC figure out how to perform something that we have not been advised by us how to do..!! Unsupervised learning can be comprehended by two straightforward methodologies: to start with, where no instructing is included by the operator by giving a particular design, yet by demonstrating the accomplishment by offering not many advantages. By and large, this sort of approach is directed where dynamic foundation as the objective is to create expanded prizes and not to deliver portions. We can utilize this way to deal with sum up the genuine world, where the specialists can be rebuffed for fouling up acts and get prizes for playing out specific activities.

Why unsupervised learning?

- It gives understanding and happens in the ongoing just, where all the information can be investigated and set apart within sight of the students.
- This strategy encourages us to find new strategies which can be valuable for strategizing.
- This information is effectively accessible with no manual intercession than the marked information.
- Unsupervised AI will discover all the obscure examples of information.
- It encourages us to learn new techniques and plans.

Case of unsupervised learning: When a kid is conceived, he watches new things around him. A house where infant lives have a cat and is well disposed around it.

In this way, one day, a family companion carries his cat to their home, and the child knows it is a cat. As he has as of now taken in the portrayal of the cat (4 legs, 2 ears, a tail, 2 eyes, and so forth). The child was not acquainted with the cat saying, *"it's a cat"* which implies he has just been instructed with his experience. At the point when we have just the information (x) and no other comparing factors. The dispersion of the information so as to get familiar with the equivalent is the objective of utilizing this method.

Unsupervised machine learning + DataRobot

The *DataRobot* computerized AI stage requires a *"target"* section—that is, it has to realize the yield variable so as to reveal designs in your information. Notwithstanding, a large number of its model outlines use unsupervised Figuring out how to mechanize convoluted element designing strategies, which are troublesome and tedious to execute without robotization.

Presently, unsupervised learning algorithms can be arranged into the accompanying parts:

1. Clustering
2. Association

Clustering: *"Clustering"* is the way toward grouping comparable substances. Grouping of comparable information focuses and to discover its likenesses is the objective of learning solo learning technique.

Features of clustering

1. Grouping comparable substances.
2. Revealing of fundamental examples of various groupings.
3. Different choices of uses to be utilized for grouping the information.
4. Reduces dimensionality.
5. Identification of groupings in various manners.

Working of clustering algorithms

1. K-mean clustering
2. Hierarchical clustering

K-mean clustering: It is the most famous and the easiest technique for AI algorithms. It makes deductions from the datasets utilizing just information without alluding to known or named results. To accomplish the goal, K-implies searches for a fixed number (k) in the dataset.

Working of K-implies algorithm—To process the information learning, the K-implies algorithms begin burrowing the information with the first grouping of arbitrarily chosen centroids. They will be utilized as the beginning stages in each group and afterward will perform dull computations to advance the centroids position.

It can stop the making in two cases:

- At the point when the centroids have balances out and we see no adjustment in its qualities on the grounds that the grouping is fruitful.
- The necessary number of redundancies have been accomplished.

"How do we calculate the similarity between two clusters?"

Figuring the closeness between two groups is critical to the consolidation or separation of the bunches. There are sure methodologies that are utilized to figure the comparability between two bunches:

- MIN
- MAX
- Group average
- Distance between centroids
- Ward's method

Limitations of hierarchical clustering technique

- *There is no numerical target for hierarchical grouping.
- All the ways to deal with computing the likeness between groups have their own drawbacks.
- High reality unpredictability for hierarchical grouping. Consequently, this clustering algorithm cannot be utilized when we have gigantic information.

Implementation of clustering

Clustering has a huge number of uses spread across different spaces. Probably the most well-known uses of grouping are:

- Recommendation motors
- Market division
- Social system investigation
- Search result grouping
- Medical imaging
- Image division

- Anomaly discovery

Hierarchical clustering: Also called hierarchical cluster assessment or HCA, is a performance grouping estimation that incorporates making bunches that have pervasive mentioning from beginning to end. For example, all records and envelopes on our hard circle are made in a chain out of significance.

The algorithm groups similar things into clusters called **groupings**. The endpoint is a great deal of clusters or social occasions, where each grouping is indisputable from each other bundle, and the things inside each grouping are widely similar to each other.

This clustering framework is isolated into two sorts:

1. Agglomerative hierarchical clustering
2. Irksome hierarchical clustering

Agglomerative hierarchical clustering

The agglomerative hierarchical clustering is the most generally perceived sort of different leveled clustering used to store up figures in bunches reliant on their closeness. It is, in any case, called **agglomerative nesting (AGNES)**. It is a *"base up"* approach: each observation starts in its own grouping, and matches of bundles are united as one trips the chain of significance.

How might it work?

- Make each datum point a single point bunch → forms N clusters.
- Take the two closest data centers and make them one grouping → forms N-1 clusters.
- Take the two closest groupings and make them one bundle → Forms N-2 clusters.
- Repeat step-3 until you are left with only one pack.

Advantages

- No, *a priori* data about the quantity of bunches required.
- Easy to execute and gives the best outcome now and again.

Disadvantages

- The algorithm can never fix what was done beforehand.
- Time multifaceted nature of in any event *O(n2 log n)* is required, where *"n"* is the quantity of information focuses.

- Based on the kind of separation grid picked for blending, various algorithms can endure with at least one of the accompanying:
  - Sensitivity to commotion and anomalies
    - Breaking huge bunches
    - Difficulty taking care of various measured bunches and arched shapes
  - No target work is straightforwardly limited
- Sometimes it is hard to distinguish the right number of bunches by the dendrogram.

A dendrogram is a tree-like outline that records the arrangements of unions or parts.

Divisive hierarchical clustering technique: since the divisive hierarchical grouping technique is not tremendously utilized in reality, we will give a brief of the divisive hierarchical clustering technique. In straightforward words, we can say that divisive hierarchical clustering is actually something contrary to agglomerative hierarchical grouping. In divisive hierarchical clustering, we consider all the information focuses as a solitary group, and in every emphasis, we separate the information focuses from the group, which is not comparative. Every datum point which is isolated is considered as an individual bunch. At long last, we will be left with n bunches.

As we are isolating the single groups into n bunches; it is named a divisive hierarchical grouping. In this way, we have talked about the two sorts of hierarchical grouping technique.

Two significant things that you should think about various leveled clustering are: This algorithm has been executed above utilizing base up approach. It is likewise conceivable to follow top-down methodology beginning with all information focuses relegated in a similar group and recursively performing parts till every datum point is appointed a different bunch. The choice of blending two groups is assumed the premise of closeness of these bunches.

Association unsupervised learning

Now we will see how the association rule works in unsupervised learning:

- **Introduction to association rules**

  Association rule is unsupervised realizing where algorithm attempts to learn without an educator as information are not marked. Association rule is enlightening, not the prescient strategy, for the most part used to find fascinating relationships covered up in huge datasets. The relationship is generally spoken to in the type of rules or incessant item sets.

Association rules mining is utilized to recognize new and fascinating bits of knowledge between various items with regards to a set, visit the design in value-based information or any kind of social database. They are generally utilized for market basket analysis (which things are purchased together), customer grouping in Retail (Which stores individuals will in general visit together), price clustering, assortment decisions, cross-selling, and others. This can be viewed as a cutting edge type of imagining a scenario where the situation, on the off chance that this, at that point that.

How does association learning work?

Association rule algorithms check the recurrence of complimentary events, or relationships, over a huge assortment of things or activities. The objective is to discover associations that happen together unmistakably more frequently than you would discover in arbitrary inspecting of conceivable outcomes. This standard-based methodology is a quick and incredible asset for mining sorted, non-numeric databases.

How association rule works

There are scarcely any key terms that we should be acquainted with to see how the association rules work.

1. **Apriori**: One of the first and most seasoned algorithms utilized for building association rules.
2. **Itemsets**: It alludes to the assortment of things. *N* thing set methods set of *n* things. Essentially, it is the arrangement of things bought by clients.
3. **Backing**: It is the level of time *X*, and *Y* happen together out of all exchanges.
4. **Certainty**: It is characterized as the proportion of conviction related to each found standard. It is the percentage of exchanges that contains both *X* and *Y* out of all exchanges that contains *X*.
5. **Lift**: It is the proportion of how *X* and *Y* are connected instead of fortuitously happening together. It gauges how frequently more regularly *X* and *Y* happen together at that point, expected in the event that they are measurably autonomous to one another. This measure will be our primary center while assessing the algorithm results. Visit item sets generation: Find the most regular itemsets from the information dependent on foreordained help and least thing and greatest thing.
    - **Real-world problem**: In this, we will utilize a shopping center dataset with the objective of finding distinctive, fascinating shopping conduct

and understanding relationships between various stores. A portion of the inquiries we are discussing to answer is, which group of stores individuals will in general visit together, which stores individuals, for the most part, follow going to store on or before going to store on or close by store A.

- **Understanding different scenarios**: So far, we have found out about guidelines and general examples. Be that as it may, imagine a scenario in which we need to burrow scoop about a specific store. This kind of investigation will be especially useful for senior supervisors to comprehend where individuals visit previously or subsequent to visiting their stores.

Conclusion

It is constantly imperative to utilize the business information and setting while at the same time deciphering association administers as they can be impacted by bewildering factors, i.e., shrouded variable excluded from an investigation, which on occasion can make watched relationship vanish or turn around, regularly known as *Simpson's Paradox*. In the next chapter, we will focus on the advanced concept of machine learning, i.e., predictive learning, deep learning, and so on.

Practical uses of association learning

- **Basket information examination**: Whether arranging item arrangements in a retail facade, running an advertising effort, or structuring a business index, association mining is a valuable instrument to remove the mystery from what your clients are searching for.
- **Web use mining and interruption location**: Finding these concealed connections is a ground-breaking prescient instrument to find fresh out of the box new security dangers and system execution gives that have not been dissected first by a human.

CHAPTER 10
Advanced Concepts to Machine Learning: Making Machine to Run the Show

In the previous chapters, we have seen that machine learning is the science of getting computers to learn/train and act like humans do and improve their learning over time in an autonomous fashion by feeding them data as input and information in the form of observations and real-world interactions. The basic premise of machine learning is to build algorithms that can receive input data and use statistical analysis to predict an output while updating outputs as new data becomes available.

AI and **machine learning (ML)**—which include technologies such as deep learning, neural networks, and natural-language processing—can also encompass more advanced systems which understand, learn, predict, adapt, and potentially operate autonomously.

In advanced concepts in machine learning, a selected number of recent developments in the field are presented and experimented with. Machine learning deals with the prediction of labels or real values for unseen objects based on a set of previously encountered examples or automatically adapting behavior according to previous experience.

Structure

This chapter will highlight the following topics:

1. Predictive learning
2. Deep learning
3. Neural networks
4. Natural language programming

Objectives

Besides an overview of recent machine learning techniques, the course also highlights the importance of representations in successful applications of machine learning. In this context, propositional representations are contrasted with multi-instance and relational representations, but also automatically generated representations through sparse coding, auto encoders, deep belief nets, and indirect representations such as distances and kernel receive substantial attention. After completion of this course, the students are able to select the most suited representations and best-fits of learning techniques for a given machine learning problem and reason about the limitations of the suggested selections.

Predictive learning—predictive analytic and machine learning

For some associations, enormous information—unfathomable volumes of crude organized, semi-organized and unstructured information—is an undiscovered asset of insight that can bolster business choices and improve tasks. As information keeps on expanding and changing, an ever-increasing number of associations are grasping predictive analytics to take advantage of that asset and advantage from information at scale. Consistently, we rely upon numerous frameworks and machines. We utilize a vehicle to travel, a lift goes here and there, and a plane to fly. Power comes through turbines, and in a medical clinic, the machine keeps us alive. These frameworks can fall flat. A few disappointments are only a burden, whereas others could mean desperate.

At the point when a lot is on the line, we perform customary support on our frameworks. For instance, vehicles are overhauled once like clockwork, and machine learning planes are adjusted day by day. In any case, as we will talk about in machine learning later in this article, these methodologies bring about asset wastage.

What is predictive learning?

A typical misinterpretation is that predictive learning and machine learning are something very similar. This is not the situation. At its center, predictive analytics envelops an assortment of factual methods (counting machine learning, predictive displaying, and information mining) and uses insights (both chronicled and current) to assess, or "anticipate", future results. These results may be practices a client is probably going to show or potential changes in the market, for instance.

Predictive analytics helps us to comprehend conceivable future events by examining the past. Machine learning, then machine learning, is a subfield of software engineering that, according to *Arthur Samuel's* definition from 1959, gives "PCs the capacity to learn without being unequivocally customized." Machine learning developed from the analytics of example acknowledgment and investigated the thought that calculations can machine learning from and make forecasts on the information. Also, as they become increasingly "insightful", these calculations can beat program guidelines to make exceptionally exact, information-driven choices.

Predictive support predicts disappointment, and the activities could incorporate remedial activities, the substitution of the framework, or even arranged disappointment. This can prompt significant cost reserve funds, higher consistency, and the expanded accessibility of the frameworks.

Predictive support investment funds come in two structures:

- Avoid or limit personal times. This will avoid a strategic distance from a miserable client, set aside cash, and once in a while spare life.
- Optimize the intermittent upkeep activities.

To comprehend the elements, we should consider a taxi organization. On the off chance that a taxi separates, the organization needs to appease a miserable client, send a substitution, and both the taxi and driver will be out of service while in a fix. The expense of disappointment is a lot higher than its clear expense.

One approach to manage this issue is to be negative and supplant error-prone parts a long time before disappointments. For instance, normal support tasks, like changing motor oil or supplanting tires, handle this. Albeit standard upkeep is superior to disappointments, we will wind up doing the support before it is required. Henceforth, it is anything but an ideal arrangement. For instance, replacing the oil of a vehicle for every 3,000 miles probably will not use oil successfully. On the off chance that we can foresee disappointments better, the taxi can go scarcely any hundred miles without supplanting oil.

Predictive support keeps away from both the boundaries and boosts the utilization of its assets. Predictive support will recognize the oddities and disappointment designs and give early admonitions. These alerts can empower proficient support of those parts.

Why predictive analytics matters—ascent of big data

Predictive analytics is frequently talked about with regards to large information, engineering information, for instance, originates from sensors, instruments, and associated frameworks out on the planet. Business framework information at an organization may incorporate exchange information, deals results, client grievances, and showcasing data. Progressively, organizations settle on information-driven choices dependent on this important trove of data.

Expanding competition

With expanded rivalry, organizations look for an edge in carrying items and administrations to swarmed markets. Information-driven predictive models can assist organizations with taking care of long-standing issues in new manners. Gear makers, for instance, can think that it is difficult to enhance equipment alone. Item designers can add predictive capacities to existing answers for increment incentive to the client. Utilizing predictive learning for gear upkeep or predictive support can foresee hardware disappointments, estimate vitality needs, and lessen working expenses. For instance, sensors that measure vibrations in car parts can flag the requirement for support before the vehicle flops out and about. Organizations likewise utilize predictive analytics to make increasingly exact estimates, for example, gauging the interest for power on the electrical matrix. These estimates empower asset-making arrangements to be accomplished all the more successfully.

Cutting edge technologies for big data and machine learning

To separate an incentive from enormous information, organizations apply calculations to huge informational collections utilizing devices, for example, *Hadoop* and *Spark*. The information sources may comprise value-based databases, hardware log records, pictures, video, sound, sensor, or different kinds of information. Advancement frequently originates from joining information from a few sources. With this information, instruments are important to remove bits of knowledge and patterns. Machine learning methods are utilized to discover designs in information and to manufacture models that foresee future results. An assortment of machine learning calculations are accessible, including machine learning and nonlinear relapse, neural systems, bolster vector machines, choice trees, and different calculations.

Predictive analytics examples

Predictive learning helps groups in enterprises as assorted as a fund, social insurance, pharmaceuticals, car, aviation, and assembling.

- Automotive—breaking new ground with independent vehicles.
- Companies creating driver help innovation and new independent vehicles utilize predictive analytics to examine sensor information from associated vehicles and to manufacture driver help calculations.
- Aerospace—monitoring aircraft engine health.
- To improve the machine learning plane up-time and lessen support costs, a motor maker made a continuous examination application to foresee subsystem execution for oil, fuel, liftoff, mechanical well-being, and controls.
- Energy production—forecasting power cost and request.
- Sophisticated anticipating applications use models that screen plant accessibility, authentic patterns, irregularity, and climate.
- Financial services—developing credit hazard models.
- Financial establishments use machine learning methods and quantitative instruments to anticipate credit chance.
- Industrial automation and machinery—predicting machine disappointments.
- A plastic and flimsy film maker spares 50,000 Euros month to month utilizing well-being checking and predictive support application that decreases vacation and limits squander.
- Medical devices—using design identification calculations to spot asthma and COPD.
- Asthma the board gadget records and investigates patients' breathing sounds and gives moment criticism through a PDA application to assist patients with overseeing asthma and COPD.

How predictive analytics works

Predictive analytics is the way toward utilizing information examination to make expectations dependent on information. This procedure uses information alongside analytics, measurements, and machine learning strategies to make a predictive model for gauging future occasions.

The expression "*predictive learning*" portrays the utilization of measurable or machine learning to make a quantitative forecast about what is to come. Regularly, managed machine learnings are utilized to foresee a future worth (How long would this be able to machine run before requiring upkeep?) or to assess a likelihood (How likely is this client to default on credit?).

Predictive learning begins with a business objective: to utilize information to decrease squander, spare time, or cut expenses. The procedure outfits heterogeneous, regularly gigantic, informational collections into models that can create clear, noteworthy results to help accomplish that objective, for example, less material waste, less supplied stock, and fabricated item that meets specifications.

Step by step workflow for predicting energy loads

Normally, the work process for a predictive learning application follows these fundamental advances:

- Import information from fluctuated sources, for example, web chronicles, databases, and spreadsheets.
- Data sources incorporate vitality load information in a CSV record and national climate information demonstrating temperature and dew point.
- Clean the information by expelling exceptions and consolidating information sources.
- Identify information spikes, missing information, or atypical focuses to expel from the information. At that point, total various information sources together—for this situation, making a solitary table including vitality burden, temperature, and dew point.
- Develop a precise predictive model dependent on the totaled information utilizing insights, bend fitting instruments or machine learning.
- Energy anticipating is a mind-boggling process with numerous factors, so you may decide to utilize neural systems to construct and machine learn a predictive model. Repeat through your preparation informational index to attempt various methodologies. At the point when the preparation is finished, you can attempt the model machine learning new information to perceive how well it performs.
- Integrate the model into a heap determining framework in a creation machine learning.
- Once you locate a model that precisely figures the heap, you can move it into your creation framework, making the analytics accessible to programming projects or gadgets, including web applications, servers, or cell phones.

Machine learning techniques for predictive maintenance

To do predictive support, first, we add sensors to the framework that will screen and gather information about its activities. Information for predictive upkeep is time arrangement information. Information incorporates a timestamp, a lot of sensor readings gathered simultaneously as timestamps, and gadget identifiers. The objective of predictive support is to anticipate at the time "t", utilizing the information up to that time, regardless of whether the hardware will flop sooner rather than later.

Predictive upkeep can be formulated in one of the two different ways:

- **Classification approach**: Predicts whether there is a chance of disappointment in the next n-steps.
- **Regression approach**: Predicts how much time is left before the following disappointment. We call this **remaining useful life (RUL)**.

The previous methodology just gives a Boolean answer yet can furnish more prominent exactness with less information. Last, it needs more information in spite of the fact that it gives more data about when the disappointment will occur. We will investigate both of these methodologies utilizing the NASA motor disappointment dataset. A key component we are missing is predictive (or unsupervised) learning: the capacity of a machine to demonstrate the earth, foresee potential fates and see how the world functions by watching it and acting in it.

This is a fascinating change and shows an inconspicuous change in his point of view concerning what he accepts is required to develop the "*cake.*" In LeCun's view, the establishment should be worked before we can machine learning ground in machine learning. As such, working off current directed learning by including more capacities such as memory, information bases, and collaborating operators will be a trudge until we are, for the most part, ready to fabricate that "*predictive fundamental layer*."

The most generally utilized predictive models are as follows:

- **Decision trees**: Decision trees are a basic, however incredible, type of different variable examination. They are delivered by calculations that distinguish different methods of parting information into branch-like sections. Choice trees parcel information into subsets dependent on classes of info factors, helping you to comprehend somebody's way of choices.
- **Regression**: Regression is one of the most well-known strategies in measurements. Relapse examination gauges connections among factors, discovering key examples in enormous and differing informational collections and how they identify with one another.
- **Neural systems**: Patterned after the activity of neurons in the human cerebrum, neural systems (additionally called counterfeit neural systems) are an assortment of profound learning innovations. They are regularly used to tackle complex example acknowledgment issues—and are inconceivably valuable for investigating huge informational indexes. They are incredible at dealing with nonlinear connections in information—and function admirably when factors are obscure.

Different classifiers:

- **Time series algorithms**: Time arrangement calculations successively plot information and are helpful for determining ceaseless qualities after some time.
- **Clustering algorithms**: Clustering calculations arrange information into bunches whose individuals are comparative.
- **Outlier detection algorithms**: Outlier recognition calculations center around abnormality identification, recognizing things, occasions, or perceptions that do not adjust to a normal example or standard inside an informational index.
- **Ensemble models**: Ensemble models utilize different machine learning calculations to acquire preferable predictive execution over what could be gotten from one calculation alone.
- **Factor analysis**: Factor examination is a technique used to depict inconstancy and means to discover autonomous dormant factors.
- **Naïve Bayes**: The naïve Bayes classifier permits us to foresee a class/classification dependent on a given arrangement of highlights, utilizing likelihood.
- **Support vector machines**: Support vector machines are regulated machine learning strategies that utilization related learning calculations to investigate information and perceive designs.

Every classifier approaches information in an alternate manner; in this manner, for associations to get the outcomes they need, they have to pick the correct classifiers and models.

Uses of predictive learning and machine learning

For associations flooding with information, however, battling to transform it into helpful bits of knowledge, predictive analytics and machine learning can give the arrangement. Regardless of how much information an association has, on the off chance that it cannot utilize that information to upgrade interior and outer procedures and meet targets, the information turns into a pointless asset.

This idea applies complex procedures of old-style insights, similar to relapse and choice trees, to give dependable responses to questions, for example, *"How precisely will my deals be impacted by a 10% expansion in promoting consumption?"* This prompts reproductions and *"imagine a scenario in which"* analytics for clients to find out additional.

All predictive learning applications include three crucial segments:

- **Data**: The adequacy of each predictive model emphatically relies upon the nature of the chronicled information it forms.
- **Statistical demonstrating**: Includes the different measurable procedures running from essential to complex capacities utilized for the determination of importance, understanding, and deduction. Relapse is the most ordinarily utilized measurable strategy.
- **Assumptions**: The ends drawn from gathered and broken down information generally expect the future will follow an example identified with the past.

Information analytics is urgent for any business on the way to progress, and predictive learning can be applied from numerous points of view to improve business profitability. These incorporate things such as showcasing effort advancement, chance, advertise examination, and misrepresentation identification.

How machine learning and predictive analytics are connected

While organizations must comprehend the contrasts between machine learning and predictive learning, it is similarly essential to know how they are connected. Fundamentally, machine learning is a predictive learning branch. Regardless of having comparative points and procedures, there are two fundamental contrasts between them:

- Machine learning works out expectations and recalibrates models continuously, consequently after structure. In the interim, predictive analytics works carefully on "*cause*" information and must be invigorated with "*change*" information.
- Unlike machine learning, predictive learning, despite everything, depends on human specialists to work out and test the relationship between cause and result.

Predictive analytics models

We will look at the main predictive analysis models as follows:

1. **Classification model:** The order model is, somehow or another, the least complex of the few sorts of predictive analytics models we are going to cover. It places information in classifications dependent on what it learns from verifiable information.

Arrangement models are ideal for responding to yes or no inquiries, giving wide examination that is useful to directing conclusive activity. These models can respond to questions, for example:

- For a retailer, *"Is this client going to beat?"*
- For a credit supplier, *"Will this advance be endorsed?"* or *"Is this candidate prone to default?"*
- For a web-based financial supplier, *"Is this a deceitful exchange?"*

The expansiveness of potential outcomes with the characterization model—and the simplicity by which it very well may be retrained with new information—implies it tends to be applied to various ventures.

2. **Clustering model:** The clustering model sorts information into discrete, settled keen gatherings dependent on comparative characteristics. In the event that an online business shoe organization is hoping to execute focused on showcasing efforts for their clients, they could experience a huge number of records to make a custom-made system for every person. Be that as it may, is this the most effective utilization of time? Likely not. Utilizing the bunching model, they can rapidly isolate clients into comparable gatherings dependent on basic qualities and devise methodologies for each gathering at a bigger scope.
3. **Forecast model:** One of the most broadly utilized predictive learning models, the figure model arrangements in the metric worth forecast, evaluating numeric incentive for new information dependent on learnings from recorded information.

   This model can be applied in any place authentic numerical information is accessible. Situations include:

   - A SaaS organization can assess what number of clients they are probably going to change over inside a given week.
   - A call focus can foresee what number of help calls they will get every hour.

   The estimated model likewise think about various information parameters. On the off chance that an eatery proprietor needs to foresee the quantity of clients she is probably going to get in the next week, the model will consider factors that could affect this; for example, is there an occasion close by? What is the climate figure? Is there an illness going around?

4. **Outliers model:** The exceptions model is situated around typical information passages inside a dataset. It can distinguish odd figures either without anyone else or related to different numbers and classes.

    - Recording a spike in help calls, which could demonstrate an item disappointment that may prompt a review.
    - Finding peculiar information inside exchanges or in protection claims to distinguish extortion.
    - Finding strange data in your NetOps logs and seeing the indications of approaching impromptu personal time.

    The anomaly model is especially valuable for predictive analytics in retail and fund. For instance, while distinguishing false exchanges, the model can evaluate sum, yet in addition area, time, buy history, and the idea of a buy (i.e., a $1,000 buy on gadgets is not as liable to be fake as an acquisition of a similar sum on books or basic utilities).

5. **Time series model:** The time arrangement model contains a succession of information focuses caught, utilizing time as the info parameter. It uses the most recent year of information to build up a numerical measurement and predicts the following three to about a month and a half of information using that measurement. Use cases for this model incorporate the quantity of everyday calls got in the previous three months, deals for as long as 20 quarters, or the quantity of patients who appeared at a given emergency clinic in the previous month and a half. It is a powerful method for understanding the manner in which a particular measurement is creating after some time with a degree of exactness past basic midpoints. It additionally considers periods of the year or occasions that could affect the measurement. On the off chance that the proprietor of a salon wishes to foresee what number of individuals are probably going to visit his business, he may go to the unrefined technique for averaging the complete number of guests in the course of recent days. Be that as it may, development is not generally static or direct, and the time arrangement model can all the more likely model exponential development and better adjust the model to an organization's pattern. It can likewise gauge for different undertakings or various districts simultaneously rather than only each in turn.

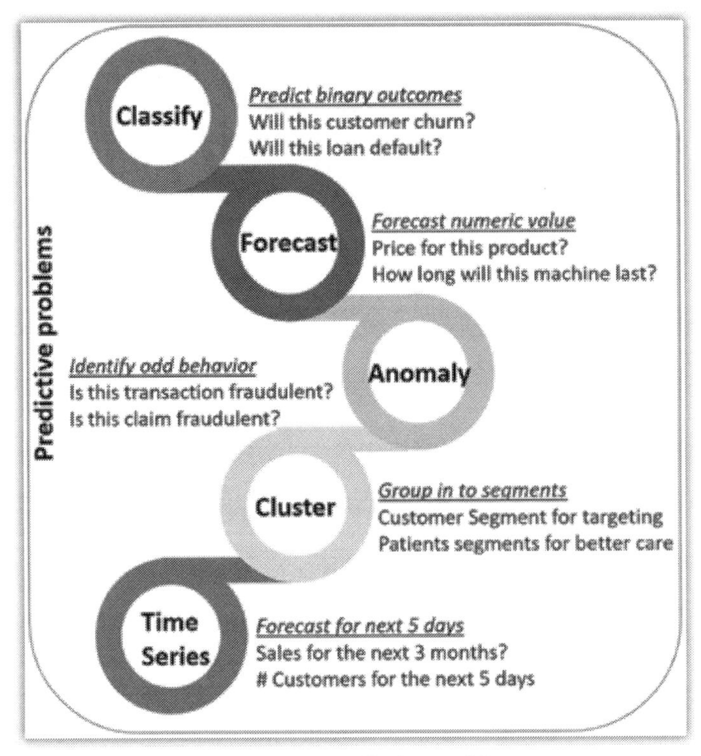

Figure 10.1: *Predictive problems*

Basic predictive algorithms

By and large, predictive analytics calculations can be isolated into two gatherings: machine learning and deep learning.

- Machine learning includes auxiliary information that we find in a table. Calculations for this involve both straight and nonlinear assortments. Straight calculations train all the more rapidly, while nonlinear are better streamlined for the issues they are probably going to confront (which are frequently nonlinear).
- Deep learning is a subset of machine learning that is progressively famous to manage sound, video, content, and pictures.

With machine learning predictive demonstrating, there are a few unique calculations that can be applied. The following are probably the most well-known calculations that are being utilized to control the predictive learning models portrayed previously:

1. **Random forest:** Random forest is maybe the most well-known arrangement calculation, equipped for both order and relapse. It can precisely order enormous volumes of information. The name "*Random Forest*" is gotten from

the way that the calculation is a blend of choice trees. Each tree relies upon the estimations of an irregular vector tested autonomously with a similar dispersion for all trees in the *"timberland."* Each one is developed to the biggest degree conceivable.

Predictive analytics calculations attempt to accomplish the least blunder conceivable by either utilizing *"boosting"* (a strategy that changes the heaviness of a perception dependent on the last arrangement) or *"packing"* (which makes subsets of information from preparing tests, picked haphazardly with substitution). Arbitrary forest uses packing. On the off chance that you have a great deal of test information, rather than preparing with every one of them, you can take a subset and train on that, and take another subset and train on that (cover is permitted). The entirety of this should be possible in equal. Different examples are taken from your information to make a normal.

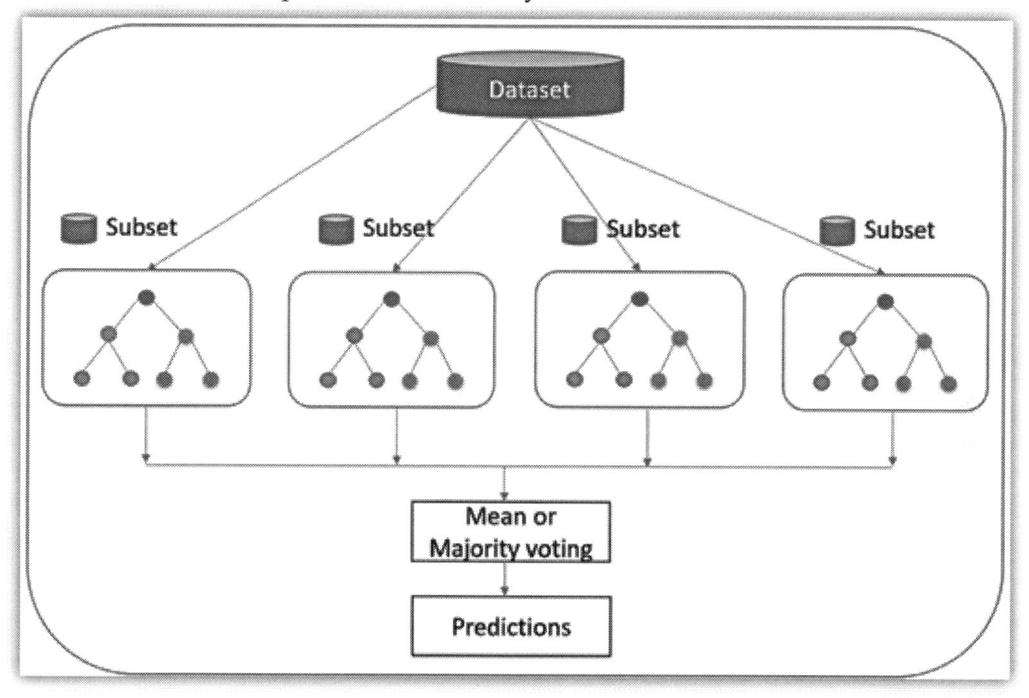

Figure 10.2: *Representation of Random Forest*

While singular trees may be *"feeble students,"* the rule of random forest is that together they can involve a solitary *"solid student."*

The ubiquity of the random forest model is clarified by its different favorable circumstances:

- Accurate and productive when running on enormous databases.

- Multiple trees diminish the change and predisposition of a littler set or single tree.
- Resistant to overfitting.
- Can handle a huge number of info factors without variable cancellation.
- Can gauge what factors are significant in grouping.
- Provides compelling techniques for evaluating missing information.
- Machine learning exactness is when an enormous extent of information is absent.

Generalized linear model for two values

The **generalized linear model** (**GLM**) is an increasing mind-boggling variation of the GLM. It takes the last model's correlation of the impacts of various factors on ceaseless factors before drawing from a variety of various conveyances to locate the *"best fit"* model.

Suppose you are keen on learning client to buy conduct for winter coats. A normal direct relapse may uncover that for each negative degree distinction in temperature, an extra 300 winter coats are bought. Although it appears to be legitimate that another 2,100 coats may be sold if the temperature goes from 9 degree to 3 degree, it appears to be less consistent that on the off chance that it goes down to –20, we will see the number increment to precisely the same degree.

The GLM would limit the rundown of factors, likely proposing that there is an expansion in deals past a specific temperature and a decline or leveling in deals once another temperature is reached.

The benefit of this calculation is that it prepares rapidly. The reaction variable can have any type of exponential dissemination type. The GLM is likewise ready to manage all out indicators whereas being moderately clear to decipher. On this, it gives an away from how every one of the indicators is impacting the result and is genuinely impervious to overfitting. Be that as it may, it requires moderately huge informational collections and is defenseless to exceptions.

Gradient boosted model (GBM)

The gradient boosted model delivers an expectation model made out of an outfit of choice trees (every last one of them a *"weak student,"* just like the case with random forest) before summing up. As its name recommends, it utilizes the *"supported"* Machine learning procedure rather than the stowing utilized by random forests. It is being used for the order model.

The distinctive quality of the GBM is that it manufactures its trees, each tree in turn. Each new tree assists with adjusting blunders made by the recently prepared tree—not at all like in the random forest model, where the trees bear no connection. It is all the time utilized in machine-picked-up positioning, as in the web indexes *Yahoo* and *Yandex*.

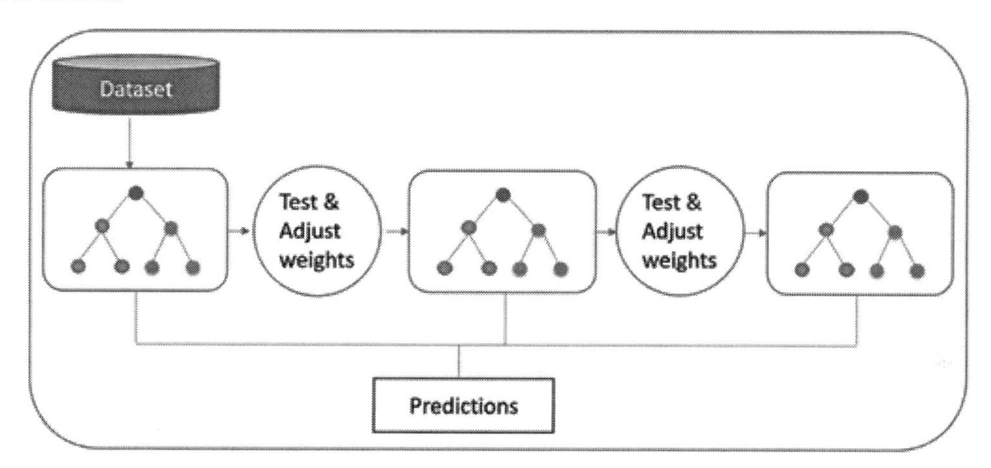

Figure 10.3: *Prediction model (GBM)*

By means of the GBM approach, information is increasingly expressive, and benchmark results show that the GBM technique is ideal as far as the general carefulness of the information. Be that as it may, as it assembles each tree successively, it additionally takes longer. All things considered, its slower presentation is considered to prompt better speculation.

K-means

A profoundly well-known, fast calculation, K-implies includes putting unlabeled information focuses in isolated gatherings dependent on likenesses. This calculation is utilized for the grouping model. For instance, Tom and Rebecca are in bunch one, and John and Henry are in bunch two. Tom and Rebecca have fundamentally the same attributes; however, Rebecca and John have totally different qualities. K-implies attempts to make sense of what the normal qualities are for people and gatherings them together. This is especially useful when you have an enormous informational collection and are hoping to execute a customized arrangement—this is hard to do with one million.

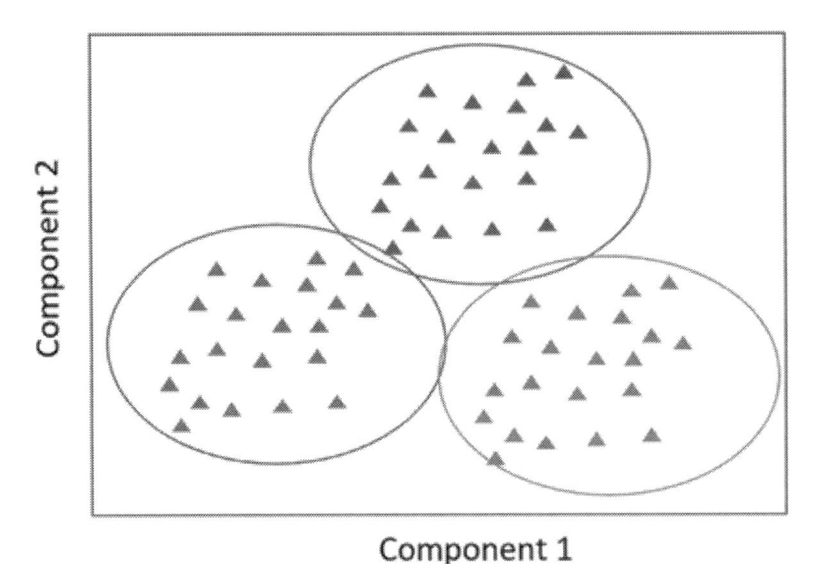

Figure 10.4: *K-means*

Deep learning

Deep learning is a man-made brainpower work that copies the operations of the human mind in preparing information and making designs for use in dynamic. Deep learning is a subset of AI in man-made reasoning (AI) that has systems equipped for taking in solo from information that is unstructured or unlabeled. Otherwise called deep neural learning or deep neural *n*, deep learning algorithms run information through a few *"layers"* of neural system algorithms, every one of which passes an improved portrayal of the information to the following layer.

Deep learning algorithms adapt dynamically progressively about the picture as it experiences each neural system layer. Early layers figure out how to identify low-level highlights like edges, and ensuing layers consolidate highlights from prior layers into a progressively comprehensive portrayal. For instance, a center layer may recognize edges to identify portions of an article in the photograph, like a leg or a branch, whereas a deep layer will distinguish the full item, for example, a canine or a tree.

Deep learning algorithms run information through a few *"layers"* of neural system algorithms, every one of which passes a rearranged portrayal of the information to the following layer.

For what reason is deep learning important?

The capacity to process huge quantities of highlights makes deep learning incredible when managing unstructured information. Be that as it may, deep learning algorithms can be needless excess for less intricate issues since they expect access to a tremendous measure of information to be successful. For example, *ImageNet*, the normal benchmark for preparing deep learning models for exhaustive picture acknowledgment, approaches more than 14 million pictures.

On the off chance that the information is excessively straightforward or fragmented, it is simple for a deep learning model to become overfitted and neglect to sum up well to new information. Therefore, deep learning models are not as successful as different procedures (for example, helped choice trees or straight models) for most commonsense business issues, for example, understanding client beat, identifying fake exchanges, and different cases with littler datasets and fewer highlights. In specific cases such as multiclass grouping, deep learning can work for littler, and organized datasets.

How does deep learning achieve such noteworthy outcomes?

In a word, exactness. Deep learning accomplishes acknowledgment exactness at more elevated levels than at any other time. This enables buyer hardware to meet client desires, and it is significant for well-being basic applications like driverless vehicles. Late advances in deep learning have improved to where deep learning beats people in certain undertakings like characterizing objects in pictures.

While deep learning was first speculated during the 1980s, there are two principal reasons it has as of late become valuable:

1. Deep learning requires a lot of named information. For instance, driverless vehicle advancement requires a great many pictures and a huge number of long stretches of video.
2. Deep learning requires significant registering power. Elite GPUs have equal engineering that is effective for deep learning. At the point when joined with bunches or distributed computing, this empowers advancement groups to lessen preparing time for a deep taking in arrange from weeks to hours or less.

Instances of deep learning at work

Uses of deep learning applications can be in enterprises from mechanized heading to clinical gadgets.

- **Robotized driving**: Automotive scientists are utilizing deep learning to figure out how to consequently recognize items, like, stop signs and traffic lights. Deep learning is used to identify people on foot, which helps decline mishaps.
- **Aviation and defense**: Deep learning is also utilized to distinguish objects from satellites that find regions of premium and recognize risky or protected zones for troops.
- **Clinical research**: The cancer specialists are using deep learning to figure out how to consequently recognize malignant growth cells. Groups at UCLA assembled a propelled magnifying lens that yields a high-dimensional informational index used to prepare a deep learning application to precisely recognize disease cells.
- **Modern automation**: Deep learning is assisting with improving laborer security around substantial hardware via naturally distinguishing when individuals or items are inside a risky separation of machines.
- **Hardware**: Deep learning is being utilized in computerized hearing and discourse interpretation. For instance, home help gadgets that react to your voice and realize your inclinations are fueled by deep learning applications.

What is the difference between machine learning and deep learning?

Deep learning is a specific type of artificial intelligence. An AI work process begins with some important highlights being physically extricated from pictures. The highlights are then used to make a model that orders the items in the picture. With the deep learning work process, significant highlights are consequently removed from pictures, and deep learning performs *"start to finish learning"*—where a system is given crude information and an assignment to perform.

Another key distinction is deep learning algorithms scale with information, whereas shallow learning joins. Shallow learning alludes to AI techniques that level at a specific degree of execution when you include more models and preparing information for the system.

A key favorable position of deep learning systems is that they regularly keep on improving as the size of your information increments.

Deep learning differences

- Deep learning frameworks speak to the first run through PCs can comprehend pictures at a helpful level and sensible expense.
- The larger part of employments includes some type of visual discernment. i.e., identification and characterization of visual data (pictures for shorthand).

- Deep learning requires non-specialized topic specialists to *"program"* it.
- Deep learning still cannot seem to be successfully utilized by little and medium organizations. We are at under <1% infiltration of the innovation.

Choosing between machine learning and deep learning

Artificial intelligence offers an assortment of procedures and models you can pick dependent on your application, the size of information you are preparing, and the kind of issue you need to explain. An effective deep learning application requires a lot of information (a great many pictures) to prepare the model, just as GPUs, or illustrations handling units, to quickly process your information.

While picking between AI and deep learning, consider whether you have a superior GPU and bunches of named information. In the event that you do not have both of those things, it might bode well to utilize AI rather than deep learning. Deep learning is commonly increasingly mind-boggling, so you will require, in any event, two or three thousand pictures to get solid outcomes. Having a superior GPU implies the model will set aside less effort to investigate every one of those pictures.

How deep learning gets better results

Deep learning utilizes layers of neural-organize algorithms to interpret more significant level data at different layers dependent on crude info information. For instance, in a picture acknowledgment application, one layer could recognize highlights, for example, sharp edges or complexities in light, while another could distinguish how extraordinary unmistakable shapes show up. Further, a third layer could translate what the picture is appearing. This is completely accomplished by taking in the various manners data from past layers are sorted out to frame recognizable items.

Neural-organize algorithms are intended to perceive information designs dependent on an early comprehension of how the human cerebrum capacities. Neural systems can help bunch focuses inside an enormous example of information dependent on the likenesses of its highlights, arrange information dependent on names from past information, and concentrate particular highlights from the information. The numerical examples these systems perceive are put away in vectors that delineate true data sources. Deep neural systems can be thought of as parts of bigger AI applications, including algorithms for support learning, order, and relapse.

Deep learning utilizes self-trained learning and calculation builds with many shrouded layers, large information, and ground-breaking computational assets. The algorithmic structure is known as the **neural system**, while the shrouded layers in the system give it the moniker of deep learning.

The *Google Brain Team* undertaking and deep learning programming like *TensorFlow* have given further footing to the improvement of deep learning strategies. Such methods depend on numerical capacities and parameters for accomplishing the ideal yield.

Deep learning architecture

Deep learning engineering is applied to informal community separating, extortion discovery, picture and discourse acknowledgment, sound acknowledgment, PC vision, clinical picture handling, bioinformatics, client relationship the executives, and a lot more fields. Deep learning models are all over the place, and the groups equipped for preparing neural systems to convey great outcomes are among the most looked after experts today. Enormous information examination as a field has gradually developed to incorporate deep learning mastery as an important expansion as well as a center and fundamental range of abilities.

The artificial neural network (ANN)

The idea of deep learning is demonstrated on standards of conduct in the layers of neurons in the neocortex of the human mind. In general, the more layers that exist, the deeper the model is, and the higher the presentation.

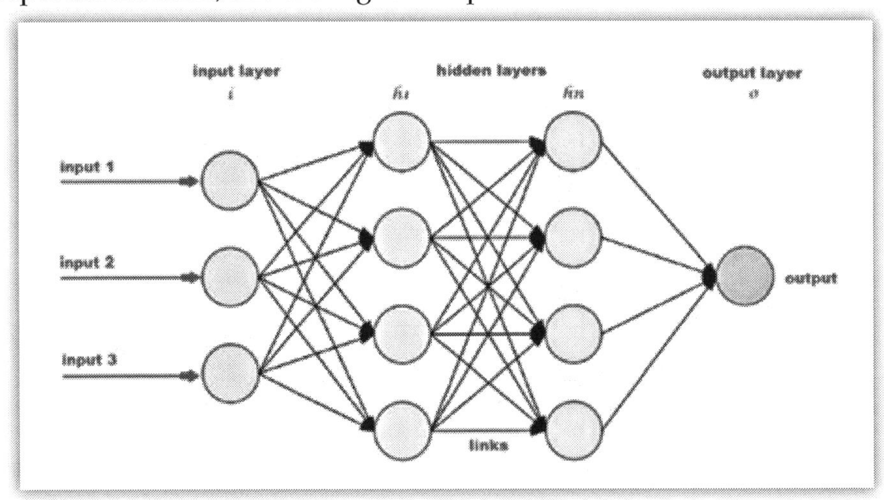

Figure 10.5: *Representation of deep learning*

A straightforward neural network (NN)

A neural system is a structure of perceptron's that are associated in various manners and that work on various enactment capacities. A perceptron is a calculation utilized in administered learning of paired classifiers. A parallel classifier is a capacity that chooses whether information (spoke to as a vector of numbers) has a place in one of two classes.

A system of perceptron's is known as a multilayer perceptron, which is likewise alluded to as a counterfeit neural system (ANN).

The deep learning engineering utilized today is essentially founded on ANNs that use different layers of nonlinear preparing for include extraction and change.

Deep Learning Algorithms

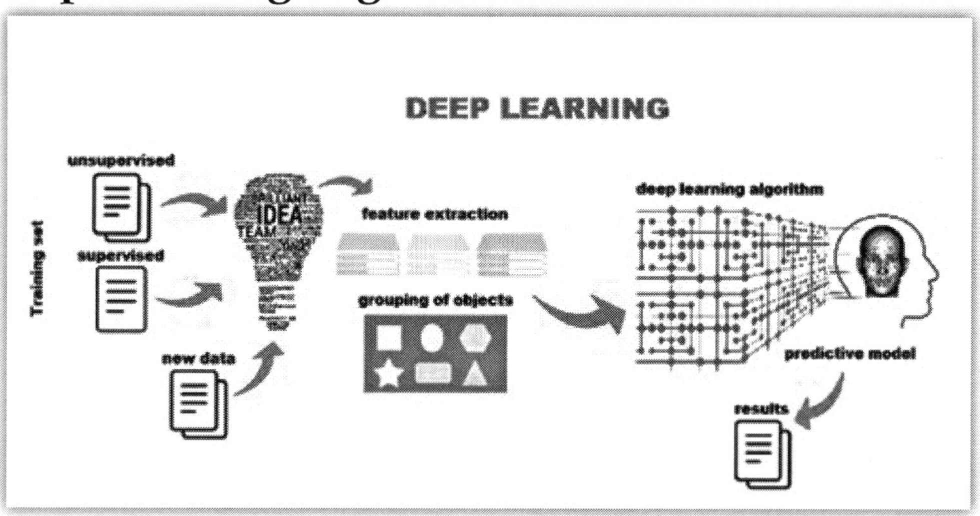

Figure 10.6: *Visualization of Deep learning*

Although deep learning algorithms include self-learning portrayals, they rely on ANNs that reflect the manner in which the cerebrum figures data. During the preparation procedure, algorithms utilize obscure components in the info dissemination to remove highlights, bunch questions, and find helpful information designs. Much like preparing machines for self-learning, this happens at various levels, utilizing the algorithms to manufacture the models.

Deep learning models utilize a few algorithms. Although nobody's organization is viewed as great, a few algorithms are more qualified to perform explicit errands. To pick the correct ones, it is acceptable to increase a strong comprehension of every single essential calculation.

The following are some significant ones utilized in deep learning structures:

1. **Multilayer perceptron neural network (MLPNN)**
   - **What it is**: The multilayer perceptron fills in as a strong prologue to deep learning. It utilizes a feed-forward directed learning calculation with up to two concealed layers to produce a lot of yields from a given arrangement of information sources. As the name proposes, it is made out of more than one perceptron.
   - **How it functions**: The system associates various layers of neurons in a coordinated chart with the goal that the sign goes through the hubs a single way. The yield vector is figured given the information sources and an arbitrary choice of loads in the feed-forward computational stream. The model is prepared to get familiar with the connection or conditions between the info and yield from preparation informational index. The mistake amount between what ought to be the yield for given info is processed, and preparing includes tuning the loads and inclinations to decrease blunder at the yield layer. The procedure is rehashed for shrouded layers moving in reverse. Backpropagation is utilized to make the weight and predisposition alterations comparative with the blunder. The blunder itself can likewise be estimated in an assortment of ways, including by **root-mean-squared mistake** (**RMSE**).
   - **Advantages**: MLPNN's can characterize non-directly divisible information focuses, tackle complex issues including a few parameters, and handle informational collections with an enormous number of highlights, particularly non-straight ones.
   - **Use cases**: MLPNN is utilized to tackle issues that require directed learning and equal appropriated preparing, as in the accompanying cases:
     - Image check and recreation
     - Speech acknowledgment
     - Machine interpretation
     - Data grouping
     - E-business, where numerous parameters are included.
2. **Backpropagation**
   - **What it is**: The backpropagation calculation is the establishment of neural system preparing. The managed learning calculation figures

an inclination plunge with the loads refreshed in reverse—from yield toward input—or backpropagation.

- **How it functions**: Initially, a neural system comprising loads and inclinations that are ineffectively adjusted to understand information. A neural system's translation of information and the physical world is done through the estimations of its loads and inclinations. In this way, an inadequately adjusted neural system infers a poor model. Whatever mistakes exist at the last forecast layer are sent back through the system to alter the loads and inclinations with the goal that future expectations have lower blunder esteems. The calculation ascertains every neuron's blunder commitment utilizing a method called the delta rule or angle plummet enhancement. The heaviness of neurons is acclimated to decrease the blunder at the yield layer. Inclination drop suggests a pace of progress of an objective set apart as *Y* for change in a parameter set apart as *X*. In this issue, *Y* would be the blunder delivered in the neural system forecast, and *X* would speak to different parameters in the information. Because there is more than one parameter, incomplete subordinates are utilized for every parameter. Additionally, in light of the fact that the layers of neural systems work consecutively, finding the subsidiaries at each layer sets up a connection of the difference in mistake at each layer for parameters in contrast with its past and next layers. This is like the chain rule of subordinates in analytics.
- **Advantages**: Backpropagation tells engineers how the purposes of mistake add to loads and can be prepared with the goal that a system can outline all the while changing all loads. It functions admirably in blunder inclined ventures and can be utilized to prepare deep neural systems.
- **Use cases**: Backpropagation can be utilized in picture and discourse acknowledgment to improve the exactness of forecasts in information mining and AI and in ventures where subordinates must be determined rapidly.

3. **Convolutional neural network**
   - **What it is**: The **convolutional neural network (CNN)** system is a multilayer, feed-forward neural system that utilizes perceptrons for directed learning and to break down information. It is used for the most part with visual information, for example, picture arrangement.

The enormous progressions in deep learning are expected partially to an energizing use of CNNs in an opposition-held in 2012. The accomplishment of deep convolutional engineering called AlexNet, which was the reason for the **ImageNet large scale visual recognition competition (ILSVRC)**, was the essential purpose behind fundamentally quickened look into in the field of deep learning in the course of recent years.

Be that as it may, CNN's are not constrained to picture acknowledgment. They have been applied legitimately to content investigation and can be applied to sound when it is spoken to outwardly as a spectrogram and diagram information utilizing chart convolutional systems.

- **How it functions**: CNN design is not the same as other neural systems. To all the more likely comprehend this differentiation, think about pictures as information. Ordinarily, with PC vision, pictures are treated as two-dimensional lattices of numbers. In any case, in CNNs, a picture is treated as a tensor or a grid of numbers with extra measurements. *Figure 10.7* shows this idea.

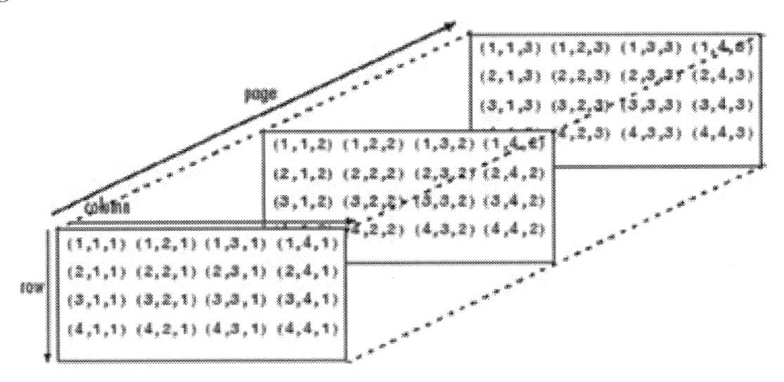

Source: www.skymind.ai

***Figure 10.7**: View of CNN*

Tensors are shaped by settling exhibits inside clusters, with settling conceivably happening limitlessly.

Pictures, specifically, are treated as four-dimensional tensors. On the off chance that a scalar is a zero-dimensional article, a vector is one-dimensional, a matrice or assortment of vectors is two-dimensional, and a heap of such grids (imagined as a shape) is three-dimensional. At that point, a four-dimensional tensor comprising various such three-dimensional articles where every component in the 3D square has a heap of highlight maps joined to it.

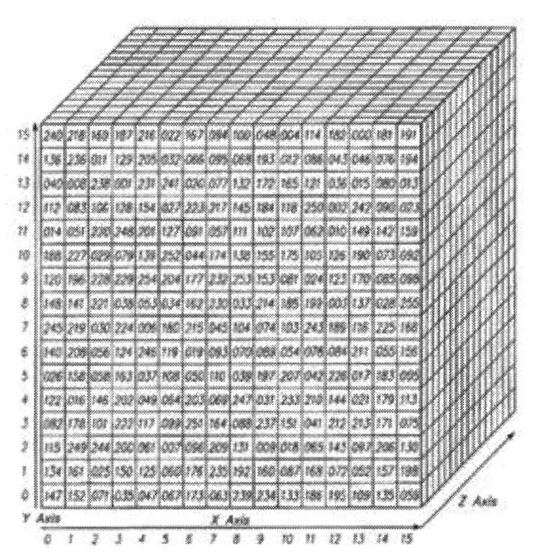

Figure 10.8: *3D shape*

The concealed layers in CNNs contain convolutional layers, standardization layers, pooling layers, and a completely associated layer. It takes an information picture, appoints critical loads and inclinations to different parts of the picture to empower separation, and applies channels with the least pre-preparing.

While the principal convolution layer catches low-level highlights, the following layers extricate more elevated level highlights, making a system with a modern examination of the pictures in the dataset.

- **Advantages**: The CNN calculation is productive at acknowledgment and exceptionally versatile. It is likewise simple to prepare in light of the fact that there are fewer preparing parameters and is adaptable when combined with backpropagation.
- **Use cases**: The CNN calculation can be utilized with:
  - Image handling, acknowledgment, and characterization.
  - Video acknowledgment.
  - Natural language-preparing errands.
  - Pattern acknowledgment.
  - Recommendation motors.
  - Medical picture investigation.

4. **Repetitive neural network (RNN)**
   - **What it is**: The intermittent neural network (RNN) system is intended to perceive an informational collection's successive ascribe and use

examples to anticipate the following likely situation. It is a ground-breaking way to deal with handling consecutive information such as sound, time arrangement information, and composed common language. The stochastic inclination drop (SGD) is utilized to prepare the system alongside a backpropagation calculation.

How it functions: Unlike conventional systems, where data sources and yields are autonomous of one another, in an RNN, the concealed layer jams consecutive data from past advances. This implies the yield from a prior advance is taken care of as the contribution to a present advance, utilizing similar loads and inclination over and over for expectation purposes. The layers are then joined to make a solitary repetitive layer. These input circles process consecutive information, permitting data to continue, as in memory, and advise the last yield.

On the off chance that an RNN is entrusted with speculating the following letter of a past information letter, it very well may be prepared by taking care of letters of realized words letter by letter, so it decides applicable examples. RNNs are layered to process data in two ways: feed-forward (to process information from introductory contribution to conclusive yield) and input circles utilizing backpropagation (circling data once again into the system).

RNNs are unique in relation to take care of forward systems since feed-forward systems acknowledge each information and give one yield in turn. This balanced imperative does not exist with RNNs, which can allude to past guides to shape expectations dependent on their implicit memory.

- **Advantages**: CNNs can become familiar with the setting in succession expectation issues, just as procedure consecutive and fleeting information. They likewise can be utilized in scope of uses.
- **Use cases**: CNNs are valuable for:
  - Sentiment grouping
  - Image subtitling
  - Speech acknowledgment
  - Natural language preparing
  - Machine interpretation
  - Search forecast
  - Video characterization

5. **Long short-term memory (LSTM)**
   - **What it is**: The long momentary memory (LSTM) calculation is a kind of RNN that permits deep repetitive systems to be prepared without making the slopes that update loads become unsteady. Examples can be put away in memory for progressively expanded periods, with the capacity to specifically review or erase information.
   - **How it functions**: It utilizes backpropagation however is prepared to learn arrangement information using memory squares associated into layers rather than neurons. As the data is prepared through the layers, the engineering can include, expel, or change information varying.
   - **Advantages**: This calculation is most appropriate for grouping and forecasting dependent on time arrangement information, offering modern outcomes for differing issues. These empower information researchers to make deep models utilizing enormous stacked systems and handle complex succession issues in AI all the more productively.
   - **Use cases**: LSTM is perfect for:
     - Captioning of pictures and recordings
     - Language interpretation and demonstrating
     - Sentiment examination
     - Stock advertise expectations.
6. **Generative adversarial network**
   - **What it is**: The **generative adversarial network (GAN)** is a strong calculation utilized for solo learning. Given a preparation set, the system consequently finds and learns regularities and examples in input information so it can self-figure out how to create new information. It can basically emulate any informational collection with little variety. GANs are deep neural net designs that included two nets, setting one in opposition to the next, accordingly the term ill-disposed.
   - **How it functions**: The GAN utilizes two submodels: generator and discriminator. The generator makes new instances of information, while the discriminator recognizes genuine area information and phony-produced tests. They run over and again, making them increasingly stronger with every redundancy.

     Generative and discriminative algorithms contrast in a couple of central ways:
     - Discriminative algorithms attempt to isolate an informational index into particular classes dependent on similitudes in their highlights,

such as characterizing messages into spam and not spam. As far as contingent likelihood, you could state the probability of an information point being class Yi given highlights $Xi - p(y \mid x)$.

  - Generative algorithms attempt to decide the probability of a lot of highlights in an information point that is as of now grouped. For instance, an email named not spam would be broken down by the generative calculation to discover how likely the real words present in the e-mail are to be available in a non-spam-type message. As far as contingent likelihood, the likelihood of highlights xi existing for an information point previously named $Yi - p(x \mid y)0$.

- **Advantages**: GANS can catch and duplicate varieties inside a given informational index, produce pictures from a given informational collection of pictures, make great information, and control information.
- **Use cases**: GANs are helpful for:
  - Cyber security
  - Health diagnostics
  - Natural language preparing
  - Speech handling

7. **Limited Boltzmann machine (RBM)**

   Highlight mapping of the RBM model:

   - **What it is**: The **restricted Boltzmann machine** (**RBM**) is a probabilistic graphical model or a sort of stochastic neural system. It is a powerful design for synergistic sifting and plays out a double factor investigation with limited correspondence between layers for productive learning.

     It is significant that RBMs have pretty much been supplanted by GANs or variational autoencoders by most AI specialists.
   - **How it functions**: The system has one layer of noticeable units, one layer of concealed units, and a predisposition unit associated with all obvious and shrouded units. Shrouded units are free as an approach to give fair examples. The neurons in the bipartite chart have a symmetric association. Be that as it may, there are no associations between the hubs inside a gathering.
   - **Advantages**: RBM offers the benefits of vitality-based learning like plan adaptability, is valuable for both probabilistic and non-probabilistic measurable models, limits network for simple learning, and is utilized with grouping, relapse, and generative models.

- **Use cases**: RBM is helpful for:
  - Recommender frameworks
  - Filtering
  - Feature learning
  - Dimensionality decrease
  - Topic demonstrating.

8. **Deep belief network (DBN)**
   - **What it is**: The **deep belief network** (**DBN**) is a solo probabilistic deep learning calculation where the system has a generative learning model. This is a blend of coordinated and undirected graphical systems, with the top layer an undirected RBM and the lower layers coordinated descending, which empowers a pre-preparing stage and a feed-forward system for the tweaking stage.
   - **How it functions**: The DBN has different layers of concealed units, which are associated, and the learning calculation is *"voracious"* from the stacked RBMs, which means there is each layer in turn, successively from the base watched layer.
   - **Advantages**: DBNs offer vitality-based taking in and can profit from unlabeled information.
   - **Use cases**: DBNs are valuable for:
     - Image and face acknowledgment
     - Video-arrangement acknowledgment
     - Motion-catch information
     - Classifying high-goals satellite picture information.

PC vision and deep learning—semantic segmentation in the period of neural networks

In semantic division, the objective is to arrange every pixel of the picture in a particular classification base. That way, we can separate the logical data of each article in the picture. To accomplish this, skip associations are utilized in neural systems, framing another design called UNets.

See how UNets work, why they perform well in the semantic division, and program one utilizing Keras?

Limitation and object detection with deep learning

The limitation is the undertaking of recognizing the area of an article in a picture, while object detection is the grouping and discovery of all items in it. To do this, the most well-known strategy is an R-CNN nearby with its upgrades Fast R-CNN and faster R-CNN.

YOLO—you just look once

Single-shot indicators like YOLO give a quick method to identify and restrict protests in a picture. In this post, you will become familiar with the privileged insights behind YOLO and why it turned into the business standard in low-power gadgets, for example, cell phones.

Applications

- Self-driving vehicles utilizing deep learning

  Get familiar with the nuts-and-bolts ventures behind the advancement of a vehicle's autopilots and utilize a game test system and python to make your own vehicle drive without anyone else.

- **Human pose estimation**

  This is a review of the most significant research papers on 2D and 3D human pose estimation. You will discover instinctive clarifications on algorithms such as OpenPose, DensePose, and VIBE.

Deep learning in clinical imaging: 3D clinical picture division with PyTorch

In this archive, we tackle the 3D clinical picture division with deep learning models utilizing PyTorch. The fundamental MRI establishments are introduced for tensor portrayal, just as the essential segments to apply a deep learning technique that handles the errand explicit problems (class lopsidedness, limited information). In addition, we present a few highlights of the open-source clinical picture division library. At long last, we talk about our starter exploratory outcomes and give sources to discover clinical imaging information.

For what reason is deep learning important?

Cell phones and chips are the substance of an associated arrange. The significance of pictures, recordings, and sound in online life, spilling examination, and web look have made another biological system where these highlights are being adapted.

The calculation of such complex highlights requires information on deep learning systems, just as the capacity to create complex progressive systems of ideas utilizing modern algorithms. Fantastic working information on deep learning strategies, sorts of deep learning, and deep learning applications can assist clients with executing it for different purposes. On account of unaided information, AI may not generally be possible since manual naming of information is costly and tedious. Deep learning systems are intended to help conquer these issues.

Deep learning still cannot seem to be viably utilized by little and medium organizations.

Deep learning is probably going to be as normal in organizations as PCs. However, up to this point, it was still so costly to fabricate that reason it was just utilized by organizations that could stand to employ a product group. Also, and still, after all that, it normally just was applied in the most expansive settings or for the most conventional of cases.

New organizations are lessening this expense to such an extent that it gets reasonable for littler groups to convey deep learning frameworks, all the more often and all the more without any problem.

Neural networks

Machines have minds. This, we definitely know. However, progressively, their minds can take care of the sorts of issues that, as of not long ago, people were particularly acceptable at. Neural systems, as the name proposes, are displayed on neurons in the cerebrum. They utilize computerized reasoning to unwind and separate amazingly complex connections.

What separates neural systems from other AI calculations is that they utilize a design roused by the neurons in the cerebrum. A mind neuron gets information and, dependent on that input, shoots a yield that is utilized by another neuron. The neural system mimics this conduct in finding out about gathering information and afterward foreseeing results. Neural nets are a method for doing AI, wherein a PC figures out how to play out some assignment by examining preparing models. As a rule, the models have been hand-named ahead of time. An article acknowledgment framework, for example, may be taken care of thousands of marked pictures of vehicles, houses, espresso cups, and so on, and it would discover visual examples in the pictures that reliably associate with specific names.

Demonstrated freely on the human cerebrum, a neural net comprising of thousands or even a large number of straightforward preparing hubs that are thickly interconnected. A large portion of the present neural nets are composed of layers of hubs, and they are *"feed-forward,"* implying that information travels through them in just a single course. An individual hub may be associated with a few hubs in the layer underneath it, from which it gets information, and a few hubs in the layer above it, to which it sends information.

Placing it in context

Neural systems are one way to deal with AI, which is one utilization of AI. We should separate it.

- Artificial insight is the idea of machines having the option to perform assignments that require apparently human knowledge.
- Machine learning, as we have talked about previously, is one utilization of computerized reasoning. It includes giving PCs access to a trove of information and letting them scan for ideal arrangements. AI calculations can improve without being expressly customized. As it were, they can discover designs in the information and apply those examples to new difficulties later on.
- Deep learning is a subset of AI, which utilizes neural systems with numerous layers. A deep neural system dissects information with learned portrayals much the same as the manner in which an individual would take a gander at an issue. In customary AI, the calculation is given a lot of pertinent highlights to investigate. Notwithstanding, in deep learning, the calculation is given crude information and infers the highlights itself.

Here are the three reasons you should contemplate neural calculation:

- To see how the mind really functions: it is enormous and exceptionally confused and made of stuff that bites the dust when you jab it, so we have to utilize PC recreations.
- To comprehend a style of equal calculation propelled by neurons and their versatile associations: it is a totally different style from the consecutive calculation.
- To tackle handy issues by utilizing novel learning calculations roused by the mind: learning calculations can be valuable regardless of whether they are not how the cerebrum really functions.

The machine learning approach

- Instead of composing a program by hand for every particular undertaking, we gather bunches of models that determine the right yield for given info.
- An AI calculation at that point takes these models and delivers a program that carries out the responsibility.

  - The program created by the learning calculation may appear to be exceptionally unique from a run-of-the-mill manually written program. It might contain a large number of numbers.
  - If we do it right, the program works for new cases just as the ones we prepared it on.
  - If the information changes, the program can change also via preparing the new information.
- Massive measures of calculation are presently less expensive than paying somebody to compose an errand explicit program.

For what reason do we need machine learning?

We need AI for errands that are unreasonably mind-boggling for people to code straightforwardly, for example, undertakings that are unpredictable to such an extent that it is illogical, if certainly feasible, for us to turn out to be the entirety of the subtleties and code for them unequivocally. So all things being equal, we furnish an AI calculation with a lot of information and let it investigate and look for a model that will work out what the software engineers have decided to accomplish.

We should take a gander at these two models:

- It is extremely difficult to compose programs that tackle issues like perceiving a 3D object, from a novel perspective, in new lighting conditions, in a jumbled scene. We do not have the foggiest idea what program to compose on the grounds that we do not have a clue how it is done in our cerebrum. Regardless of whether we had a smart thought for how to do it, the program may be horribly muddled.
- It is difficult to compose a program to register the likelihood that a Visa exchange is deceitful. There may not be any standards that are both basic and solid. We have to consolidate countless frail principles. Extortion is a moving objective; however, the program needs to continue evolving.

At that point comes the machine learning approach: rather than composing a program by hand for every particular errand, we gather bunches of models that indicate the right yield for given information. An AI calculation at that point takes these models and delivers a program that carries out the responsibility. The program delivered by the learning calculation may appear to be unique from commonplace written by hand program—it might contain a huge number of numbers. In the event that we do it right, the program works for new cases, just as the ones we prepared it on. On the off chance that the information changes, the program can change also via preparing the new information. You should take note that directing gigantic measures of calculation is currently less expensive than paying somebody to compose an assignment explicit program.

A few instances of assignments best comprehended by AI include:

- **Recognizing designs**: Protests in genuine scenes, facial personalities, or outward appearances, as well as expressed words.
- **Recognizing abnormalities**: Surprising groupings of charge card exchanges, strange examples of sensor readings in an atomic force plant.
- **Prediction**: Future stock costs or money trade rates, which motion pictures an individual will like.

Enhancement algorithms

A few instances of enhancement calculations include:

- ADADELTA
- ADAGRAD
- ADAM
- NESTEROVS
- NONE
- RMSPROP
- SGD
- CONJUGATE GRADIENT
- HESSIAN FREE
- LBFGS
- LINE GRADIENT DESCENT

Activation functions

The actuation work decides the yield a hub will produce in view of its info.

A few models include:

- CUBE
- ELU
- HARDSIGMOID
- HARDTANH
- IDENTITY
- LEAKYRELU

- RATIONALTANH
- RELU
- RRELU
- SIGMOID
- SOFTMAX
- SOFTPLUS
- SOFTSIGN

Logistic regression

On a deep neural system of numerous layers, the last layer has a specific job. When managing marked info, the yield layer groups every model, applying the most probable name. Every hub on the yield layer speaks to one mark, and that hub turns on or off as per the quality of the sign it gets from the past layer's information and parameters. Each yield hub produces two potential results, the double yield esteems 0 or 1, on the grounds that an info variable either merits a mark or it does not. All things considered, there is nothing of the sort as somewhat pregnant. While neural systems working with marked information produce double yield, the info they get is regularly nonstop. That is, the signs that the system gets as information will traverse a scope of qualities and incorporate any number of measurements, contingent upon the difficulty it tries to explain.

For instance, a suggestion motor needs to settle on a parallel choice about whether to serve an advertisement or not. In any case, the information it puts together its choice with respect to could incorporate how much a client has spent on *Amazon* in the most recent week or how regularly that client visits the site. So the yield layer needs to gather signals, for example, $67.59 spent on diapers, and 15 visits to a site, into a range somewhere in the range of 0 and 1; for example, a likelihood that given info ought to be named or not.

Deep neural networks

Neural systems can be made from, in any event, three layers of neurons: the info layer, the covered-up layer(s), and the yield layer. The concealed layer—or layers—in the middle of comprising numerous neurons, with associations between the layers. As the neural system *"learns"* the information, the loads, or quality, of the associations between these neurons are *"calibrated,"* permitting the system to think of exact expectations.

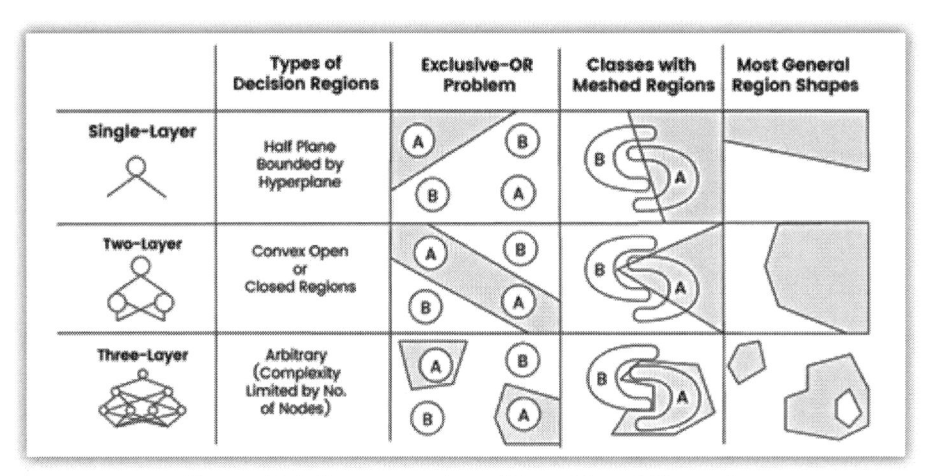

Figure 10.9: Representation of Deep Neural Networks

As we have talked about, neural system AI calculations are displayed in transit the mind works—explicitly, the manner in which it speaks to data. At the point when a neural system has numerous layers, it is known as a **deep neural system**, and the way toward preparing and utilizing deep neural systems is called deep learning, deep neural systems, for the most part, allude to especially complex neural systems. These have more layers (upwards of 1,000) and—regularly—more neurons per layer. With more layers and more neurons, systems can deal with progressively complex undertakings; however, that implies they take more time to prepare. Because GPUs are upgraded for working with grids and neural systems depend on direct variable-based math, the accessibility of incredible GPUs has made structure deep neural systems attainable.

In a "*classic*" neural system, data is transmitted a solitary way through a system, where each layer is completely associated with its neighbors, from the contribution to the yield layers. In any case, there are two different sorts of neural systems that are especially appropriate for specific issues: **convolutional neural networks (CNNs)** and **intermittent neural systems (RNNs)**.

Convolutional neural networks

Convolutional neural **networks** (CNNs) are much of the time utilized for the errands of picture acknowledgment and order.

For instance, assume that you have a lot of photos, and you need to decide if a feline is available in each picture. CNNs process pictures starting from the earliest stage. Neurons that are found before in the system are answerable for looking at little windows of pixels and distinguishing basic, little highlights, for example, edges and corners. These yields are then taken care of into neurons in the transitional layers, which search for bigger highlights, for example, stubbles, noses, and ears. This second arrangement of yields is utilized to make the last judgment about whether the picture contains a cat.

Convolutional neural networks are so progressive since they take the assignment of limited element extraction out of the hands of people. Before utilizing CNNs, specialists would regularly need to physically choose which qualities of the picture were generally significant for recognizing a feline. In any case, neural systems can develop these component portrayals naturally, deciding for themselves which parts of the picture are the most significant.

Recurrent neural networks

Although CNNs are appropriate for working with picture information, repetitive neural systems (RNNs) are a solid decision for working up consecutive portrayals of information after some time: assignments, for example, penmanship acknowledgment and voice acknowledgment. Similarly, as you cannot identify a feline taking a gander at a solitary pixel, you cannot perceive content or discourse taking a gander at a solitary letter or syllable. To appreciate regular language, you have to comprehend the present letter or syllable as well as its unique situation. RNNs are equipped for "recalling" the system's past yields and utilizing these outcomes as contributions to later calculations. By including circles as a feature of the system model, data from past advances can endure after some time, helping the system settle on more intelligent choices. Long-momentary memory (LSTM) units or **gated intermittent units (GRUs)** can be added to a RNN to permit it to recollect significant subtleties and overlook the insignificant ones.

A historical context

The entirety of this may feel contemporary; however, it returns decades. Enormous information specialist *Bernard Marr* and Import.io, among numerous others, have arranged the historical backdrop of neural systems and deep learning. Here is a short diagram.

- In 1943, *Walter Pitts*, a scholar, and *Warren McCulloch*, a neuroscientist, made the model of a neural system. They proposed a blend of science and calculations that was meant to reflect human points of view. The model—named the *McCulloch-Pitts* neurons—has, obviously, developed, yet it stays standard.
- In 1980, *Kunihiko Fukushima* proposed the Neoconitron, a progressive, multilayered, counterfeit neural system utilized for penmanship acknowledgment and other example acknowledgment assignments.

- In the mid-2000s, the expression *"deep learning"* picked up footing after papers by *Geoffrey Hinton*, Ruslan Salakhutdinov, and others demonstrated how neural systems could be pre-prepared a layer at once.
- In 2015, *Facebook* executed *DeepFace* to naturally tag and distinguished clients in photos.
- In 2016, *Google's AlphaGo* program beat a top-positioned worldwide Go player.

Games, particularly system games, have been an incredible method to test as well as exhibit the intensity of neural systems. Be that as it may, there are various, progressively reasonable applications.

Top 10 neural network architectures you need to know:

1. **Perceptron:** The perceptron model, proposed by *Minsky-Papert*, is one of the least difficult and most established models of Neuron. It is the littlest unit of the neural system that does certain calculations to distinguish highlights or business knowledge in the information. It acknowledges weighted information sources and applies the actuation capacity to get the yield as the conclusive outcome. Perceptron is otherwise called **threshold rationale unit (TLU)**. Perceptron is a managed learning calculation that orders the information into two classifications; along these lines, it is a parallel classifier. A perceptron isolates the information space into two classifications by a hyperplane spoken to by the accompanying condition represented by the following equation.

$$X_T G + D_K = 0$$

2. **Feedforward neural networks:** Applications on feedforward neural networks:
   - Simple characterization (where conventional machine-learning based arrangement calculations have impediments).
   - Face acknowledgment [Simple straight forward picture processing].
   - Computer vision [Where target classes are hard to classify].

   Speech recognition.

   The simplest form of neural networks is where input data travels in one direction only, passing through artificial neural nodes and exiting through output nodes. Where hidden layers may or may not be present, input and output layers are present there. Based on this, they can be further classified as a single-layered or multi-layered feed-forward neural network.

A number of layers depends on the complexity of the function. It has uni-directional forward propagation but no backward propagation. Weights are static here. An activation function is fed by inputs which are multiplied by weights. To do so, a classifying activation function or step activation function is used. For example, the neuron is activated if it is above the threshold (usually 0), and the neuron produces 1 as an output. The neuron is not activated if it is below the threshold (usually 0), which is considered as −1. They are fairly simple to maintain and are equipped to deal with data that contains a lot of noise.

3. **Multilayer perceptron**

   - Applications on multi-layer perceptron
   - Speech recognition
   - Machine translation
   - Complex classification

   An entry point towards complex neural nets where input data travels through various layers of artificial neurons. Every single node is connected to all neurons in the next layer, which makes it a fully connected neural network. Input and output layers are present, having multiple hidden Layers i.e., at least three or more layers in total. It has a bi-directional propagation i.e., forward propagation and backward propagation.

   Inputs are multiplied with weights and fed to the activation function, and in backpropagation, they are modified to reduce the loss. In simple words, weights are machine learned values from neural networks. They self-adjust depending on the difference between predicted outputs versus training inputs. Nonlinear activation functions are used, followed by SoftMax as an output layer activation function.

4. **Convolutional neural network:** Applications on convolution neural network:

   - Image processing
   - Computer vision
   - Speech recognition
   - Machine translation

   A convolution neural network contains a three-dimensional arrangement of neurons instead of the standard two-dimensional array.

   - The first layer is called a **convolutional layer**. Each neuron in the convolutional layer only processes the information from a small part of the visual field. Input features are taken batch-wise like a filter.

- The network understands the images in parts and can compute these operations multiple times to complete the full image processing.
- Processing involves the conversion of the image from RGB or HSI scale to grey-scale. Furthering the changes in the pixel value will help to detect the edges, and images can be classified into different categories.

Propagation is uni-directional where CNN contains one or more convolutional layers followed by pooling and bidirectional, where the output of the convolution layer goes to a fully connected neural network for classifying the images as shown in the above diagram. Filters are used to extract certain parts of the image. In MLP, the inputs are multiplied with weights and fed to the activation function. Convolution uses RELU, and MLP uses a nonlinear activation function followed by softmax. Convolution neural networks show very effective results in image and video recognition, semantic parsing, and paraphrase detection.

5. **Radial basis function neural networks:** The radial basis function network consists of an input vector followed by a layer of RBF neurons and an output layer with one node per category. Classification is performed by measuring the input's similarity to data points from the training set where each neuron stores a prototype. This will be one of the examples from the training set. When a new input vector [the n-dimensional vector that you are trying to classify] needs to be classified, each neuron calculates the Euclidean distance between the input and its prototype. For example, if we have two classes, i.e., class A and Class B, then the new input to be classified is closer to class A prototypes than the class B prototypes. Hence, it could be tagged or classified as class A.

   Each RBF neuron compares the input vector to its prototype and outputs a value ranging, which is a measure of similarity from 0 to 1. As the input equals to the prototype, the output of that RBF neuron will be 1, and with the distance growing between the input and prototype, the response falls off exponentially towards 0. The curve generated out of the neuron's response tends towards a typical bell curve. The output layer consists of a set of neurons [one per category]

6. **Recurrent neural networks:** Applications of recurrent neural networks
   - Text processing such auto suggest, grammar checks, and so on
   - Text to speech processing
   - Image tagger
   - Sentiment analysis

- Translation

Designed to save the output of a layer, the recurrent neural network is fed back to the input to help in predicting the outcome of the layer. The first layer is typically a feed-forward neural network followed by a recurrent neural network layer where some information it had in the previous time-step is remembered by a memory function. Forward propagation is implemented in this case. It stores information required for its future use. If the prediction is wrong, the learning rate is employed to make small changes. Hence, making it gradually increase towards making the right prediction during the backpropagation.

7. **Sequence to sequence models:** A sequence to sequence model consists of two RNNs. Here, there exists an encoder that processes the input and a decoder that processes the output. The encoder and decoder work simultaneously—either using the same parameter or different ones. This model, contrary to the actual RNN, is particularly applicable in those cases where the length of the input data is equal to the length of the output data. While they possess similar benefits and limitations to the RNN, these models are usually applied mainly in chatbots, machine translations, and question answering systems.
8. **Modular neural network:** Applications of modular neural network
   - Stock market prediction systems
   - Adaptive MNN for character recognitions
   - Compression of high-level input data.

   A modular neural network has a number of different networks that function independently and perform sub-tasks. The different networks do not really interact with or signal each other during the computation process. They work independently towards achieving the output.

   As a result, a large and complex computational process is done significantly faster by breaking it down into independent components. The computation speed increases because the networks are not interacting with or even connected to each other.

Neural networks are one of the most beautiful programming paradigms ever invented. In the conventional approach to programming, we tell the computer what to do and break big problems up into many small, precisely defined tasks that the computer can easily perform. In contrast, we do not tell the computer how to solve our problems for a neural network. Instead, it learns from observational data and figures out its own solution to the problem.

Today, deep neural networks and deep learning achieve outstanding performance for many important problems in computer vision, speech recognition, and natural language processing. They are being deployed on a large scale by companies such as *Google*, *Microsoft*, and *Facebook*. I hope that this post helps you learn the core concepts of neural networks, including modern techniques for deep learning.

Natural language programming

AI for normal language handling and text examination includes utilizing AI calculations and *"restricted"* computerized reasoning (AI) to comprehend the significance of text reports. These reports can be just about whatever contains the text: internet-based life remarks, online audits, overview reactions, even money-related, clinical, lawful, and administrative records. Fundamentally, the job of AI and AI in characteristic language preparing (NLP) and text investigation is to improve, quicken, and mechanize the hidden text examination capacities, and NLP includes that transforming this unstructured text into useable information and experiences.

In contrast to algorithmic programming, an AI model can sum up and manage novel cases. On the off chance that a case looks like something the model has seen previously, the model can utilize this earlier *"learning"* to assess the case. The objective is to make a framework where the model persistently improves at the errand you have set it. AI for NLP and text examination includes a lot of factual methods for recognizing grammatical features, substances, supposition, and different parts of the text. The strategies can be communicated as a model that is then applied to other text, otherwise called regulated AI. It likewise could be a lot of calculations that work across enormous arrangements of information to separate importance, which is known as solo AI. It is imperative to comprehend the contrast between administered and solo learning and how you can defeat both in one framework. Text information requires an exceptional way to deal with AI. This is on the grounds that text information can have a huge number of measurements (words and expressions) yet will, in general, be exceptionally scanty. For instance, the English language shares around 100,000 words practically speaking use. Be that as it may, some random tweet just contains two or three dozen of them. This contrasts from something like video text where you have exceptionally high dimensionality, yet you have tons and gobs of information to work with; in this way, it is not exactly as inadequate.

Natural language processing (**NLP**) is a field of **artificial intelligence** (**AI**) that centers around evaluating human language to make it coherent to machines. It consolidates the intensity of phonetics and software engineering to consider the standards and structure of language and make wise frameworks fit for comprehension, examining, and removing importance from text and discourse.

When a dream of sci-fi motion pictures, the capacity of machines to decipher human language is currently at the center of numerous applications that we use each day—from interpretation programming, chatbots, spam channels, and web crawlers to sentence structure checking programming, voice aides, and web-based life observing apparatuses.

Take your *Gmail*, for instance. You may have seen that your messages are consequently ordered as promotions, social, primary, or spam; that is conceivable gratitude to an NLP task called text characterization.

Another case of NLP in real life is data about booked flights showing up naturally in your schedule—that is an NLP task that separates data. In spite of the advancement made around various NLP issues, there are as yet numerous difficulties ahead, similar to those identified with **natural language understanding** (**NLU**), a subfield of NLP that is centered around understanding a text similarly we would.

Why is NLP important?

A large number of tweets, messages and web looks are produced each day, bringing about a monster measure of information that is developing continuously. Be that as it may, a large portion of this advanced information is unstructured—meaning it is not sorted out in a predefined way—making it difficult for machines to examine and extricate significant data.

NLP assumes a significant job in organizing information since it gets ready to text and discourse for machines, with the goal that they are ready to decipher, process, and arrange data. A portion of the fundamental preferences of NLP include:

- **Large-scale examination**: Characteristic language processing can assist machines with performing language-based undertakings, for example, understanding text, distinguishing what is significant, extricating conclusion, or hearing discourse, for an enormous scope. Envision you need to break down the opinion of thousands of tweets referencing your image and discover which ones allude to your item in a positive or negative manner. On account of NLP, machines can mechanize this procedure rapidly and adequately while applying steady and fair measures.
- **Structuring unstructured information**: Human language is mind-boggling, shifted, and equivocal, while machine language depends on legitimate and profoundly organized dialects and data. NLP overcomes any barrier between the manner in which we talk and how PCs disentangle data. By utilizing linguistic principles, calculations, and measurements, it can decipher the natural language and give a fitting reaction or activity.

How does NLP work?

At the point when we read a text, our minds are basically disentangling a progression of words and making associations. Those human capacities that permit us to comprehend language are decisively the ones that NLP attempts to recreate and pass on to machines. NLP works by separating words into their least difficult structure and distinguishing examples, rules, and connections between them.

As we clarified before, NLP utilizes a blend of etymology and software engineering. Etymology is utilized to comprehend the structure and significance of a book by investigating various angles such as grammar, semantics, pragmatics, and morphology. At that point, software engineering changes this etymological information into rule-based or AI calculations that can tackle explicit issues and perform wanted undertakings. Because you have a superior thought of what NLP is, how about we investigate its various strategies, techniques, and calculations:

NLP levels and techniques

In this area, we will center around the two essential NLP levels: syntactic and semantic, and their particular sub-undertakings.

- NLP levels
- Syntactic

Syntactic investigation—otherwise called parsing or linguistic structure examination—considers the linguistic guidelines in natural language to reveal the structure of a book.

Distinguishing the syntactic structure of a book and the dependency connections between words—which are spoken to on a chart called a parse tree—likewise add to understanding the importance of words.

Punctuation examination includes a wide range of methods, including:

- **Tokenization:** This is the way toward separating a series of words into semantically helpful units called **tokens**. You can utilize sentence tokenization to part sentences inside a text or word tokenization to part words inside a sentence. This NLP task works by characterizing limits, that is, a standard of where a token starts or finishes. By and large, word tokens can be isolated by clear spaces and sentence tokens by stops. In any case, you can perform elevated level tokenization for increasingly complex structures, similar to words that frequently go together, also called **collocations** (for instance, New York). Tokenization makes a book increasingly basic and simple to deal with, and it is the most fundamental undertaking in-text pre-preparing. Here is a case of word tokenization of a basic sentence: client assistance could not be better! = ["customer administration", "could", "not", "be", "better"].

Grammatical feature labeling: grammatical feature labeling (condensed as PoS labeling) includes including a grammatical feature class to every token inside a text. Some normal PoS labels are action word, descriptor, thing, pronoun, combination, relational word, crossing point, among others. For this situation, the model above would resemble this: "Client assistance": NOUN, "could": VERB, "not": ADVERB, "be": VERB, "better": ADJECTIVE, "!": PUNCTUATION PoS labeling is valuable for distinguishing connections among words and, in this manner, comprehend the significance of sentences.

- **Dependency parsing:** Dependency syntax alludes to the manner in which the words in a sentence are associated with one another. A dependency parser, in this manner, breaks down how "head words" are connected and adjusted by different words so as to comprehend the syntactic structure of a sentence:

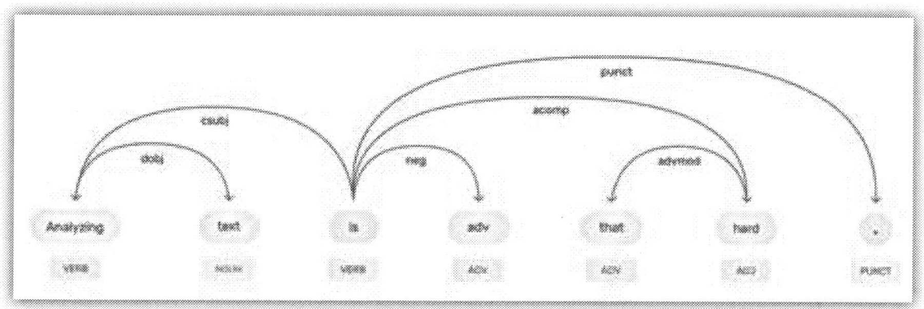

***Figure 10.10**: Dependency Parsing*

Constituency parsing: Plans to imagine the whole syntactic structure of a sentence by recognizing phrase structure syntax. You can attempt diverse parsing calculations and methodologies relying upon the idea of the text you expect to investigate and the degree of multifaceted nature you had prefer to accomplish.

- **Lemmatization and stemming:** At the point when we talk or compose, we typically utilize curved types of a word (words that get from others). Lemmatization and stemming are two comparable NLP errands that comprise of decreasing words to their base structure with the goal that they can be dissected by their normal root. The word as it shows up in the word reference—its base structure—is called a **lemma**. For instance, the words "are, is, am, were, and been", are assembled under the lemma "be". Along these lines, on the off chance that we apply this lemmatization to "*African elephants have 4 nails on their front feet*", the outcome will look something like this: African elephants have 4 nails on their front feet = ["African", "elephant", "have", "4", "nail", "on", "their", "foot"] This model is helpful to perceive how the lemmatization changes the sentence utilizing its base structure (for example "feet" was changed over into "foot"). At the point when we allude to stemming, then again, the root type of a word is called the stem. Stemming works by cutting the start and endings of words, so word stems may not generally be semantically right. For instance, utilizing stemming for the word's "counsel", "expert", "counseling", and "advisors", would bring about the stem "counsel".

The contrast between these two methodologies is that lemmatization is word reference-based and can pick the fitting lemma dependent on setting, while at the same time stemming works on single words without thinking about the specific circumstance. Along these lines, for instance, in the sentence "*this is better*", "better" is comprehended as a lemma for "*good*", yet this connection is missed by stemming. Despite the fact that they can prompt less-precise outcomes on certain events, stemmers are simpler to manufacture and perform quicker than lemmatizes.

- **Stopword removal:** This procedure comprises of sifting through high recurrence words that enhance a sentence. For instance, which, to, at, for, is, and so forth, are for the most part, words that do not assist you with understanding a text. Evacuating stop words is a significant advance in preprocessing text information that will later be utilized to make NLP models. You can even alter arrangements of stopwords so as to improve exactness. Suppose you had prefer to characterize client care tickets dependent on their subjects. In this model: "*Hi, I'm experiencing difficulty signing in with my new secret key*", it might be valuable to evacuate stop words like "*hi*", "*I*", "*am*", "*with*", and "*my*", so you are left with the words that assist you with understanding the subject of the ticket: "*inconvenience*", "*signing in*", "*new*", and "*secret key*".
- **Semantic:** Semantic examination centers around recognizing the significance of text. By dissecting the structure of sentences and the cooperation between words in a given setting, semantic investigation attempts to locate the best possible significance of words that may have various definitions. Joined with software engineering, the semantic examination can help comprehend the subject of a book, as it can recognize the nearness of related ideas. That way, a news story containing the words speculators, market, and a downturn would be named as "*financial matters*". Because language is polysemic and vague, semantics is viewed as one of the most testing zones in NLP, and its issues have not been completely settled at this point.

These are a portion of the sub-assignments in the semantic examination:

1. **Word sense disambiguation:** Contingent upon their specific situation, words can have various implications. Take *"book"*, for instance:
   - You should peruse this book, it is an incredible novel!
   - You should book the trips as quickly as time permits.
   - You should close the books before the year's over.
   - You ought to get everything done right to maintain a strategic distance from potential confusion.

   There are two fundamental strategies that can be utilized for **word sense disambiguation (WSD)**: information-based (or word reference approach) and managed approach. The first attempts to surmise importance by watching the word reference meanings of equivocal terms inside a text, whereas the last requires preparing information and depends on AI calculations that can gain from models. Recognizing the significance of a word dependent on the setting is as yet a significant (and open) challenge looked by natural language processing.
2. **Relationship extraction:** This undertaking comprises of recognizing semantic connections between at least two elements in a book. Elements can be names, places, associations, and so on, and connections can be set up in an assortment of ways. For instance, in the expression *"Susan lives in Los Angeles"*, an individual (Susan) is identified with a spot (Los Angeles) by the semantic classification *"lives in."*

Techniques

There are two principle specialized ways to deal with natural language processing that make various kinds of frameworks: one depends on phonetic standards and the other on AI strategies. In this area, we will look at the points of interest and burdens of every one, and the chance of joining both (half and half methodology).

- **Rule-based approach:** Rule-based frameworks are the soonest way to deal with NLP and comprise of applying hand-created phonetic standards to text. Each standard is framed by a precursor and a forecast. Along these lines, when the framework finds a coordinating example, it applies the anticipated measures. For instance, envision you had preferred to perform assumption examination to discover positive and negative assessments in item audits. To begin with, you would need to make a rundown of positive words (for example, great, best, magnificent, and so on) and a rundown of negative words (terrible, most noticeably awful, disappointing, and so forth). At that point, you will have to experience each survey and tally the quantity of positive words and the quantity of negative words. In view of the quantity of positive and negative words, you will order every sentiment as positive, negative, or unbiased. Because the principles are dictated by people, this sort of framework is straightforward and gives genuinely precise outcomes with little exertion. Another preferred position of deciding based frameworks is that they do not require preparing information, which makes them a decent alternative in the event that you do not have a lot of information and are simply beginning your investigation. Be that as it may, physically creating and upgrading rules can be a troublesome and lumbering undertaking and frequently requires an etymologist or an information engineer. Additionally, including an excessive number of rules can prompt complex frameworks with conflicting standards.

- **AI models:** AI comprises calculations that can figure out how to comprehend language dependent on past perceptions. The framework utilizes factual strategies to manufacture its own *"insight bank"*, and is prepared to make the relationship between specific info and its comparing yield. How about we return to the opinion examination model. With AI, you can assemble a model to naturally characterize sentiments as positive, negative, or unbiased. On the whole, you have to prepare your classifier by physically labeling the models until it is prepared to make its own forecasts over inconspicuous information. You will likewise need to change the text models into something a machine can get (vectors), a procedure known as highlight extractor or text vectorization. When the writings have been changed into vectors, they are taken care of to an AI calculation along with their normal yield (labels) to make an arrangement model. The greatest favorable position of AI models is their capacity to learn all alone, with no compelling reason to characterize manual guidelines. All you will require is a decent arrangement of preparing information, with a few models for every one of the labels you had prefer to examine. AI models can have higher exactness and review than rule-based frameworks after some time, and the all the more preparing information you feed them, the more precise they are. Be that as it may, you will need enough preparing information pertinent to the difficulties you need to tackle so as to fabricate a precise framework.
- **Hybrid approach:** A third methodology includes consolidating both standard-based frameworks and AI frameworks. That way, you can profit from the upsides of every one of them and increase precision in your outcomes.
- **NLP algorithms:** Normal language processing includes utilizing a wide range of calculations to distinguish etymological guidelines, separate

importance, and reveal the structure of a book. The following are the absolute most mainstream calculations that can be utilized in NLP, relying upon the undertaking you need to perform.

Text classification algorithms

Text classification is the way toward sorting out unstructured text into predefined classes (labels). Text grouping assignments incorporate notion investigation, plan discovery, theme demonstrating, and language location. These are the absolute most famous calculations for making text arrangement models:

- **Naive Bayes**: An assortment of probabilistic calculations that draw from the likelihood hypothesis and Bayes' Theorem to anticipate the tag of a book. As indicated by Bayes' Theorem, the likelihood of an occasion occurring (A) can be determined if an earlier occasion (B) has occurred.

  This model is called innocent since it expects that every factor (highlights or indicators) is free, has no impact on the others, and every factor equally affects the result. Credulous Bayes calculation is utilized for text arrangement, slant examination, suggestion frameworks, and spam channels.

- **Support vector machines (SVM)**: This is a calculation, for the most part, used to tackle arrangement issues with high precision. Administered arrangement models intend to foresee the classification of a bit of text-dependent on a lot of physically labeled preparing models.

  So as to do that, SVM transforms preparing models into vectors and attracts a hyperplane to separate two classes of vectors: those that have a place with a specific tag and those that do not have a place with that one tag. In light of which side of the limit they land, the model will have the option to dole out some tag. SVM calculations can be particularly valuable when you have a constrained measure of information.

- **Deep learning**: This arrangement of AI calculations depends on fake neural systems. They are ideal for handling huge volumes of information; however, thusly, they require an enormous preparing corpus. Profound learning calculations are utilized to take care of complex NLP issues.

Text extraction algorithms

Text extraction comprises extricating explicit bits of information from a book. You can utilize extraction models to pull out catchphrases, substances (for example, organization names or areas), or sum up text. Here are the most well-known calculations for text extraction:

- **TF-IDF (term recurrence reverse record recurrence)**: This measurable methodology decides how significant a word is inside a text in an assortment of reports and is naturally used to separate important watchwords from the text. The significance of a word increments dependent on the occasions it shows up in a book (text recurrence), yet diminishes dependent on the recurrence it shows up in the corpus of writings (opposite record recurrence).
- **Natural expressions (regex)**: A normal articulation is a grouping of characters that characterize an example. Regex checks if a string contains a decided pursuit design, for instance, in-text managers or web indexes, and is naturally utilized for separating watchwords and elements from the text.
- **Contingent random fields** (CRF): This AI approach learns examples and concentrates information by allotting a load to a lot of highlights in a sentence. This methodology can make designs that are more extravagant and more mind-boggling than those examples made with regex, empowering machines to decide better results for increasingly questionable articulations.
- **Rapid automatic keyword extraction** (RAKE): this calculation for catchphrase extraction utilizes a rundown of stopwords and expression delimiters to distinguish applicable words or expressions inside a text. Essentially, it dissects the recurrence of a word and its co-event with different words.

Subject modeling algorithms

Subject displaying is a strategy for bunching gatherings of words and comparative articulations inside a lot of information. In contrast to theme grouping, point demonstrating is a solo strategy, which implies that it induces designs from information without expecting to characterize classifications or label information already.

The fundamental calculations utilized for point demonstrating include:

- **Latent semantic analysis** (LSA): This strategy depends on the distributional speculation, and distinguishes words and articulations with comparable implications that happen in comparative bits of text. It is the most continuous strategy for theme display.
- **Latent dirichlet allocation** (LDA): This is a generative measurable model that expects that records contain different themes and that every subject contains words with specific probabilities of an event.

What is NLP used for?

The motivation behind NLP is to examine, structure, and discover significance in text and discourse. You can utilize NLP to play out an assortment of undertakings, for example, interpreting text starting with one language then onto the next, distinguishing pertinent points inside the text, or extricating the most significant watchwords in an enormous assortment of text, among others.

A couple of instances of NLP that individuals utilize each day are:

- Spell check
- Autocomplete
- Voice text informing
- Spam channels
- Related watchwords on web search tools
- Siri, Alexa, or Google Assistant.

We do not routinely consider the complexities of our own dialects. It is instinctive conduct used to pass on data and significance with semantic signals, for example, words, signs, or pictures. It is been said that language is simpler to learn and comes all the more normally in immaturity since it is repeatable, prepared conduct—much like strolling. Also, language does not observe an exacting arrangement of rules, with such huge numbers of exemptions like *"I before E aside from after C."* What falls into place without any issues for people, nonetheless, is exceedingly hard for PCs with the measure of unstructured information, absence of formal guidelines, and nonappearance of true setting or aim. That is the reason AI and man-made brainpower (AI) are picking up consideration and energy, with more prominent human dependency on processing frameworks to impart and perform assignments. Furthermore, as AI gets progressively modern, so will NLP. Although the terms AI and NLP may summon pictures of cutting-edge robots, there are as of now essential instances of NLP at work in our everyday lives. Here are a couple of noticeable models.

- **Email channels:** Email channels are one of the most fundamental and starting uses of NLP on the web. It began with spam channels, revealing certain words or expressions that signal a spam message. However, separating has been redesigned, much the same as early adjustments of NLP. One of the more pervasive, more up-to-date utilization of NLP is found in Gmail's email arrangement. The framework perceives if messages have a place in one of three classifications (essential, social, or advancements) in light of their substance. For all Gmail clients, this keeps your inbox to a sensible size with significant, important messages you wish to survey and react to rapidly.

- **Smart assistants:** Smart assistances like Apple's Siri and Amazon's Alexa perceive designs in the discourse on account of voice acknowledgment, at that point surmise meaning and give a helpful reaction. We have gotten used to the way that we can say *"Hello Siri,"* pose an inquiry, and she comprehends what we said and reacts with pertinent answers dependent on the setting. Furthermore, we are becoming accustomed to seeing Siri or Alexa spring up all through our home and day-by-day life as we have discussions with them through things such as the indoor regulator, light switches, vehicle, and that is only the tip of the iceberg.

  We presently expect colleagues like *Alexa* and *Siri* to comprehend relevant pieces of information as they improve our lives and make certain exercises simpler, like requesting things and even acknowledge when they react entertainingly or answer inquiries regarding themselves. Our communications will develop progressively close to home as these collaborators become acquainted with increasingly us. As a New York Times article *"Why We May Soon Be Living in Alexa's World,"* clarified: *"Something greater is in the air. Alexa has the absolute best of turning into the third incredible shopper figuring foundation of this decade."*

- **Search results:** Web indexes use NLP to surface pertinent outcomes dependent on comparative inquiry practices or client aim, so the normal individual finds what they need without being a pursuit term wizard. For instance, *Google* not just predicts what famous quests may apply to your inquiry as you begin composing; however, it takes a gander at the entire picture and perceives what you are attempting to state as opposed to the specific hunt words. Somebody could put a flight number in *Google* and get the flight status, type a ticker image and get stock data, or an adding machine may come up while contributing a math condition. These are a few varieties you may see while finishing a pursuit as NLP in search relates the questionable inquiry to a relative substance and gives helpful outcomes.

- **Predictive text:** Things such as autocorrect, autocomplete, and prescient text are so typical on our cell phones that we underestimate them. Autocomplete and prescient text are like web indexes in that they foresee comments dependent on what you type, completing the word, or proposing a significant one. What is more, autocorrect will once in a while even change words with the goal that the general message bodes well. They likewise gain from you. Prescient text will modify itself to your own language eccentricities the more you use it. This makes for the sake of entertainment tests where people will share whole sentences made up altogether of prescient text on their telephones. The outcomes are shockingly close to home and illuminating; they have even been featured by a few news sources.

- **Language translation:** One of the indications of undermining your Spanish schoolwork is that linguistically, it is a wreck. Numerous dialects do not take into account straight interpretation and have various requests for sentence structure, which interpretation administrations used to ignore. In any case, they have progressed significantly. With NLP, online interpreters can decipher dialects all the more precisely and present syntactically right outcomes. This is vastly useful when attempting to speak with somebody in another dialect. That, however, whereas making an interpretation of from another dialect to your own, apparatuses now perceive the language-dependent on inputted message and decipher it.
- **Digital calls:** We as a whole hear *"this call might be recorded for preparing purposes,"* yet once in a while do we wonder what that involves. It turns out these accounts might be utilized for preparing purposes if a client is oppressed, however more often than not, they go into the database for an NLP framework to gain from and improve later on. Computerized frameworks direct client calls to an assistance delegate or online chatbots, which react to client demands with accommodating data. This is an NLP practice that numerous organizations, including enormous media communications suppliers, have put to utilize. NLP additionally empowers PC-created language near the voice of a human. Calls to plan arrangements like an oil change or hairstyle can be mechanized, as proven by this video indicating Google Assistant creation a hair arrangement.

Data analysis

Natural language abilities are being incorporated into information investigation work processes as more BI merchants offer a characteristic language interface to information perceptions. One model is more intelligent visual encodings, presenting the best representation for the correct undertaking dependent on the semantics of the information. This opens up more open doors for individuals to investigate their information utilizing characteristic language articulations or question pieces comprised of a few watchwords that can be deciphered and relegated a significance. Applying language to research information improves the degree of openness; however, it brings down the boundary to examination across associations, past the normal network of experts and programming designers.

Conclusion

Deep learning is the first run through which PCs can see the world that will impact most the occupations, and we are at the beginning of this innovation.

NLP is utilized to apply AI calculations to text and discourse. **Natural language toolkit** (**NLTK**) is the main stage for building Python projects to work with human language information. Sentence tokenization is the issue of separating a string of composed language into its part sentences. Word tokenization is the issue of partitioning a string of composed language into its segment words. The objective of both stemming and lemmatization is to lessen inflectional structures and here and there derivationally related types of a word to a typical base structure. Stop words will be words that are sifted through previously or subsequent to preparing of text. They, for the most part, alluding to the most widely recognized words in a language. An ordinary articulation is an arrangement of characters that characterize a pursuit design. The sack of-words model is a well-known and basic component extraction procedure utilized when we work with text. It portrays the event of each word inside a record. TF-IDF is a factual measure used to assess the significance of a word to a report in an assortment or corpus. The next chapter will explain the applications of ML in different sectors.

Points to remember

To enhance your skills, you had like to remember the following terms/points:

- Predictive analytics helps us to comprehend conceivable future events by examining the past.
- Machine learning and predictive analytics both are connected because machine learning is a predictive learning branch.
- The random forest can precisely order enormous volumes of information.
- The name "*Random Forest*" is gotten from the way that the calculation is a blend of choice trees. Each tree relies upon the estimations of an irregular vector tested autonomously with a similar dispersion for all trees in the "*timberland.*" Each one is developed to the biggest degree conceivable.
- Deep learning is a man-made brainpower work that copies the operations of the human mind in preparing information and making designs for use in dynamic.

CHAPTER 11
Application of Machine Learning

In the previous chapters, we have seen the power of AI and ML, which include technologies such as deep learning, neural networks, and natural-language processing that can also encompass more advanced systems, which understand, learn, predict, adapt, and potentially operate autonomously.

The beauty of applications that use machine learning is that it seems to be extremely simple on the surface, hiding away much complexity from users.

The 21st century is just two decades old, and it is sure that one of the greatest transformative advancements and empowering agents for the human culture of this century will be **artificial insight** (**AI**). It is an entrenched thought that machine learning and related administrations and stages are set to change worldwide profitability, working examples, and ways of life and make tremendous riches. For instance, *McKinsey* sees it conveying worldwide financial action of around $13 trillion by 2030. For the time being, research firm *Gartner* expects the worldwide AI-based financial movement to increment from about $1.2 trillion every 2018 to about $3.9 trillion by 2022. It is an obvious fact that this change is being, to a huge degree, filled by the ground-breaking ML instruments and strategies, for example, deep convolutional networks, **generative adversarial networks** (**GAN**), Gradient-helped tree models (GBM), **deep reinforcement learning** (**DRL**), and so forth.

Structure

This chapter will highlight the machine learning applications in:

- Healthcare
- Finance
- Retail
- Travel
- Media

Objective

After reading this chapter, you will be able to apply your machine learning concept in healthcare, finance, retail, travel, and media.

Machine learning applications in healthcare

In any chapter, conventional business and innovation segments are not by any means the only fields being affected by machine learning. Medicinal services are a field that is believed to be profoundly appropriate for the utilizations of AI devices and procedures. Obligatory practices, for example, **electronic medical records (EMR)**, have just prepared human services frameworks for applying big data instruments for cutting-edge information investigation. Computer-based intelligence/ML instruments are bound to increase the value of this stream. They are required to improve the nature of computerization and shrewd dynamic in essential/tertiary patient consideration and open human services frameworks. This could be the greatest effect of AI instruments as it can conceivably change the personal satisfaction of billions of individuals around the globe. The regularly expanding populace of the world has squeezed the social insurance area to give quality treatment and human services administrations. Presently, like never before, individuals are requesting brilliant social insurance administrations, applications, and wearables that will assist them with leading better lives and draw out their life expectancy.

By 2025, artificial intelligence in the social insurance area is anticipated to increment from \$2.1 billion (as of December 2018) to \$36.1 billion at a CAGR of 50.2%. The social insurance area has consistently been probably the best defender of creative innovation, and artificial intelligence and machine learning are no exemptions. Similarly, as AI and ML pervaded quickly into the business and web-based business parts, they likewise found various use cases inside the social insurance industry. Indeed, machine learning (a subset of AI) has come to assume a critical job in the domain of social insurance—from improving the conveyance arrangement of medicinal services administrations, reducing down expenses, and taking care of patient information to the improvement of new treatment methodology and medications, remote checking thus significantly more.

This requirement for a *"superior"* medicinal services administration is progressively making the degree for AI and ML applications to enter the social insurance and pharma world. With no deficiency of information in the human services division, now is the ideal opportunity to outfit the capability of this information with AI and ML applications. Today, AI, ML, and profound learning are influencing each comprehensible space, and social insurance, as well, does not stay immaculate. In the wide compass of AI's present common desire, AI social insurance applications appear to top the rundown for financing and press over the most recent three years.

Since mid-2013, IBM's Watson has been utilized in the clinical field, and in the wake of winning a dumbfounding arrangement of games against with world's best living Go player, Google DeepMind's group chose to toss their weight behind the clinical chances of their advances too. A considerable lot of the AI (ML) industry's most sweltering youthful new businesses are hunkering down critical parts of their endeavors to social insurance, including Nervanasys (as of late gained by *Intel*), *Ayasdi* (raised $94MM starting at 02/16), *Sentient.ai* (raised $144MM starting at 02/16), *digital reasoning systems* (raised $36MM starting at 02/16) among others. With all the energy in the financial specialist and examination networks, we at Emerj have discovered most AI officials make some hard memories putting the finger on where AI is positively shaping medicinal services today.

Likewise, the way that the social insurance part's information trouble is expanding continuously (inferable from the ever-developing populace and higher frequency of illnesses) is making it even more fundamental to consolidate machine learning into its canvas. With machine learning, there are unlimited prospects. Through its front-line applications, ML is changing the medicinal services industry to improve things. Examination firm Frost and Sullivan keep up that by 2021, machine learning will create almost $6.7 billion in income in the worldwide human services industry. As per *McKinsey*, large information and AI in the human services area can possibly produce up to $100 billion every year! With the persistent developments in information science and ML, the medicinal services segment presently holds the possibility to use progressive devices to give a better mind.

Diagnosis in medical imaging

PC vision has been one of the most amazing achievements on account of AI and profound learning, and it is an especially dynamic human services application for

ML. Microsoft's Inner Eye activity (began in 2010) is by and by dealing with picture symptomatic devices, and the group has posted various recordings clarifying their turns of events, remembering this video for machine learning for picture examination: profound learning will most likely play an increasingly more significant job in symptomatic applications as profound learning turns out to be progressively open, and as more information sources (counting rich and fluctuated types of clinical symbolism) become some portion of the AI demonstrative procedure. In any case, profound learning applications are known to be constrained in their illustrative limit. As it were, a prepared profound learning framework cannot clarify *"how"* it showed up at its expectations—in any event, when they are right. This sort of *"discovery issue"* is all the more testing in human services, where specialists will not have any desire to settle on life-and-passing choices without a firm comprehension of how the machine showed up at its proposal (regardless of whether those suggestions have demonstrated to be right before).

For pursuers who are not acquainted with profound adapting yet might want an educated, streamlined clarification, we prescribe tuning in to our meeting with Google DeepMind's Nando de Freitas.

Treatment queries and suggestions

The conclusion is an exceptionally confusing procedure and includes—at any rate for the time being—a bunch of elements (everything from the shade of whites of a patient's eyes to the food they have for breakfast) of which machines cannot and by gather and bode well; in any case, there is little uncertainty that a machine may help in helping doctors make the correct contemplations in finding and treatment, just by filling in as an augmentation of logical information.

That is the thing that **memorial sloan kettering's** (**MSK**) oncology division is focusing on in its ongoing association with IBM Watson. MSK has reams of information on malignant growth patients and medicines utilized over decades, and it is ready to introduce and propose treatment thoughts or choices to specialists in managing remarkable future disease cases—by pulling from what worked best before. The sort of an insight-expanding apparatus, whereas hard to sell into the hurly-brawny universe of clinics, is as of now in primer use today.

Scaled up/crowdsourced medical data collection

There are many spotlights on pooling information from different cell phones to total and understand all the more live well-being information. Apple's research kit is intending to do this in the treatment of Parkinson's sickness and Asperger's disorder by permitting clients to get to intelligent applications (one of which applies

AI for facial acknowledgment) that evaluate their conditions after some time; their utilization of the application takes care of continuous advancement information into a mysterious pool for future investigation.

IBM is making a huge effort to procure all the well-being information it can get its hands on, from cooperating with Medtronic to understand diabetes and insulin information continuously to purchasing out social insurance examination organization *Truven Health* for $2.6B. In spite of the gigantic downpour of human services information given by the web of things, the business, despite everything, is by all accounts testing how to comprehend this data and make continuous changes to treatment. Researchers and patients, the same can be hopeful that, as this pattern of pooled buyer information proceeds, analysts will have more ammo for handling extreme maladies and exceptional cases.

Medication discovery

Although great part of the human services industry is a bog of laws and befuddling motivating forces of different partners (clinic CEOs, specialists, medical caretakers, patients, insurance agencies, and so forth), sedate revelation stands apart as a generally direct monetary incentive for AI medicinal services application makers. This application additionally manages one moderately clear client who happens to, for the most part, have profound pockets: sedate organizations. IBM's own wellbeing applications have had activities in sedate disclosure since its initial days. Google has likewise bounced into the medication revelation quarrel and joins a large group of organizations previously collecting and bringing in cash by taking a shot at sedate disclosure with the assistance of machine learning. We have secured tranquilize revelation and pharma applications in more noteworthy profundity somewhere else on Emerj. A considerable lot of our speculator interviews (counting our meeting named *"Specialists Don't Want to be Replaced"* with *Steve Gullans* of Excel VM) include a moderately idealistic viewpoint about the speed of advancement in tranquilizing disclosure versus numerous other human services applications (see our rundown of *"exceptional hindrances"* to clinical AI at the finish of this article).

Robotic surgery

The da Vinci robot has gotten the main part of the consideration in the mechanical medical procedure space, and some could contend in light of current circumstances. This gadget permits specialists to control dexterous mechanical appendages so as to perform medical procedures with fine detail and in restricted spaces (and with few tremors) that would be conceivable by the human hand alone. Here is a video featuring the inconceivable aptitude of the Da Vinci robot: while not all automated medical procedure strategies include machine learning, a few frameworks use PC vision (helped by AI) to recognize separations or a particular body part (for example, distinguishing hair follicles for transplantation on the head, on account of hair transplantation medical procedure). What is more, machine learning is now and again used to consistent the movement and development of automated appendages when taking headings from human controllers.

The following are 11 well-known AI applications that are becoming showbiz royalty in the medicinal services industry:

1. **Pattern imaging analytics:** Today, medicinal services associations around the globe are especially keen on improving imaging investigation and pathology with the assistance of AI instruments and calculations. AI applications can help radiologists to recognize the unobtrusive changes in examines, in this manner helping them distinguish and analyze the medical problems at the beginning times. One such pathbreaking progression is Google's ML calculation to recognize carcinogenic tumors in mammograms. Likewise, as of late, at *Indiana University-Purdue University Indianapolis*, scientists have made a critical achievement by building up an AI calculation to anticipate (with 90% exactness) the backslide rate for myelogenous leukemia (AML). Other than these discoveries, analysts at Stanford have additionally built up a profound learning calculation to distinguish and analyze skin malignancy.
2. **Personalized treatment and behavioral modification:** Between 2012 and 2017, the infiltration pace of electronic health records in social insurance rose from 40% to 67%. This normally implies more access to singular patient wellbeing information. By assembling this individual clinical information of individual patients with ML applications and calculations, social insurance suppliers (HCPs) can recognize and evaluate medical problems better. In light of directed learning, clinical experts can anticipate the dangers and dangers to a patient's wellbeing as indicated by the manifestations and hereditary data in his clinical history. This is correctly what IBM Watson oncology is doing. Utilizing patients' clinical data and clinical history is helping doctors to configuration better treatment plans dependent on a streamlined choice of treatment decisions.

   Conduct adjustment is a significant part of preventive medication. ML advancements are helping take conduct change up a score to help impact positive behavioral fortifications in patients. For instance, Somatix, a B2B2C-based information examination organization that has propelled an ML-based application that inactively screens and perceives a variety of physical and passionate states. This enables doctors to comprehend what sort of social and way of life changes are required for a solid body and psyche. Medicinal services new businesses and associations have additionally begun to apply ML applications to encourage conduct changes. Somatix, an information examination B2B2C programming stage, is a fine model. Its ML application utilizes *"acknowledgment of hand-to-mouth motions"* to assist people with comprehension and survey their conduct, subsequently permitting them to open up to settle on invigorating choices.

3. **Drug discovery and manufacturing:** AI applications have discovered their way into the field of medication disclosure, particularly in the fundamental stage, directly from the introductory screening of a medication's mixes to its assessed achievement rate dependent on organic components. This is essentially founded on cutting-edge sequencing. AI is being utilized by pharma organizations in the medication disclosure and assembling process. Be that as it may, at present, this is restricted to using solo ML that can distinguish designs in crude information. The concentration here is to create exactness medication controlled by solo realizing, which permits doctors to distinguish components for *"multifactorial"* infections. The MIT clinical machine Learning Group is one of the main players in the game. Its exactness medication research intends to grow such calculations that can assist with understanding the malady forms better and in like manner chalk out powerful treatment for medical problems like Type 2 diabetes.

   Aside from this, R&D innovations, including cutting edge sequencing and exactness medication, are additionally being utilized to discover which elective ways for the treatment of multifactorial illnesses. Microsoft's Project Hanover utilizes ML-based advances for creating accuracy in medication. Indeed, even Google has joined the medication disclosure fleeting trend. As indicated by the UK Royal Society, AI can be of extraordinary assistance in enhancing bio-fabricating for pharmaceuticals. Pharmaceutical makers can tackle the information from the assembling procedures to decrease the general time required to create drugs, in this way additionally lessening the expense of assembling.

4. **Identifying diseases and diagnosis:** AI, alongside deep learning, has helped make an astounding discovery in the conclusion procedure. On account of these trendsetting innovations, today, specialists can analyze even such maladies that were already past determination—be it a tumor/or malignant growth in the underlying stages to hereditary sicknesses. For example, IBM Watson Genomics incorporates intellectual registering with genome-based tumor sequencing to advance the finding procedure so treatment can be begun head-on. At that point, there is Microsoft's InnerEye activity propelled in 2010 that plans to create advancement analytic apparatuses for better picture investigation.

Computerized reasoning: Taking or rather taken over.

5. **Robotic surgery:** On account of mechanical medical procedures, today, specialists can effectively work even in the most muddled circumstances and with accuracy. A valid example—the Da Vinci robot. This robot permits specialists to control and control mechanical appendages to perform medical procedures with accuracy and fewer tremors in restricted spaces of the human body. The automated medical procedure is likewise broadly utilized in hair transplantation strategies as it includes fine specifying and outline. Today mechanical autonomy is initiated in the field of medical procedure. Mechanical autonomy controlled by AI and ML calculations upgrades the exactness of careful instruments by fusing constant medical procedure measurements, information from fruitful careful encounters, and information from pre-operation clinical records inside the surgery. As indicated by *Accenture*, mechanical technology has diminished the length of remain in medical procedures by practically 21%.

   Major robotics utilizes AI to improve customization and keep intrusiveness at the very least in surgeries, including body leaves behind complex life structures, for example, the spine.

6. **Personalized treatment:** By utilizing quiet clinical history, ML innovations can help create tweaked medicines and meds that can target explicit illnesses in singular patients. This, when joined with the prescient examination, receives further rewards. In this way, rather than browsing a given arrangement of conclusions or assessing the hazard to the patient dependent on his/her indicative history, specialists can depend on the prescient capacities of ML to analyze their patients. IBM Watson Oncology is a prime case of conveying customized treatment to disease patient's dependent on their clinical history.

7. **Clinical trial research:** AI applications present a huge degree for improving clinical preliminary examination. By applying keen prescient examination to applicants of clinical preliminaries, clinical experts could evaluate a progressively complete scope of information, which would, obviously, diminish the expenses and time required for leading clinical analyses. *McKinsey* keeps up that there is a variety of ML applications that can additionally upgrade the clinical preliminary productivity, for example, assisting with finding the ideal example sizes for expanded adequacy and lessening chance information blunders by utilizing EHRs. AI is quickly developing to turn into a staple in the clinical preliminary and exploration process. Why?

   Clinical preliminaries and examinations include a great deal of time, exertion, and cash. Now and again, the procedure can extend for quite a long time.

ML-based prescient examination help cut down the time and cash interest in clinical preliminaries yet would likewise convey exact outcomes. Besides, ML advances can be utilized to recognize potential clinical preliminary applicants, get to their clinical history records, screen the up-and-comers all through the preliminary procedure, select best testing tests, diminish information-based mistakes, and significantly more.

ML instruments can likewise encourage remote checking by getting to the continuous clinical information of patients. By taking care of the wellbeing measurements of patients in the Cloud, ML applications can permit HCPs to anticipate any potential dangers that may bargain the soundness of the patients.

8. **Predicting epidemic outbreaks:** Social insurance associations are applying ML and AI calculations to screen and anticipate the conceivable plague flare-ups that can take over different pieces of the world. By gathering information from satellites, continuous updates via web-based networking media, and other crucial data from the web, these computerized apparatuses can anticipate pestilence flare-ups. This can be a help, especially for the underdeveloped nations that need a legitimate medicinal services framework. Although these are only a couple of utilization instances of machine learning today, later on, we can anticipate substantially more upgraded and spearheading ML applications in human services. Since ML is as yet advancing, we are in for some increasingly such shocks that will change human lives, forestall illnesses, and help improve the social insurance benefits significantly.

   For example, support vector machines and fake neural systems have anticipated the episode of intestinal sickness by considering elements, for example, temperature, normal month-to-month precipitation, and so forth. ProMED-mail, an online program, permits wellbeing associations to screen illnesses and anticipate infection flare-ups progressively. Utilizing robotized order and perception, HealthMap effectively depends on ProMED to track and ready nations about the conceivable pestilence episodes.

9. **Crowdsourced data collection:** Today, the medicinal services area is amazingly putting resources into publicly supporting clinical information from numerous sources (versatile applications, social insurance stages, and so forth), obviously, with the assent of individuals. In light of this pool of live wellbeing information, specialists and human services suppliers can convey rapid and essential treatment to patients (no time squandered in fulfilling formal administrative work). As of late, IBM teamed up with Medtronic to gather and decipher diabetes and insulin information, continuously dependent on publicly supported information. Of course, Apple's research

kit awards clients access to intuitive applications that utilization ML-based facial acknowledgment to treat Asperger's and Parkinson's infection.

10. **Improved radiotherapy:** AI has ended up being colossally useful in the field of radiology. In clinical picture examination, there is a large number of discrete factors that can get activated at any arbitrary second. ML-based calculations are valuable here. Since ML calculations gain from the numerous unique information tests, they can more readily analyze and distinguish the ideal factors. For example, ML is utilized in clinical picture investigation to characterize objects like sores into various classes—typical, unusual, sore or non-sore, kindhearted, harmful, and so on. Analysts in UCLH are utilizing Google's DeepMind Health to grow such calculations that can recognize the distinction between sound cells and harmful cells thus improving the radiation treatment for dangerous cells.
11. **Maintaining healthcare records:** Regularly refreshing and keeping up medicinal services records and patient clinical history is a comprehensive and costly procedure. ML advancements are illuminating this issue by diminishing the time, exertion, and cash contribution to the record-keeping process. Record characterization strategies utilizing **vector machines (VMs)** and ML-based OCR acknowledgment procedures like Google's cloud vision API help sort and group medicinal services information. At that point, there is likewise brilliant wellbeing records that help associate specialists, human services professionals, and patients to improve research, care conveyance, and general wellbeing. Today, we remain on the cusp of a clinical upheaval, all gratitude to AI and computerized reasoning. In any case, utilizing innovation alone will not improve human services. There likewise should be interested and committed personalities who can offer importance to such splendid mechanical advancements as AI and AI.

Closing thoughts on machine learning in healthcare

Finding, treatment, and avoidance are generally tremendous issues that are situated to a limited extent on abundant information, and their improvement speaks to endless worth. This is only the sort of thing that Silicon valley should jump on, is not that so? Clearly, there is an opportunity; however, there are likewise interesting deterrents in the clinical field that are not generally present in different areas:

1. **Stakeholder-transport is dispersed**: When you purchase a *Toyota Camry*, it is an exchange that fulfills your own needs. You get it from *Toyota*, you make the most of its advantages, and you are answerable to fix and look after it. When an emergency clinic welcomes on another machine learning human services symptomatic gadget, who pays for it? Would patients pay a

premium to be treated at emergency clinics with such gadgets? Would clinics spread the cost so as to boast about better analytic devices and draw in more patients? Would protection spread the cost here and there? Specialists may like such a gadget in the event that it improves indicative precision; however, a few patients may despise or not acknowledge being treated by a machine. Likewise, a few patients may mobilize for more AI demonstrative instruments, yet specialists or attendants in dread of their occupations may revitalize against their across-the-board reception. On the off chance that such a machine made a mistake (possibly a deadly one), when might we say this was the duty of the machine producer, and when might we say it was the flaw of the specialists for not utilizing it effectively? This is only a hint of something larger of the cross-section of partners in the clinical space, and it is one of the numerous reasons why advancement and change are at times troublesome in the clinical field.

2. **Security is tight:** When you purchase a feast at Wendy's or some pants from GAP, you do not have to give those organizations considerably more than a wad of money or a Visa. At the point when you experience indicative tests to decide the most ideal approach to treat your skin malignant growth, substantially more delicate data must be gathered by a social insurance supplier. **Health Insurance Portability and Accountability Act (HIPAA)**, passed by Congress in 1996 laws exist—among different reasons—to authorize federal guidelines on any transmission of patient clinical data. In the event that you make an application to share pictures of food, you will have much less Federal formality to cut through than if you make an application for diagnosing malady indications through blood tests. Sharing wellbeing information across clinics, through cell phones, or in different databases suggests numerous novel difficulties with HIPAA consistency.
3. **Medicine is more than math**: A specialist is not just a propelled *"choice tree,"* taking in information focuses and siphoning out the most probable analysis. Specialists are surveying surges of data that machines today are either unequipped for evaluating or are unequipped for incorporating into a *"specialist replicator"* robot. Consider the expression on a patient's face, their stride and walk, what their relatives state about their past conduct (notwithstanding what they round out themselves on an admission structure), the smell of their breath, their degree of apprehension (as communicated by non-verbal communication and the inner mind), and the rundown continues endlessly. The activity of supplanting a whole specialist—at any rate for general conclusion and treatment—is impossible. Trend-setters should discover the pieces of these issues that they can really unravel without taking on more than they could possibly deal with.

4. **A "black box" will not do**: Machine learning and profound learning (dissimilar to stodgier AI approaches like master frameworks) cannot communicate why they accomplished the outcome that they did. Now and again, this does not make a difference. For *Facebook*, it is not totally important to know precisely why an ML program distinguished your face as your face in a picture. In the event that it effectively labeled you in a picture, that is a sufficient success. Then again, a patient who is being informed that he/she should experience chemotherapy is probably not going to acknowledge the appropriate response, "*The AI calculation said as much, in view of past case information and your present condition.*" This is one more explanation that most specialists ought not to be trembling in fear about getting supplanted by machines in the following decade.

The above difficulties are no motivation to quit advancing, and I am certain there are a few clinicians who have their fingers crossed that a greater amount of the world's information researchers and PC researchers will focus on improving human services and medication.

In any event with regards to AI, all things considered, valuable and far-reaching applications will grow first in limited use-cases—for instance, an AI human services application that identifies the rate development or shrinkage of a tumor after some time dependent on picture information from handfuls or several X-beam pictures from different points.

While AI may help with "*proposals*" in an indicative circumstance, a specialist's judgment would be required so as to factor for the particular setting of the patient. An increasingly limited PC vision application, then again could, without much of a stretch, beat out any human master (expecting the model had enough preparation). Moreover, the Federal "*formality*" or HIPAA may make the clinical field, even more, a "*Goliath*" game rather than a "*David*" one. It appears to be conceivable that some new interpersonal organization could get on with adolescents and beat out Snapchat and Facebook by ideals of its virality, promotion, and UI.

Like Instagram, you may just need twelve designers and the correct thought at the ideal time; in any case, it is impossible that twelve architects—regardless of whether they raised a large number of a great many dollars—would have the imperative business associations and legitimate understandings to enter the profound layers of partners so as to turn into an accepted clinical norm. That maze may include more assets, associations, and ability than any little Silicon Valley startup can assemble and more persistence than most VC's can hold up under. It appears that an organization like IBM or Medtronic may have an unmistakable preferred position in clinical advancement for simply those reasons.

Machine learning applications in finance

Machine learning in an account may do something amazing, despite the fact that there is no enchantment behind it (well, perhaps only a tad). All things considered, the accomplishment of the machine learning venture relies more upon building a proficient framework, gathering appropriate datasets, and applying the correct calculations. Machine learning is making critical advances in the monetary administrations' industry. How about we see why money-related organizations should mind, what arrangements they can execute with machine learning and AI, and how precisely they can apply this innovation. By and large, the more information you feed, the more precise are the outcomes. Adventitiously, huge datasets are basic in the budgetary administrations' industry. There are petabytes of information on exchanges, clients, charges, cash moves, and so on. That is an ideal fit for machine learning. As the innovation develops and the best calculations are publicly released, it is difficult to envision the eventual fate of the money-related administrations without machine learning. Today, machine learning has come to assume a vital job in numerous pieces of the monetary biological system, from endorsing advances to FICO ratings to overseeing resources and surveying dangers. In any case, few actually smart monetary administrations experts have an exact perspective on where machine learning can assume a job at their organizations.

At Emerj, the AI Research and Advisory Company, we work with enormous budgetary administrations firms that need to survey where machine learning could drive an incentive at their organizations. We give our customers this asset as an establishment for understanding the wide prospects of machine learning in their industry as a component of our progressively broad machine learning opportunity landscape administration.

- **How to make use of machine learning in finance?** With unrealistic gauges and drains financial plans, it is not sufficient to have a reasonable programming framework set up (in spite of the fact that that would be a decent beginning). It takes an unmistakable vision, specialized information, and center to convey an important machine learning advancement venture. When you get a decent comprehension of this innovation, it will assist you with achieving business targets and continue with thought approval. This is an errand for information researchers. They examine the thought and subsequently assist you with figuring the feasible KPIs and make reasonable evaluations.

  Note: You have to have all the information gathered now. On the off chance that you do not, at that point, you would require an information specialist to gather and tidy up this information.

- **Why machine learning is suitable in finance?** Machine learning is tied in with processing a lot of information and gaining from that information in how to complete a particular errand, for example, recognizing false authoritative archives from real records. Machine learning in an account is the usage of an assortment of procedures to wisely deal with enormous and complex volumes of data. ML exceeds expectations at taking care of huge and complex volumes of information, something the money business has in overabundance of. Because of the high volume of authentic monetary information created in the business, ML has discovered numerous helpful applications in the fund. The innovation has come to assume an essential job in numerous periods of the money-related biological system, from supporting advances and doing financial assessments to overseeing resources and surveying hazards.

Today, machine learning has come to assume an essential job in numerous periods of the budgetary environment, from supporting credits to overseeing resources to evaluating risks. Yet, few actually shrewd experts have an exact perspective on exactly what number of ways AI discovers its way into their day-by-day money-related lives. The following are instances of AI being put to utilize effectively today. Remember that a portion of these applications influence different machine learning draws near—not only machine learning.

1. **Algorithmic trading:** With inceptions returning to the 1970s, algorithmic exchanging (once in a while called "*Robotized Trading Systems*," which is ostensibly a progressively precise portrayal) includes the utilization of complex AI frameworks to settle on amazingly quick exchanging choices. Algorithmic frameworks regularly make thousands or a huge number of exchanges a day, thus the expression "high-recurrence exchanging" (HFT), which is viewed as a subset of algorithmic exchanging. Most speculative stock investments and budgetary foundations do not straightforwardly reveal their machine learning ways to deal with exchanging (in light of current circumstances); however, it is accepted that machine learning and profound learning are assuming an inexorably significant job in adjusting exchanging choices ongoing.
2. **Credit/Insurance underwriting:** Guaranteeing could be depicted as an ideal activity for machine learning in the fund, and to be sure there is a lot of stress in the business that machines will supplant an enormous area of the endorsing places that exist today. Particularly everywhere organizations (large banks and traded on open market protection firms), machine learning calculations can be prepared on a great many instances of purchaser information (age, work, conjugal status, and so on) and money

related loaning or protection results (did this individual default, repay the credit on schedule, get in a fender bender, and so on?). The hidden patterns that can be evaluated with calculations and constantly examined to distinguish patterns that may impact loaning and safeguarding into what is to come (are an ever-increasing number of youngsters in a specific state getting in auto crashes? Are there expanding paces of default among a particular segment populace in the course of the most recent 15 years?). These outcomes have a huge substantial yield for organizations; however, at present are fundamentally saved for bigger organizations with the assets to employ information researchers and the gigantic volumes of at various times information to prepare their calculations.

3. **Portfolio management:** The expression *"auto-consultant"* was basically unfathomable only five years back; however, it is currently typical in the budgetary scene. The term is deluding and does not include robots by any means. Or maybe, auto-counsels are calculations worked to align a money-related portfolio to the objectives and hazard resilience of the client. Clients enter their objectives (for instance, resigning at age 65 with $250,000.00 in investment funds), age, pay, and current monetary resources. The guide (which would all the more precisely be alluded to as an *"allocator"*) at that point spreads ventures across resource classes and money-related instruments so as to arrive at the client's objectives. The framework at that point aligns to changes in the client's objectives and ongoing changes in the market, pointing consistently to locate the best fit for the client's unique objectives. Auto-consultants have increased huge footing with millennial purchasers who need not bother with a physical guide to feeling good contributing and who are less ready to approve the charges paid to human counselors.

4. **Fraud detection and prevention:** Join progressively available processing power, web getting all the more generally utilized, and an expanding measure of significant organization information being put away on the web, and you have a *"flawless tempest"* for information security hazard. While past money-related fraud discovery frameworks relied vigorously upon perplexing and powerful arrangements of rules, present-day misrepresentation location goes past after an agenda of hazard factors—it effectively learns and aligns to new potential (or genuine) security dangers. This is the spot of machine learning in money for fraud—yet similar standards remain constant for other information security issues. By using machine learning, frameworks can identify interesting exercises or practices (*"irregularities"*) and banner them for security groups. The test for these frameworks is to maintain a strategic distance from bogus positives—circumstances where *"dangers"* are hailed that were never hazards in any case. Money-related specialist organizations have no more noteworthy

duty than ensuring their customers against false movement.

By looking at every exchange against account history, machine learning calculations can evaluate the probability of an exchange being false. Unordinary exercises, for example, out-of-state buys or huge money withdrawals, raise signals that can make the framework acquaint ventures with deferring the exchange until a human can settle on a choice. By and large, contingent upon the idea of the endeavored exchange, a buy or withdrawal endeavor might be consequently declined by the framework.

In contrast to a human operator, the calculation can rapidly gauge the exchange subtleties against a huge number of information focuses and make an assurance whether the endeavored movement is unique of the record proprietor. Also, not at all like non-machine learning programming, machine learning programs gain from each move the record proprietor makes and from every choice the product makes. After some time, the calculations alter themselves because of changing propensities with respect to the record proprietor. Altogether, for machine learning to be successful, it must have the option to rapidly access and condensation a lot of information. Understanding the estimation of machine learning, *Amazon*, *Microsoft*, *IBM*, and *Google* are each coordinating AI capacities into their cloud-based designer interfaces.

5. **Customer service:** Chatbots and conversational interfaces are a quickly growing zone of adventure venture and client assistance spending plan and positioned as the most encouraging transient machine learning purchaser application. Organizations are, as of now, fabricating fund explicit chatbots to assist clients with posing inquiries by means of visits, for example, "*What amount did I spend on goods a month ago*?" and "*What was the parity of my own investment account 60 days back*?" These colleagues have must be worked with powerful regular language handling motors just as reams of money explicit client connections. Banks and money-related foundations that consider such quick questioning and communication may get clients from banks that expect individuals to sign onto a customary web-based financial gateway and do the burrowing themselves. This sort of visit (or later on—voice) experience is not the standard today in banking or account, yet perhaps a feasible choice for millions in the coming five years. This application goes past AI in money and is probably going to show itself as specific chatbots in an assortment of fields and businesses.

6. **Security 2.0:** Usernames, passwords, and security questions may never again be the standard for client security in five years. Client security in banking and fund is an especially high stakes game. Notwithstanding oddity discovery applications like those right now being created and utilized in fraud, future safety efforts may require facial acknowledgment, voice acknowledgment,

or other biometric information.

7. **Feeling/news analysis:** Speculative stock investments hold their cards tight to their chest, and we can hope to hear next to no by a method of how assumption investigation is being utilized explicitly. In any case, it is assumed that a significant part of things to come utilization of machine learning will be in understanding web-based life, news patterns, and other information sources—not simply stock costs and exchanges. The securities exchange moves in light of heap human-related elements that have nothing to do with ticker images, and the expectation is that machine learning will have the option to recreate and upgrade human *"instinct"* of money-related action by finding new patterns and telling signs. Machine learning in the account will be a long way from constrained to stock and ware information—and that the machine learning mutual funds come out of top should do considerably more than study ticker images alone.
8. **Sales/recommendations of financial products:** Utilizations of mechanized budgetary item deals exist today, some of which may not include machine learning (but instead, other standard-based frameworks). An auto-counsel may propose portfolio changes, and there are a lot of protection proposal destinations; this may utilize some level of machine learning for recommending a specific vehicle or home protection plan. Later on, progressively customized and adjusted applications and individual associates might be seen (not simply by recent college grads) as increasingly dependable, objective, and solid than in-person counsels. Similarly, as *Amazon* and *Netflix* can suggest books and films better than any living human *"master,"* progressing discussions with budgetary individual associates may do likewise for money-related items, as we witness starting in the protection business
9. **Marketing:** Having perused the numerous manners by which machine learning can keep accounts secure, improve hazard the board, and offer venture methodologies, you probably will not anticipate that the innovation should likewise be a decent promoting apparatus. Despite what might be expected. The capacity to make expectations dependent on past practices is crucial to any effective advertising exertion. By investigating web action, versatile application use, reaction to past promotion battles, machine learning programming can foresee the adequacy of an advertising system for a given client. With the web-based showcasing intensity of *Google,* presently expanded by machine learning, it is feasible for engineers working in the monetary division to make keen instruments that make the activity of promoting officials simpler than any time in recent memory. The capability

of machine learning to supercharge the promoting business has led to a spray-in machine learning-based publicizing of new companies.

10. **System security:** Among the top contemplations for any system chairman or information security proficient is the manner by which to perceive dubious examples happening over their systems. The test to distinguish such example loans is impeccable to the capacities of machine learning. The intensity of astute example examination joined with large information capacities absolutely gives machine learning innovation an edge over conventional, non-machine learning instruments. One may venture to such an extreme as to announce AI as the last any expectation of making sure about basic systems against expert and state-supported digital assaults.

Machine learning has just helped a great deal to take care of complex issues by developing as one of the most mainstream and ground-breaking techniques for learning errands. The money-related area is likewise not left immaculate by the current influx of machine learning and man-made reasoning.

Future applications of machine learning in finance

Supposition analysis ML calculations and their fitness for supposition examination will progressively impact exchanging what is to come. Supposition investigation is a principal case of machine learning in an account. It includes the examination of colossal volumes of unstructured information like recordings and video interpretations, photographs, sound records, web-based life posts, introductions, website pages, articles, sites, and business archives to decide the market assumption.

Opinion investigation lets organizations comprehend what individuals are stating, and critically, what they mean by what they are stating. Supposition examination is vital for all business chiefs in the present working environment and a fantastic case of machine learning in the fund. Many accept that this innovation can change future money-related markets. Where people frequently exchange on instinct, ML calculations have such a great amount of data available to them; they need not bother with instinct. Their conjectures will be founded on the exact investigation of continuous occasions.

What does the future hold? Another *World Economic Forum* report, The New Physics of Financial Services—how computerized reasoning is changing the money-related biological system, cautions that across-the-board appropriation of AI could present new fundamental and security dangers to the budgetary framework.

The report takes note of early enormous movers are offering their machine learning applications (that incorporates AI) as an "*administration*" to their rivals, drawing in clients to quicken their framework's learning and transforming cost focuses into benefit focuses. As this pattern extends, the money-related framework may confront new dangers. The WEF public statement clarifies that bank clients are progressively encountering a *"self-driving"* AI money world. This advancement may accompany fundamental and security dangers.

Why? This new budgetary world will be concentrated with just a couple of organized players, including, possibly, huge tech. For example, in the US, BlackRock's Aladdin speculation stage gives advanced hazard investigation and far-reaching portfolio the executive's instruments that influence AI. BlackRock's Chief Executive Officer *Larry Fink* anticipates that Aladdin should get 30% of the company's income by 2022. The report predicts that machine learning will likewise quicken the *"race to the base"* for some items, as cost turns out to be profoundly practically identical by means of accumulation administrations and outsider administrations commoditize back-office greatness. Budgetary establishments will progressively use AI and ML to separate themselves and give altered items varying.

Machine learning in the fund will be vital to these turns of events—the net outcome for clients will act naturally *"driving fund"*—a client experience where a person's or an association's accounts are adequately running themselves, drawing in the customer to go about as a confided in counselor on choices of significance, expresses the official statement.

Synopsis

The estimation of machine learning in money is getting progressively obvious; however, the genuine long-haul worth will most likely just come clear in the coming years. There are many use cases for AI in money and banks, and other budgetary organizations are putting billions in the innovation. Their ventures bring their organizations' numerous advantages, including decreased operational costs, expanded incomes, expanded client dependability because of improved client experience, and better consistency and hazard the executives. Meanwhile, ML calculations are giving venture exhortation, combatting misrepresentation in the fund, confirming archives, exchanging on stock trades, and assembling pivotal data that may influence markets and speculations.

And keeping in mind that ML calculations are occupied with every one of these errands, they are learning and getting more astute, carrying the world more like a totally mechanized monetary framework, which would add up to a definitive accomplishment of machine learning in an account.

Machine learning applications in retail

AI and machine learning (ML) are among the top innovation drifts in the retail world. They are greatly affecting the business, specifically in internet business organizations that depend on online deals, where the utilization of an AI innovation is exceptionally regular these days. Large players and first-movers such as *eBay*, *Amazon*, or *Alibaba* have effectively coordinated AI innovations over the whole deals cycle, from capacity coordinations to post-deal client care. Nonetheless, you do not need to be a major organization or sell solely online to exploit the gigantic intensity of machine learning.

In this guide, we will perceive how both online retailers and physical stores of any size can incorporate machine learning innovation to remain in front of their rivals by expanding deals and diminishing expenses. From garments to goods to family unit things, the conceivable outcomes in the retail space are brimming with a guarantee. The applications and use cases introduced in this guide are a small amount of the possible machine learning activities and fill in as instances of what should be possible today in the retail space. That being stated, numerous organizations have one-of-a-kind needs that could be presented with information.

At the point when directors and pioneers consider machine learning in retail, they regularly envision accommodating in-store robots, robotized forms like checkout or loading racks, or conversational operators that propose items and answer inquiries for clients. Although these applications ought to be considered as problematic components for retail's future, it is improbable that these variables will be the primary rush of machine learning's effect on the segment. Our own exploration on machine learning in retail proposes that the underlying ramifications of computerized reasoning and machine learning will include considerably less physical automation and direct substitution of human specialists (rack stockers, checkout representatives, and so forth) and significantly more expansion of the current retail involvement in information and dynamic.

1. **Machine learning in retail**: While there is a ton of discussion about the utilization of machine learning in retail, we are as yet ignorant regarding how it really functions. How about we see the job of machine learning in item value improvement for the retailer. Social affair data for training the machine: by get-together information relating to the selection of items and their particular value run, the evaluating model is pre-prepared.

Figure 11.1: *Machine learning in retail*

2. **Utilizing an algorithm**: Now, the retailer additionally needs to utilize a calculation for examining the highlights of the items referenced in the preparation information and accompany the exact forecast about the correct cost of the item.
3. **Preparing the model for pricing optimization**: Now, the Pricing improvement model of the calculation checks the forecasts about the correct cost for the client against the genuine item costs.
4. **Changing the prediction mechanism**: The retail calculation furnished with the machine learning innovation keeps on changing and modifying the forecast component after some time.
5. **Valuing optimization for the model**: As soon as the pre-preparing is finished, forecasts on an assortment of selling costs estimated against item highlights and quality credits come to the surface.
6. **Criticism loop**: Whenever an item is sold, the cost of the item in that particular deal is considered as a new contribution to the input circle for preparing the estimating model to accompany progressively exact costs.

7. **New data inputs**: To use the estimating enhancement model to the upside of item promoting on a nonstop premise, new item information is constantly fused for the model to refine the value forecasts further.

Key benefits of machine learning in retail

Artificial intelligence has opened another vista of showcasing and business process advancement in the retail area. To comprehend the chief favorable circumstances of machine learning for retail, let us view the different settings in which this innovation is utilized for retail.

- To offer retail clients genuinely customized item proposals.
- Offering a superior cost to help deals by continuous and dynamic modification of costs.
- Making better stock arranging and guaranteeing better upkeep with the right forecasts.
- Offering quicker and progressively proficient conveyance dependent on past client information and client conduct.
- Better expectation of deals and client assistance dependent on prior client conduct information.
- Perfecting application client experience and upgrading site content dependent on in-application and on-web client conduct and communications.
- Better division of clients based on past client conduct.

Gaining from top retail brands about the implementation of machine learning

1. **Walmart**: This US retail goliath headquartered in Bentonville; Arkansas needs no presentation. Walmart utilizes AI innovation to outline conveyance courses, offer quicker checkout, and improve suggestions and item coordinates dependent on singular web perusing and buy history. AI is likewise utilized by Walmart to make and demonstrate explicit promotions to the objective clients.
2. **Amazon**: Amazon is, as of now, an easily recognized name as the undisputed retail pioneer on the planet. Amazon is approaching the biggest volume of retail client information, applies AI to get exact bits of knowledge from that information for different purposes. For instance, it applies Machine Learning on client information to cause an exact gauge for some items, to recognize deceitful exercises, and offer clients explicit item proposals.

3. **Target**: Target is another eminent *"one-stop shop"* selling nearly all that we need in everyday lives extending from pieces of clothing to staple goods. Target began using machine learning to investigate its client information to distinguish explicit client conditions and to make proposals as needs to be. For instance, the machine learning program began to recognize ladies with the most extreme odds of being pregnant. Subsequent to distinguishing such conditions, it is simpler for the program to recognize key purchasing conduct and inclinations. In light of such bits of knowledge, the retail shop could make recommendations or give the applicable product to the focused-on clients.
4, **Alibaba**: Making big data accessible for smaller retailers: *Alibaba,* the Chinese mammoth in B2B retail internet business really serves a huge number of little retailers. In the wake of using huge information examination for certain years, the retail goliath began utilizing ML to break down in-shop client conduct and locate the most well-known value focuses for the items bought by its retailer clients.
5. **The north face**: Headquartered in Alameda, California, North Face is a world-well-known experience gear and open-air wear brand that, as of late, tied up with the IBM Watson to exploit the machine learning innovation to push clients to the item they need. Natural Language Processing (NLP) ability of IBM Watson and the intelligent interface gave the brand's essence a human touch while utilizing the forefront of machine learning innovation.
6. **American eagle outfitters**: Situated in Pittsburgh, Pennsylvania, American Eagle is a notable piece of a clothing brand that as of late made an association with Slyce, a promising picture acknowledgment startup brand utilizing machine learning and picture search innovation to peruse and discover items in a store. Slyce offers a visual web crawler through its versatile application that permits its clients to look for explicit articles of clothing through pictures taken by their handheld gadget camera.

Wrapping up

From the previously mentioned models, it is very certain that an expanding number of business brands are currently depending on machine learning innovation for pushing business transformation, development, and client commitment. In the future time, we can see increasingly imaginative approaches to utilizing machine learning for explicit business settings.

Cases of machine learning in retail

There are different organizations that are using machine learning to improve their client's understanding and furthermore to help deals. Check underneath some machine learning use cases in the retail segment:

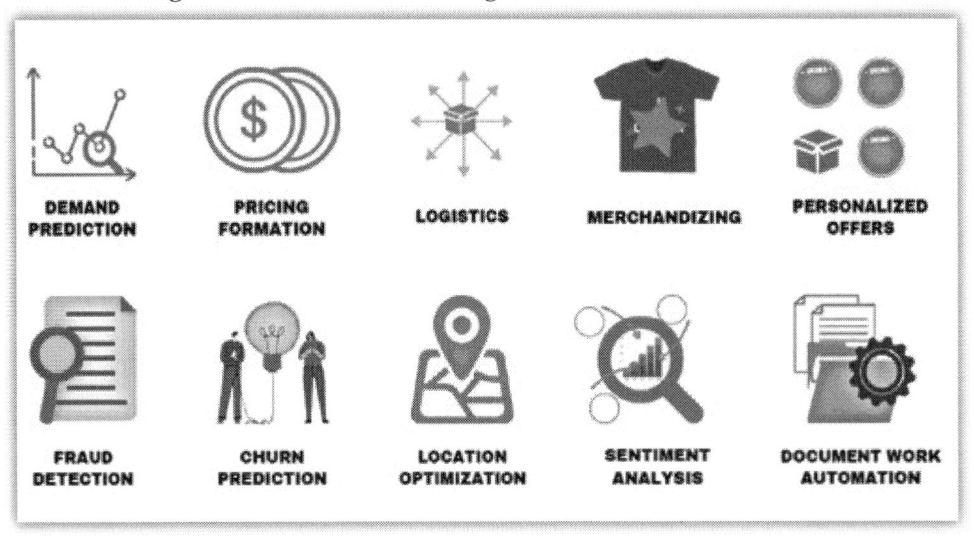

Figure 11.2: *Cases of Machine learning in retail*

- **Price optimization**: A colossal measure of information handled in machine learning frameworks permit you to see a comprehensive picture that unfurls available. For instance, AI frameworks permit retailers to follow the conduct of their affiliates and know without a doubt if any of them abuse the minimum advertised price. Because of the far-reaching investigation of information on clients and their dissolvability, it gets conceivable to decide the clearest value that they are happy to pay for a specific item. Also, on this premise, either change your variety by fitting the item to an appropriate cost or procure considerably more.
- **Demand prediction:** So as to offer a client a really customized understanding, a business needs to anticipate requests. AI will assist with improving stock arranging and will likewise guarantee that the item is loaded up as indicated by the interest forecast. Also, prescient investigation and machine learning make it conceivable to anticipate variances sought after and change the cost dependent on these vacillations altogether not to lose possible benefit.
- **Logistics support**: The information on which machine learning calculations are based is additionally the reason for the arrangement of courses for the conveyance of merchandise to a specific shopper. Shrewd frameworks make coordination increasingly attentive, accomplishing two objectives simultaneously—the most extreme conceivable improvement of client assistance because of quick conveyance and the greatest decrease of

retailer's expenses. Furthermore, frameworks can consider the need to lessen destructive air discharges from street transport.

- **Predictive analytics**: Prescient investigation is a ground-breaking weapon that a couple of years back appeared to retailers as a dream. Back then, they could just dream of somebody revealing to them how occasions would create, what patterns would rise and how clients would react to them with the greatest precision. At that point, exchanging procedures were constructed distinctly on suppositions, guesses, and presence of mind. Today, because of machine learning and computerized reasoning, they are based on sound judgment and an enormous exhibit of chronicled, current, and asserted information. This is one of the principal advantages of prescient examination.
- **Churn rate prediction:** As indicated by ICECDS research, this is a significant point since when a retail business loses one of its clients, it likewise loses all possible benefits as well as cash that was put resources into drawing in and building associations with this purchaser. Additionally, presently the business should pay to draw in another customer, and this is multiple times costlier than keeping the bygone one. AI frameworks can follow circumstances that are probably going to bring about the departure of a customer so the organization can take the most earnest measures to hold him.
- **Location optimization:** Organizations can target clients based on their land area and can likewise utilize the innovation to think about quicker and better courses with the goal that an effective conveyance to the clients should be possible.
- **Fraud detection:** Since the framework is equipped for self-learning, machine learning and AI are extremely solid in perceiving and forestalling fake movement with charge cards when shopping on the web or disconnected. In addition, approaching a boundless measure of information, machine learning frameworks can likewise help forestall deceitful exercises with coupons and limits by following client conduct from a particular IP address. As per a similar standard, the calculation can decide the client's aims, for instance, on the off chance that the fraudster is going to purchase an item and afterward return the phony inside the structure of the arrival conditions.
- **Document work automation**: AI is additionally ready to examine your interior information, for instance, data about how your organization sorts out HR the board. On this premise, you, as a retailer, are getting the chance to make your representatives increasingly adaptable, spare them from routine assignments, and all the more ably plan their work routine with the goal that they stay enlivened, proficient, and focused on client assistance.

- **Merchandising**: Machine learning can be utilized to do visual promoting, where an online client will have a similar encounter as a disconnected store client. It has been expressed by clients that item pictures assume an essential job in the business part. AI is currently utilized by organizations to give a special visualization to clients.

Advantages of predictive analytics for machine learning in retail

Machine learning can offer an increasingly customized understanding to its clients by bringing the clients information and utilizing the bits of knowledge picked up from it.

- **Fetches data**: Prior, there was very little organizations could do to gather clients' information; however, today, we have innovation like enormous information that has reversed the situation for the organizations. By getting information, huge information characterizes each new key move comparable to the customer, item, and market.
- **Advanced marketing strategies**: Huge data in business permits you to adjust showcasing methodologies relying upon changing economic situations and expectations got from them. Consequently, retailers guarantee themselves against shocks, have the chance to assess which advertising action gives better outcomes, and create singular promoting approaches.
- **Predicts users' behavior**: Thus, for instance, having the chance of recommending pregnancy with the assistance of AI, the retailer can make a customized proposal for a specific lady on schedule until this is finished by contenders.
- **Improves customer service**: We have just discussed the chance of forestalling fraud, offering improved conveyance, enhancing the cost, and making individual offers. Likewise, communication with chatbots and virtual fitting rooms additionally makes cooperation with organizations progressively helpful and focused on. This is about client care, the degree of which is developing.
- **Boost deals**: Thinking about the entirety of the above favorable circumstances, it is sure that it closes as an increment in deals, reinforcing steadfastness and trust, just as the capacity to give individuals what they need right now.

Applications in Brick-and-Mortar retail

- **Retail stocking and inventory**: Improving stock arranging and prescient upkeep is a key issue and a significant strategic worry for retailers.

- **Anticipating inventory needs**: Machine learning calculations can misuse buy information to foresee stock needs continuously. In light of the day of the week, the season, close-by occasions, web-based life information, and client past conduct, these calculations can give a day-by-day dashboard of proposed requests to a buying director.
- **The power of computer vision**: Physical retailers can exploit the amazing late outcomes of PC vision. The new methodologies in the field could be utilized to create continuous, precise appraisals of the items in a given store. With this data, an AI calculation could advise head supervisors of startling examples of stock information that could be because of robbery or an unordinary increment in the interest for an item. Another application is to utilize pictures to investigate the utilization of rack space and distinguish imperfect setups. A generally excellent case of this innovation is LoweBot, Lowe's self-sufficient retail administration robot that, other than helping the client to shop, continually screens stock and gives constant criticism to the store workers.

What do I need to start?

The stock arranging models need purchaser conduct information. That is, for instance, buying history or purchasing patterns; however, it could likewise incorporate web-based life movement and space explicit information.

PC vision calculations need pictures to process. They can emerge out of the surveillance cameras introduced in the store or be taken by representatives.

Use case	Requirements
Predicting inventory needs	Data from customers (purchases, searches, and social media) Data from external events (if available)
Computer vision	Store images and videos Data from products (descriptions and images)

Table 11.1: *PC vision calculations*

- **Conduct tracking by means of video analytics**: Something worth being thankful for about physical stores is that the conduct and cooperation of people with items can create significant bits of knowledge in manners that online retail cannot. PC vision calculations can perceive faces and individuals' attributes, for example, sexual orientation or scope old enough, producing valuable exploitable information.

- Breaking down navigational routes: Where to put various things is a critical issue for physical retailers, who consistently search for extra approaches to comprehend the client's way to buy. PC vision calculations can follow clients' excursion in stores to see how they are cooperating with it. These calculations can distinguish the strolling designs and the heading of the look of the clients. Retailers can utilize this data to rebuild store designs or to quantify the enthusiasm for their items. They can likewise find areas that get a great deal of traffic and visual consideration.

  Do older individuals shop more on weekdays? Do adolescents will, in general, spread just a piece of the store, for instance, the forward portion? Is the store more visited in winter? Factors, for example, age, day of the week, or season, could be utilized to create bits of knowledge that help to progressively change item arrangements and make effective advancements.
- Robbery prevention: Robbery prevention is a typical issue in retail with a solid ROI, where AI advancements can go past the run-of-the-mill utilization of camcorders to identify shoplifters. Facial acknowledgment calculations can be prepared to spot known shoplifters when they enter the store. Walmart tried this innovation in 2015 as an enemy of burglary instruments. Similarly, PC vision can identify on the off chance that somebody picks a thing; it could distinguish on the off chance that somebody conceals a thing in their rucksack or coat. In addition, a similar methodology can be utilized to identify when checkout agents skip filtering things, either unintentionally or deliberately. A framework dependent on machine learning can caution continuously security workforce or administrators and send them video passages so they can decide without anyone else before going up against the person in the store.

Item tracking and gesture recognition: Physical retailers, for the most part, have no data about the things that clients get, look at, and set back on the rack. They do not have any data either about what clients take a gander at next. A PC vision calculation can screen customers facial and hand motions to assess how fruitful a thing is. This sort of utilization produces valuable information about how frequently a thing is gotten from the rack, set back on oneself or in the shopping basket, or bought.

What do I have to start?

In the event that your store is furnished with surveillance cameras having a specific picture quality, at that point, you as of now have all that is expected to begin actualizing the arrangements recently referenced.

- **Virtual mirrors**: Virtual or intelligent mirrors bring customers a blended encounter between physical stores and computerized cooperation. This is an innovation particularly important for style retailers and cosmetics boutiques. Rather than evaluating garments, virtual mirrors permit clients to explore through virtual garments models to discover and pick the one they generally like. Coupled to a proposal framework, virtual mirrors could recommend embellishments and related garments. In addition, a *"look book"* could be made by joining outfits, so the customers can choose which garments suit them best.

  Corrective boutiques can likewise improve clients experience by letting them, for all intents, and purposes attempt items. A particular virtual mirror can likewise go about as a stunner advisor, breaking down somebody's skin, searching for wrinkles, dim spots, and stopped-up pores, and producing a report with solid activities to be completed.

  This is an exceptionally hot market, and there are a few turnkey arrangements in the market, for example, *HiMirror,* a delight and wellbeing expert, or *SenseMi,* a mirror for design stores. Past the current arrangements, a retailer may require a custom advancement as indicated by the necessities of its organization and the qualities of its items.

- **In-store assistants**: A portion of the arrangements proposed for internet retailing can be incorporated in versatile applications to get canny in-store partners. These are among the most well-known AI use cases in retail. Such an aide could tell clients where an item or a group of items are found in the store, help them to intelligently locate what is best for their necessities, or propose to them the best excursion in the hides away gets a rundown of items. Realizing their shopping list, the versatile application could propose things that are presumably absent from the rundown. In this situation, a tablet or telephone could be utilized as a pointing gadget that permits the client to get moment data about things. Thank to discourse acknowledgment, connection with the associate feels progressively human. A case of this sort of innovation is Macy's On Call, an application that causes customers to get data while they are exploring the organization's stores. Another fascinating use case is the Digital Tire Journey in-store web application proposed via Sears Automotive, which encourages customers to discover what they need among the extraordinary collection of tires.

  In-store associates create a twofold advantage. From one perspective, they give genuine incentives to clients, which expands reliability and maintenance. Then again, they empower retailers to gather a lot of information that can be utilized as a contribution by other machine learning arrangements.

What do I need to start?

To build up an in-store aide, data about items, stock, and clients is generally required. Also, a blueprint of potential cooperation is important to start improvement. Remember that a right hand can be created in a gradual manner.

- Necessities:
  - Information from clients (buys, collaboration history).
  - Information from items (pictures, portrayals).
  - Information from stock (store, items).
  - Tests of collaborations (if accessible) or a lot of utilization cases.

At Tryolabs we fabricate custom information-driven answers for improving organization's KPIs. This implies we accomplice up with retailers to conceptualize and construct custom AI frameworks that either increment income or decrease costs.

Wrap up

The retail and buyer industry is information substantial, and numerous retailers work over various channels. Creating unmistakable bits of knowledge from information gathered over these different channels requires the utilization of calculations and models that can procedure and gain from enormous datasets and make significant expectations and proposals. For instance, suggestion motors need to depend on huge informational collections to keep customers intrigued, and when they are done well, they help the retailer gauge request and settle on flexible choices well ahead of time. Value advancement is another zone where various boundaries must be considered, which makes it hard for some inheritance programming instruments and the human mind to ace. The AI calculation can make various choice trees dependent on an assortment of sub-gatherings before consolidating everything into a far-reaching prescient model and, at last, recommending the ideal cost for an item on a particular week or even day of the month. Machine learning unrest is genuine—and its applications inside retail are tremendous. Organizations that comprehend the advantages of ML—and along these lines send the correct procedure, the correct programming for the correct difficulties—are those set to receive the most benefits.

Machine learning applications in travel

Inferable from our expanded reliance on devices, individuals today are bound to design trips by means of keen applications. They can really spend numerous hours stuck to the screen—finding the best spot, best cost, and the best schedule. This is the place artificial intelligence and Machine Learning become integral factors. This can create super-customized proposals to imminent explorers by examining huge datasets. It is clear that outside of chatbots, the field of AI and AI in the movement and the travel industry is still at its outset. A great part of the effect of man-made reasoning on the movement and the travel industry centers on client care and commitment.

With segments, for example, banking, medicinal services, and online business, plainly the movement and the travel industry do not have a strong seller scene for machine learning and AI-related arrangements. This is likely in light of the fact that it is a generally little area, and the vast majority of the investment cash and the focal point of the new businesses are rather than bigger segments instead of on movement without anyone else. As per a review, advanced travel deals are anticipated to cross $800 billion by 2020. Such applications are reproducing the full-administration experience by utilizing AI and ML for movement programming advancement.

A considerable lot of the advantages of ML and AI occur in the background, which is the reason we concentrated more on new companies and SMEs utilizing AI-based programming or stages that would help travel and the travel industry organizations with their transformations and commitment on the backend. Travel and the travel industry is on their ascent these days. This might be clarified by the way that it has gotten progressively moderate to a more extensive crowd. Be that as it may, in the present quick-paced world, discovering time to make a trip to a ticket office and get your tickets is an extravagance few can bear. Like some other industries, machine learning, AI, and enormous information examination have changed the movement and friendliness of industry too. In this post, we will talk about the significant applications and future extents of AI, AI, and large information examination in the movement and neighborliness industry—over the globe and in India. Furthermore, we will likewise view how machine learning, AI, and huge information examination are reshaping the neighborliness work advertise.

Because of fast computerized change, more than 500 billion dollars ($564.87 billion) was made in the movement and accommodation area in the year 2016 alone. The number is required to reach $817.54 billion by 2020. Travel port forms 10 to 12 billion hunts every day from explorers investigating or booking trips. Along these lines, so as to deal with such an enormous measure of information, to push out contenders, and give a decent client experience, machine learning, AI, and huge information examination are incredibly basic.

- **Nuts and bolts of AI and ML:** It is getting harder to discover an example of overcoming adversity of how to travel organization X made innovation improvement Y that expanded deals by *Z%* without recognizing the words *"AI"* or *"man-made brainpower"*. Once in a while utilized conversely, these two ideas really have various implications.

Man-made reasoning is a huge zone of software engineering that reviews how to instruct PCs to think and act like a human. ML is a subset of AI, significant, however not alone. More or less, ML is tied in with building models that anticipate the outcome with high precision based on the info information. Utilizing factual techniques empowers machines to improve their precision as more information is taken care of in the framework.

The last yield of ML models relies upon the following:

- **Quality of the data:** The more information is different and rich, the better the machine can discover designs and the more exact the outcome. For instance, here are certain ways how and which information can be caught by movement industry suppliers:

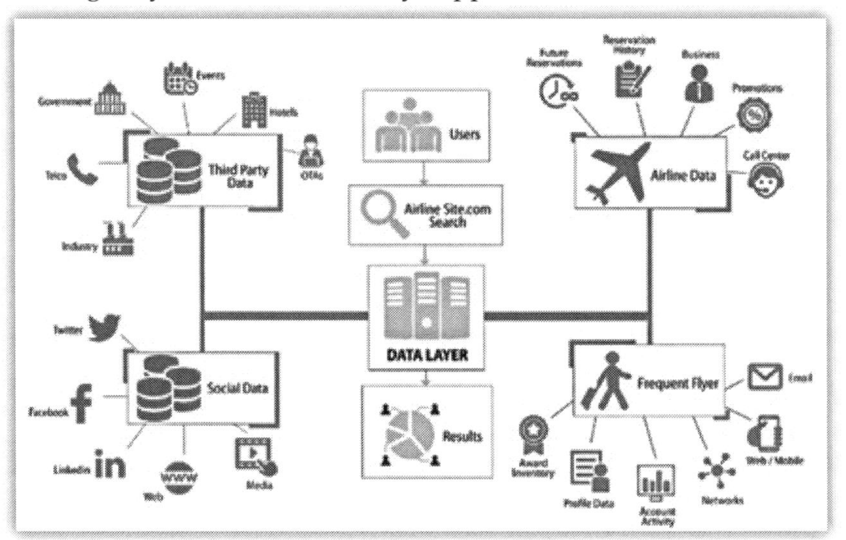

***Figure 11.3**: Certain ways of information used by movement industry suppliers (Source: Markrs.co)*

The datasets of good quality are as a rule in extremely appeal and the organizations here, and there truly need to chase for the average datasets.

- Features are important sources of info that the current information contains, similar to client sex/area/program augmentation and so on. Normally information has more data that is expected to assemble the model, so it is important to choose the significant highlights. During this procedure, either the investigator or displaying apparatus chooses or disposes of the characteristics relying upon how helpful they are for examination. A huge number of highlights make the calculation work slower, so generally, the procedure of information planning and having slick **.xlsx** and **.csv** documents at long last takes additional time than the entire procedure of preparing.

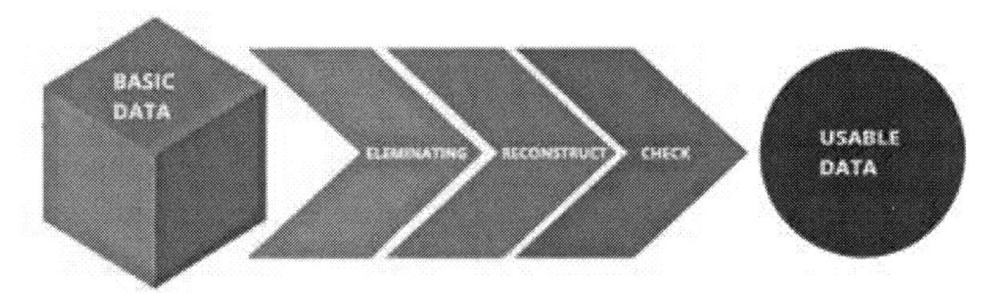

Figure 11.4: *Basic Data to Usable Data flow*

- The algorithm that breaks down the information searches for examples or patterns and afterwards finds the ideal boundaries for making the model. It is a serious test to pick the best calculation to comprehend a particular errand as every calculation can create an alternate outcome, and some of them produce more than one sort of result.

Here is the means by which machine-learning-fueled model is fabricated:

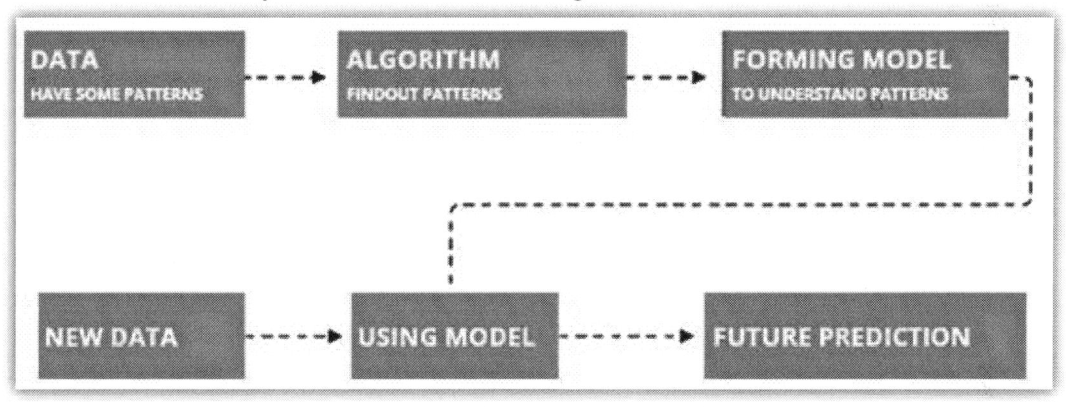

Figure 11.5: *Machine-Learning-fueled model*

AI model can outflank old-style inflexible business insight where business rules cannot catch the concealed examples. Travel organizations are effectively actualizing AI and ML to delve somewhere down in the accessible information and improve the stream on their sites and applications, and convey really prevalent encounters.

ML, AI, and big data analytics in the travel and hospitality industry

In the cutting-edge period of the computerized economy, innovative progressions are not, at this point, an extravagance for the associations, yet a need to outfox their rivals and business development. With the mechanical headways as of late, the effect of **machine learning** (**ML**) and **artificial intelligence** (**AI**), information investigation is basic than any time in recent memory. Both constant examination and prescient investigation have numerous applications in the movement and accommodation industry.

Ten major applications of machine learning, AI and big data analytics in the travel and hospitality sector worldwide are as follows:

1. **Proposal engines:** One of the most standard use cases for information science, some proposal arrangement is as of now consolidated in 99% of every single fruitful item. Like customized content proposals dependent on neural systems on *Netflix* or the *"Highlighted Recommendations"* box on *Amazon,* online travel booking suppliers frequently give custom-made recommendations in light of your ongoing pursuits and appointments.

   For instance, while scanning on *MakeMyTrip* or Expedia for trips to London, you will be offered a few convenient choices for your outing. Also, Booking.com offers elective goals you may like for your next outing. Mechanized proposals dependent on client information functions admirably to build deals, upsell, and keep steadfast clients returning for additional.

2. **Flight fare and hotel price forecasting:** Flight passages and lodging costs are ever-changing and fluctuate enormously, relying upon the supplier. Nobody has the opportunity to follow every one of those progressions physically. In this way, shrewd devices which screen and convey ideal alarms with hot arrangements are at present popular in the movement business. As indicated by Travelport's 2018 Digital Traveler Survey, half of US explorers and 51% of Canadian voyagers distinguished the time spent attempting to locate the best cost as a top torment point for looking and booking relaxation trips.

   Locales like Hopper are extraordinary instances of assistance like this, helping its clients to book modest flights utilizing examination. Adding a device like this to an online travel office entrance is a keen method to snare clients in and tempt them to book more excursions. Container spares clients time, cash, and tension in their mission to book the ideal excursion by offering explorers suggestions and cautions dependent on exceptionally exact valuing forecasts. The application additionally uses AI to reveal value drops and select arrangements for a customized search and booking experience on cell phones.

   Another extraordinary model is the inventive admission indicator instrument by Fareboom.com, which gets to and gathers authentic information around a great many tolls look through returning quite a while. With such rich information and AI calculations, the stage predicts the future value developments dependent on various variables, for example, occasional patterns, request development, aircrafts uncommon offers, and arrangements. A lot of this application is subject to predictive analytics and ML.

3. **Intelligent travel assistants:** As comfort is the lord in this day and age, brilliant attendant services controlled by AI are picking up energy in different businesses. Travel booking is just one of the zones being intensely computerized by AI calculations. Shrewd projects (bots) are prepared to play out specific assignments on clients' solicitations. Texting stages like WhatsApp are likewise getting well known for client assistance. With the best four talk applications having more than 4 a huge number of month-to-month dynamic clients only for April 2018, texting stages are broadly embraced by some noticeable brands as an extraordinary method to contact the customers and assemble better client relations. They can be additionally utilized as versatile travel colleagues, taking care of a few issues in a hurry, for example:
    a. What are the things remittances for my flight?
    b. Where is the closest business lounge?
    c. What is my boarding door number?
    d. How long will it take to get to the air terminal?
4. **Optimized disruption management**: What is a robotized interruption on the board? It fundamentally implies settling barriers that a voyager may look on their way to the goal. As the name recommends, it is a method to naturally deal with interruptions to the arrangement. This target is settling real issues a voyager may look on his/her way to a goal point, and especially pertinent for business and corporate travel.

    Interruption of the executives is consistently a period delicate assignment, requiring a moment reaction. Although the odds to get affected by a tempest or a spring of gushing lava emission are extremely little, the danger of a movement disturbance is still very high: there are a huge number of deferrals and a few several dropped flights each day. With the ongoing advances in innovation, it got conceivable to foresee such interruptions and effectively moderate the misfortune for both the voyager and the transporter. This is the place real-time analytics assumes an indispensable job.

    Theopendoorforinformationsciencehereliesinforeseeingtravelinterruptions dependent on accessible data about climate, current postponements, and other air terminal assistance information. Subsequently, a calculation prepared to screen this information can convey ideal warnings, alarming the clients and their movement chiefs about forthcoming interruptions, and consequently put an emergency course of action vigorously. The 4 site instrument, worked by *cornerstone information systems*, targets upgrading the productivity of big business travel. The item obliges explorers; travel the executive's organizations and undertaking customers, giving a one-of-a-kind arrangement of highlights for ongoing travel disturbance to the board.

5. **Customer support:** Like individual travel partners and shrewd disturbance the executives, carriers can use the intensity of man-made brainpower to smooth out the client assistance process. Particularly now, when practically 50% of all purchasers concur that the speed of reaction to a request is the most significant segment of fruitful client assistance. Man-made intelligence and talk bot are extraordinary methods to smooth out specific parts of client assistance and backing. Fundamental instructive and value-based administrations can be offered through a specially modified chatbot. Consolidating menial helpers with human ones not exclusively can assist organizations with developing their image dedication yet additionally improve business execution.
6. **Customized offers for most valuable customers (MVCs)**: The significance of reliability programs for the movement and accommodation industry keeps on developing. In 2016, the quantity of faithfulness program individuals for significant inns chains expanded by 13.1%. The individuals from steadfastness programs, for example, most significant clients, are those clients that the movement business players should concentrate on first to maintain a strategic distance from the stir. Also, this is the low-draping organic product for the AI application. Utilizing inheritance information and client buys, you can build up a strong model for offering extraordinary arrangements to your most faithful customers.
7. **Opinion analysis in social media:** As indicated by Amadeus, 90% of US voyagers with a cell phone share their encounters and photographs in internet-based life and surveys administrations. TripAdvisor has 390 million one of a kind guests and 435 million surveys. Consistently, around 280 voyager surveys are submitted to the site. This is a huge pool of important information that brands can break down to improve their administrations. While the traditional measurable investigation of audits subsets is conceivable, the figuring power and fundamental AI methods take into account dissecting all brand-related surveys. Feeling examination is the part of administered discovering that targets are investigating printed information to characterize and rate enthusiastic and authentic characteristics of it. For example, Google cloud natural language API is an off-the-rack application programming interface that can be changed and incorporated with investigative devices to give ongoing examinations of all brand-related surveys. This can assist you with recognizing issues and resolving them to improve client altruism. By using regulated learning

and regular language acknowledgment, information apparatuses can take advantage of the extraordinary wild of online networking discussion to distinguish open doors for mediation.

8. **Dynamic pricing in the hospitality industry**: Dynamic estimating depends on changing room costs relying upon different market conditions. This is not something new for the movement and friendliness industry. Numerous properties like Hilton and Marriot have been changing their room rates on more than one occasion per day since 2004. In 2015, *Starwood* Hotels began building up a prescient investigation apparatus that represents many elements to show the most productive cost for the occasion. These incorporate serious evaluating information, climate, a client's reserving design, inhabitance information, room types, everyday rates, and different factors. This is another great use of predictive analytics.

   Although the framework can work in a completely programmed way, it likewise permits human administrators to see the information dashboard and physically change rates if necessary. Utilizing AI and information investigation for dynamic evaluating can improve the viability and gainfulness of such plans.

9. **In-stay experience**: Client experience matters a ton. Computer-based intelligence arrangements can help an explorer in transit to a goal, yet in addition, during an inn remain. With voice-empowered menial helpers in rooms, visitors can make themselves increasingly agreeable. For instance, they can set a temperature in a room, modify the light, and switch the TV on and off. With facial acknowledgment, inns can accelerate registration and remain increasingly secure. As per the Oracle report Hotel 2025, 78% of lodgings will redesign suites with voice-controlled contraptions, and 68% of them will utilize robots for registration and registration by 2025.

   Wynn Las Vegas has furnished every one of its rooms with *Amazon Echo*, Safeco field suits is not just utilized in the rooms, yet additionally recommends the visitors what to do in the city during their remain. *Radisson Blu Edwardian Hotel* in London uses a chatbot named Edward, and Las Vegas Hotel *Cosmopolitan* has Rose, another virtual attendant who responds to any inquiries and helps 24 hours every day, 7 days per week. Clarion Hotel *Amaranten*, in Stockholm, likewise utilizes a chatbot dependent on Alexa. With facial acknowledgment innovation, the involvement with the lodging turns out to be a lot more secure. For instance, *Lemon Tree Hotel*, in Deli, introduced a facial acknowledgment framework to propel security. This framework catches facial pictures from the CCTV camera and contrasts them and existing pictures in the database. Furthermore, a Japanese lodging, *Henn*

Na, is totally overseen by robots. In Henn Na Hotel, the receptionists are robots; the attendant is likewise a robot and rather than giving the electronic keys, the visitors must enlist their facial pictures during the enrollment.

Information science is demonstrating the method of how we will go later on. The fields recorded above for your application are only a hint of something larger.

10. **Fraud detection**: As per the Juniper research report, aircraft and travel enterprises experience the ill effects of e-commerce fraud the most. The movement business and friendliness industry lose billions of dollars consistently discounting taken cash to clients.

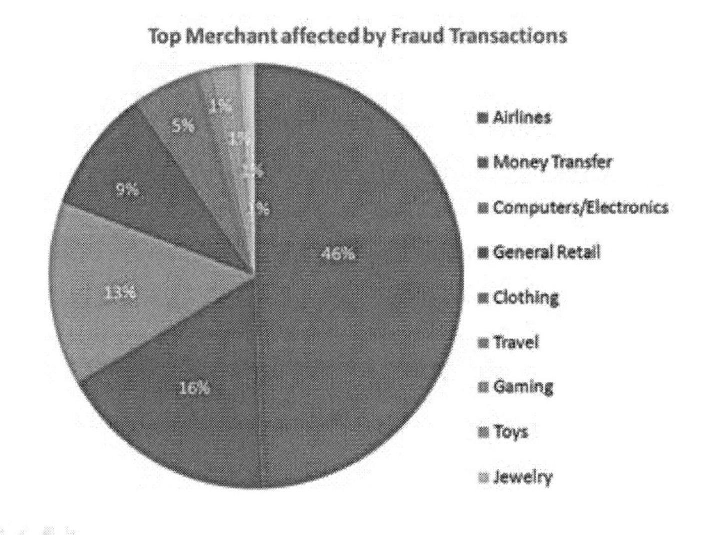

Figure 11.6: *Fraud Detection (Source: Juniper Research)*

Installment misrepresentation is one of the most mainstream sorts of tricks in this industry that involves utilizing a taken Visa for booking flights or settlement. Another well-known kind of fraud is an inviting misrepresentation, when a client pays for a buy and afterwards asserts that the card was taken, requesting a chargeback. Client conduct examination utilizing profiling and AI advancements can help forestall and identify illicit exchanges from occurring. Italian web-based booking stage Wanderries helped out Pi School that applied an AI-innovation of fraud identification. Portable booking application Hotel Tonight additionally applied a machine learning model to anticipate and identify fraud that permitted them to lessen chargebacks to half.

ML: Just the ticket Advertising administrators in the movement division are very much aware that ML is a wellspring of vital advantage, and they have grasped the innovation in like manner. Milden hall sees that nowadays, everything in the movement division—the purchaser, the contenders, the innovation itself—moves quickly. To keep up, he says, "you need constant information that is driving continuous procedure that is driving ongoing business sector usage." ML innovation, along with the fitting utilitarian KPIs and structure to help it, will in all likelihood assume an extending job in the information is driven travel advertiser's toolbox.

Bottom line

With a huge assortment of cool glossy things that AI and ML propose, it is anything but difficult to get the flash and hunker down with the "I need everything" thought. Recollect that innovation works great just when it is appropriately executed. Consider the accompanying things and fuel those innovations in your business:

a. Gather quality information. They state *"trash in—trash out"* which is unforgiving yet obvious. It is critical how rich the information is, regardless of whether it is joinable and how it is named as information quality, legitimately impacts the yield of the model. An information researcher may assist you with arranging those datasets out and assembling that entire framework.

b. Know your item. Truly, that may seem like *"much appreciated, Captain Obvious,"* however it is the beginning stage of usage of any innovations. We at Django Stars tell our customers that we can fabricate the calculation of any refinement, yet the item proprietor needs to obviously see how to plug and play those calculations, what are the business objectives, and in what manner should it work.

c. Consider the development of your business. Joining artificial intelligence is an intense call that requires awesome area information, propelled abilities and information on legitimate limitations (for example, information catching guidelines). This is the reason you could think about connecting with specialists to help, as it is very elusive and keep the architects in-house.

d. Focus on what is important most. There is somewhat opportunity to prevail with *"everything you-can-eat"* approach. A few models give just 5% improvement, however for an enormous scope, that is a considerable advancement that brings better understanding and incomes. Then again, concentrating on ML chatbots may let loose your workforce and bring client experience to new levels.

Machine learning applications in media

Artificial intelligence presents a critical chance to improve main concern proficiency yet in addition, top-line income age for **media and entertainment (M&E)** organizations to counter a significant number of the current difficulties in the business, as old income models deteriorate, while new ones develop. It is the ideal opportunity for M&E organizations to investigate AI, especially the subset of AI called ML. In contrast to prior variants of AI, which looked to reproduce human knowledge through human-customized rules, ML is the way toward making a factual model from different kinds of data that perform different capacities without being modified by a human. There are different methodologies inside ML, for example, **deep learning (DL)**, which utilizes neural system algorithms to mirror the manner in which the human cerebrum capacities, fundamentally interconnecting neurons to perceive complex examples in pictures, text, sounds, and other data to create bits of knowledge, recommendations, and expectations. Enormous players in the media and entertainment advertise each day face new difficulties of the computerized reality. The clients will, in general, quest for the administration that might be accessible whenever and wherever, paying little heed to the conditions. This circle turns out to be increasingly more serious consistently.

Present-day inclines in the use of data science in different parts of regular day to day existence set up new guidelines and require extra inventive deduction from media and entertainment holders. Enormous data might be utilized for some, objectives shifting from rising the benefit to improving perspectives and remarks. The advantage of data science applications is apparent for enormous telecom or gaming undertakings, the media, and so on. In this very manner, they make their data work for them. On account of media and diversion, extensive consideration is paid to the crowd. In this manner, there is an immediate reliance between the client's decision and the organization's activity.

The E&M industry is a differing part made out of different fragments, including film, TV and media spilled on the web. By 2021, the U.S. E&M industry is anticipated to reach $759 billion in income, expanding at a compound yearly development rate (CAGR) of 3.6%. In spite of the foreseen development, there are worries about income decreases in progressively customary market sections. Thus, industry investigators, for example, PwC contend that client experience must take expanding need, and AI is among driving rising advances ready to decidedly add to this exertion. To measure the developing job of AI in the E&M business, we investigated this segment inside and out to help answer addresses business pioneers are asking today, including:

- What kinds of AI applications are right now being used in the entertainment and media industry?

- How has the market reacted to these AI applications?
- Are there any regular patterns among these advancement endeavors—and how could these patterns perhaps influence the eventual fate of the entertainment and media division?

In this chapter, we separate utilization of man-made reasoning in the entertainment and media industry market to give business pioneers a comprehension of current and developing patterns that may affect their division. We will start with a summation of the areas we secured:

Entertainment and media AI applications overview

In light of our appraisal of the applications in this segment, most diversion and media use-cases seem to fall into three significant classifications:

- **Marketing and advertising:** Companies are preparing AI algorithms to help create film trailers and plan promotions.
- **Personalization of user experience:** Entertainment suppliers are utilizing AI to suggest customized content dependent on data from client movement and conduct.
- **Search optimization:** Media content makers are utilizing AI programming to improve the speed and proficiency of the media creation process and the capacity to sort out visual resources.

Following, we will investigate the AI utilization of every application by segment and give agent models.

Marketing and advertising

In August 2016, IBM declared the arrival of the trailer for a twentieth Century Fox tension/blood and gore movie Morgan supposedly created utilizing AI. The coming sections will give more light to it.

Fox and IBM Watson—Morgan film trailer

The exploration group prepared the AI framework on scenes from *"100 blood and gore flicks."* Features from every one of the film scenes were sorted into what the group called *"minutes"* and were then examined dependent on visual, sound, and scene organization components.

- **Personalized advertising:** The fascination of clients' consideration is a critical right of any organization, fundamentally when it is associated with media and diversion business. At the point when brisk and noteworthy online experience turned out to be exceptionally recognizable for some individuals, it is considerably additionally testing to hold the consideration of the client picked up. Now, customized showcasing algorithms act as the hero the enormous media domains. These algorithms mostly spread their operational potential to four measurements. Most importantly, the calculation is fit for perceiving new and old clients and hauling out helpful data from them progressively mode. Additionally, the calculation may play out a cross-channel following of both natural and new guests. Customized offers and messages are custom-made by the social bits of knowledge, and individual data picked up. Finally, this individual data is utilized to advance the media content among the clients' gatherings which may end up being the most responsive and persuasive. Customized promoting procedures permit fitting of the general site substance to the flavor of any guest.

- **Customer sentimental analysis:** All the media and diversion organizations look to separate how the guests feel about their substance, site page, or web applications. This data gives a possibility to change in accordance with the watcher's taste. For this reason, client assessment analysis is broadly applied.

Figure 11.7: *Representation of Watcher's taste*

Customer sentiment analysis algorithms exist in estimating positive and negative language signs. For this situation, common language preparation ensures the analysis of literary discussions. The algorithms are fit to order the posts, messages, discussion sections by the slant they express, characterizing the feelings taken cover behind the unique situation. Present-day apparatuses utilized for client assumption analysis can recognize six enthusiastic states as characterized by *Paul Ekman*. Subsequently, the client's conclusion may not exclusively be named positive or negative yet, in addition, give increasingly solid data. Thusly, media and diversion organizations can expand positive notices of their names to make a positive picture and create important substance.

- **Real-time analytics**: Real-time analytics, by its very name, provides the data handling to introduce the yield in the amazingly brief timeframes. To the extent, media and entertainment ventures have an immense measure of data furnished by the client with all their snaps, the speed of its analysis is an important factor.

  Real-time analysis algorithms give the yield very quick. In this way, urgent choices and enhancements to the substance might be completed right away. Using ongoing analysis gives the organization more opportunities to win the race with the contenders.

- **Recommendation engines**: Recommendation engines give the entertainment, and media suppliers and opportunity to concentrate on the clients' wants and sentiments. Other than the historical backdrop of a client inside one organization, a supplier gives extraordinary consideration to the sensations identified with this client. Present-day suggestion motors utilize coordinating algorithms preparing the data and append labels to the words bearing passionate demeanor just as coordinating recently referenced or looked through things. On this premise, precise, significant and engaging recommendations and recommendations are made.

  The suppliers are anxious to build up a substance bearing the passionate connection to a watcher. In this way, the fitting substance would arrive at the correct watchers at the right time.

- **Content circulation on social media**: The advanced universe of interpersonal interaction offered the media and diversion suppliers an astonishing opportunity to implement their promoting techniques with an incredible asset of online networking content circulation. General inclinations, clients' conduct, inclinations, experience, interests, and chronicles are presently accessible in a single tick for immense media endeavors.

Figure 11.8: Representation of content circulation

Content distribution, to a great extent, relies upon analysis of the online life measurements. Uncommonly created devices permit distinguishing the objective pursuers, the best channels and in any event, when the client will be the most receptive to the message. These activities become conceivable because of modern algorithms spotting fortuitous events and coordinating them to the clients' needs. The cooperative energy with a client by means of informal community ends up being very proficient in the advancement of the media and entertainment results. To the extent, public activity goes connected at the hip with diversion, news channels, tattling, film, gaming, and so forth. Fruitful substance conveyance system is efficient, arranged, directed, applicable, adaptable, and slow.

- **Object identification and classification**: The web includes heaps of data, and these huge sums are ceaselessly developing. It has a great many sites and stages committed to media and entertainment containing joins, posts, video and sound records, movies, games, and applications, and so forth. This reality may cause a few troubles in the hunt.

  Object discovery and order algorithms help to channel, coordinate, characterize data, perceive pictures, make third party referencing. In this way, the including of a fitting or unessential object will not show up on your way. Part of bothers and misconstruing might have stayed away from. Thus, media or entertainment supplier guarantees a decent substance, pull in and hold clients and advance their administrations.

- **Collecting and analyzing customer insights**: A general propensity of data science application got various advantages to individuals' businesses everywhere throughout the world. The algorithms help to gather and break down the customer bits of knowledge and utilize the yield.

  Comparable to territories of media and entertainment, all the remarks, posts, different preferences, sees, membership, and so on present a tremendous ground for extricating the experiences. The algorithms procedure the data, channel, order and gather the fortuitous events, acquire the most significant pieces and reach determinations permitting the media and entertainment organizations to realize their clients better. Anticipating the clients' response and mentality, future benefits, arranging and building fruitful promoting arrangements—all these become a reality because of the bits of knowledge.

- **Leveraging mobile and social media content**: Mobile and social media content is viewed as a key to guarantee cooperation between the organization and the client. Reports, energetic conversations of posts, likes and offers are, for the most part, the media and entertainment organizations chase for.

  As a matter of first importance, utilizing portable and web-based life content expands the quantity of channels and the measure of data traded continuously. In its turn, the data give upgraded focusing on abilities. As it were, having the experiences of watchers, the media and entertainment organizations tailor offers and suggestions to suit the necessities of much focused-on crowd gathering. Furthermore, embracing the mobile substance makes the organizations' administrations progressively accessible and simple to reach. Text mining, discourse and picture acknowledgment, and feeling analysis end up being valuable for this situation.

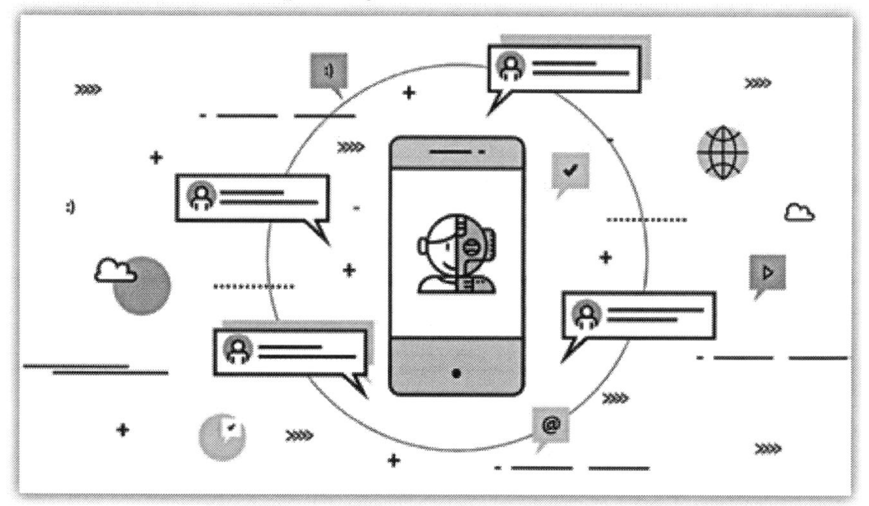

***Figure 11.9**: Representation of social media contents using mobile*

- **Analysis of media content use**: Because of the presence of the overall system, its ubiquity is ceaselessly developing. It has become a general stage for business, public activity, diversion, and recreation. Consistently a large number of individuals everywhere throughout the world leave their fingertips in the system. These are their snaps, likes, posts, reposts, remarks, offers, or perspectives. Disregarding such important data would be a huge misfortune, particularly when it concerns the media substance and its immediate effect on the crowd.

  Because of the data science algorithms, large media undertakings can make data work and bring benefits. Media content analysis is a very much evolved technique targeting breaking down the message of the substance and its undertone. The procedure of the media content analysis comprises three significant levels: catch, get, and present. The algorithms track the examples and incidents in the content. From that point forward, the data is set up for preparation. The systems characterize the supposition of the content. In this manner, its effect on the client might be anticipated.

  As per the yield, the message of the content might be adjusted, or a general inclination of the substance might be characterized.

Using AI in media intelligence

Many automated media observing arrangements state they utilize computerized reasoning and machine learning. Be that as it may, if there is no committed human examiner anyplace in the process to check or name the info data (for example, your association's media), it implies one of two things:

1. The outcomes you are getting from your organization's media insight arrangement are off base since it utilizes unaided AI. The arrangement using AI is training itself, and you most likely should not rely on it to settle on educated choices without marked data.
2. You, the client, are relied upon to resemble the coders talked about in the Bloomberg article. This implies removing the time from your own timetable to prepare the algorithms on what is good and bad or recruiting somebody to do as such.

A few people say a managed machine learning arrangement is costly, however, directed AI supports media insight precision and enables correspondences stars to settle on better choices. To get exact data, you have to either recruit an investigator to prepare the calculation with the goal that it learns the correct way or invests energy doing it without anyone else's help. Else, you may wind up paying in an alternate manner with off base outcomes.

Effect of AI on media intelligence in the future

Computer-based intelligence and AI will enormously affect advertising and media insight. Artificial intelligence will give you something other than analysis; it will offer you responses to what exactly is occurring in your media inclusion and why—all on request. That, yet it will conjecture what subjects could be an issue later on, where those issues will happen, and to what extent the issues may last. These prescient analyses will make you proactive as opposed to simply responsive.

As AI gets *"more intelligent"* it will improve you and increasingly arrange. Be that as it may, AI will just become as shrewd as the human educators who train it en route. It is a temperate upward pattern of people and innovation improving one another. People can prepare the machines and get the last bits of the most unpredictable analysis that AI cannot care for informal expressing and mockery. Whenever done right, the advantages are really worth the venture. PublicRelay keeps on putting resources into AI. Truth be told, directed AI is inserted into our answer both as far as improving the analysis and quicker just as in the yields to the customer.

Companies using machine learning in cool ways

1. **Yelp—image curation at scale**: Barely any things contrast with evaluating another eatery at that point going on the web to whine about it a while later. This is among the numerous reasons why Yelp is so well known (and helpful). Although Yelp probably will not appear to be a tech organization from the start, Yelp is utilizing AI to improve clients' understanding. Because pictures are nearly as indispensable to Yelp as client audits themselves, it should come as a meager shock that Yelp is continually attempting to improve how it handles picture preparation.

   This is the reason Yelp went to machine learning a few years back when it originally executed its image characterization innovation. Cry's machine learning algorithms help the organization's human staff to order, classify, and name pictures all the more productively—no little accomplishment when you are managing a huge number of photographs.

2. **Pinterest—improved content discovery**: Regardless of whether you are an in-your-face pinner or have never utilized the site, Pinterest possesses an inquisitive spot in the web-based life biological system. Because Pinterest's essential capacity is to minister existing substance, it bodes well that putting resources into innovations that can focus on this procedure increasingly compelling would be—and that is certainly the situation at Pinterest. Today, AI contacts for all intents and purposes each part of Pinterest's

business tasks, from spam control and substance disclosure to publicizing adaptation and decreasing agitate of email bulletin endorsers.

3. **Facebook—chatbot army**: Despite the fact that Facebook's Messenger administration is still somewhat… argumentative (individuals have solid sentiments about informing applications, it appears), it is one of the most energizing parts of the world's biggest web-based social networking stage. That is on the grounds that Messenger has become something of an exploratory testing lab for chatbots.

   Any engineer can make and present a chatbot for consideration in *Facebook Messenger*. This implies organizations with a solid accentuation on client care and maintenance can use chatbots, regardless of whether they are a small startup with restricted building assets. Obviously, that is, by all account, not the only use of AI that Facebook is keen on. Man-made intelligence applications are being utilized at Facebook to sift through spam and low-quality substance, and the organization is additionally exploring PC vision algorithms that can "read" pictures to outwardly hindered individuals.

4. **Twitter—curated timelines:** Twitter has been at the focal point of various debates recently (not least of which were the much-disparaged choices to balance everybody's symbols and changes to the manner in which individuals are labeled in @ answers); however, one of the more combative changes we have seen on Twitter was the advance toward an algorithmic channel.

   Regardless of whether you like to have Twitter show you "*the best tweets first*" (whatever that implies) or as a sensibly sequential course of events, these progressions are being driven by Twitter's AI innovation. Twitter's AI assesses each tweet progressively and "*scores*" them as indicated by different measurements. Eventually, Twitter's algorithms at that point show tweets that are probably going to drive the most commitment. This is resolved on an individual premise; Twitter's AI tech settles on those choices dependent on your individual inclinations, coming about in the algorithmically curated channels, which kind of sucks in case we are, as a rule, totally fair. (Does anyone really favor the algorithmic feed? Disclose to me why in the remarks, you stunning weirdos.)

5. **Google—neural networks and "Machines That Dream":** Nowadays, it is presumably simpler to list territories of logical R&D that Google—or, rather, parent organization Alphabet—is not chipping away at, as opposed to attempting to sum up Google's mechanical aspiration. Obviously, Google has been occupied lately, having enhanced into such fields as hostile to maturing innovation, clinical gadgets, and—maybe generally energizing for tech geeks—neural systems.

The most obvious advancements in Google's neural system research has been the DeepMind organize, the "*machine that fantasies*." It is a similar system that created those hallucinogenic pictures everyone was discussing some time back. As indicated by Google, the organization is investigating "*essentially all parts of AI,*" which will prompt energizing improvements in what Google calls "*old style algorithms*", just as different applications including common language handling, discourse interpretation, and search positioning and forecast frameworks.

The future of machine learning

One of the fundamental issues with fast, innovative headway is that, out of the blue, we wind up underestimating these jumps. A portion of the uses of AI recorded above would have been practically inconceivable as of late as 10 years prior, but then the pace at which researchers and specialists are progressing is completely astounding. All in all, what is next in AI patterns?

- **Machines that learn more effectively**: After a short time, we will see computerized brains that can learn considerably more successfully. This will prompt advancements in how algorithms are dealt with, for example, AI organizations that can perceive, modify, and enhance their own inside engineering with insignificant human oversight.
- **Computerization of cyberattack countermeasures**: The ascent of cybercrime and ransomware has constrained organizations of all sizes to rethink how they react to foundational online assaults. We will before long observe machine learning play a lot more noteworthy job in checking, forestalling, and reacting to cyberattacks such as database breaks, DDoS assaults, and different dangers.
- **Persuading generative models**: Generative models, for example, the ones utilized by Baidu in our model above, are, as of now, unimaginably persuading. Before long, we will not have the option to differentiate by any stretch of the imagination. Improvement demonstrating will bring about progressively advanced pictures, voices, and even whole personalities created completely by algorithms.
- **Better machine learning training**: Indeed, even the most modern machine learning can just learn as viably as the preparation it gets; generally, machine learning frameworks require colossal volumes of data to be prepared. Later on, AI frameworks will require fewer and fewer data to "*get the hang of,*" bringing about frameworks that can learn a lot quicker with essentially little data index.

Conclusion

Data science is utilized in numerous circles of human life. The estimation of the algorithms and their effectiveness can scarcely be thought little of. The utilization of data science in the field of media and diversion has become workmanship. It is not, at this point, enough just to spread news, gossipy tidbits or offer engaging exercises. An organization should arrive at the connection with a client, summon sentiments and feelings and have an attractive effect. The capacity of data science to gather, process, investigate, store, give suggestions is a tremendous advantage for the media and the performers.

Points to remember

Revise your reading with the following points:

- PC vision has been one of the most amazing achievements on account of AI.
- Robotic surgery is a great success in the field of AI.
- The most demanding application in the medical industry are:
  - Pattern imaging analytics
  - Drug discovery
  - Identifying diseases
  - Clinical trial research.
- Fraud detection and prevention is one of the important benefits of the use of AI in finance.

Index

A

B

C

D

E

J

K

L

M

N

O

P

Q

R

S

T

U

V

W

X

Y

Z

Printed in Great Britain
by Amazon